FLUID
POWER PNEUMATICS

OLAF A. JOHNSON
*Consultant, Design of Machines
and Mechanisms*

D1597342

*An analysis of basic theory and behavior
of gaseous media for practical applications
with appendices on fluid power symbols
and metric conversion.*

 American Technical Society • Chicago 60637

Preface

Fluid power for industry has been important in the development of automatic machinery and equipment for general use in industrial plants. In the early days of automation the fluid media for power transmission were considered with skepticism and therefore were used only in the simplest forms. However, as progress was made it was soon discovered that these media had many advantages over solid-state mechanical elements for transmitting power.

As is the case with any successful, new improvement, fluid power was greeted with great enthusiasm. Some engineers became over-enthused, feeling sure that fluid media could completely replace the old established mechanical systems. They attempted many applications that proved complete failures or caused trouble never encountered with purely mechanical transmissions because they rushed ahead without first making a comprehensive study. As a result, fluid power lost ground.

Later, with the start of mass production of complicated shapes for airplane parts, the interest in fluid mechanics was again renewed. With more experience, engineers found that the application of fluid mechanics is definitely predictable, and many successful applications were made.

This book has been written based on the author's long, successful experience in this field, and is intended for students with little or no previous knowledge of fluid power as well as a ready reference for established engineers.

There are two main branches of fluid power:

1. Pneumatics
2. Hydraulics

Since these two branches of fluid power are so different in behavior and performance, the best approach is to treat each branch separately. Often the two branches are used in conjunction with each other, but unless the basic laws are studied separately the result could be confusing.

The gaseous media, of which the atmosphere is the principal medium, were used on a larger scale in the early days of fluid power than were liquid media. In some cases where both gaseous and liquid media are used in conjuction, air is the prime mover and hydraulic oil the secondary medium. A few applications of this kind are presented in this book, with full explanations of only the pneumatic operations and brief comment concerning the hydraulic parts of these systems.

It is necessary for anyone directly connected with the design and operation of equipment depending partially or fully on the fluid power media to have a thorough knowledge of the fundamental laws governing the successful functioning of these media.

In the early years of fluid power presentation much time was spent in preparing diagrams that would adequately reveal the behavior of these media for power transmission. These diagrams often were prepared with a variation of colors and sometimes, when functions were complicated, lengthy descriptions were necessary to reveal distinctly the intended operation.

For several years there was a justified concern among engineers and management in the United States for a clearer, universal method of presenting systems for fluid power transmission. Finally a standard, based on experience and meetings in the United States and also worldwide, has been adopted and made available. This standard is presented and arranged in its entirety as an appendix in this book in a way easy to follow by the practicing engineer and student alike.

The metric system of measurements is another universal development that has been in progress a great many years. It was legally adopted in France in 1793. Even though this system later was legalized in the United States by an Act of Congress in 1866, it has never been adopted for common use in this country. We have, however, used the metric system here for scientific work. For instance, you will discover several metric terms such as *torr* for pressure and *liter* for volume in the presentation of vacuum technology. These terms, which came into existence long before the SI or International System of metric measurements were adopted by the ISO (International Standards Organization) in 1960, are likely to be retained in their present form long after conversion to the SI metric system has been completed, changing the *torr* to the *pascal*.

Serious developments are now in progress for complete conversion to the metric system in the future even though a bill authorizing this conversion was defeated in the U.S. Congress in May, 1974. Efforts in the direction of metrication will continue. In the meantime we have to prepare ourselves for conversion. The major part of this book has been presented in the present U.S. system of measurement, with occasional reference to the metric system.

We have intentionally omitted complicated metric calculations in the main text. We have, however, provided a metric appendix, outlining briefly the history and developments of this system and giving tables and factors for conversion. Because pre-SI measurements still co-exist with SI units at this point in time (1975) and the United States as a nation is still uncommitted officially, we have no choice but to present both pre-SI metric units, which in Britain are referred to as MT, or "Metrical Technical," and the latest SI units. Many metric countries which have agreed to phase out earlier metric practices, and in due time will do so completely, are still in the process. Facing real and present needs as well as looking at what appears to be shaping up for the future, we take an ambivalent stand in the presentation of data for conversion contained in this metric appendix.

In this book, as you will see, great emphasis has been placed on successful applications. The selection of material and problems is simple enough to be of value to the student and operator of the equipment. This material should also be helpful as a ready reference to the engineer established in the field.

Olaf A Johnson

Contents

cont.

Introduction to Pneumatics

The word *fluid* in the term "fluid power", as used in industry, may surprise many students because the study of pneumatics deals with systems operated with air or other gaseous media. In ordinary speech, the word *fluid* is nearly or entirely synonymous with the word *liquid*. Scientifically, however, both liquids and gases are classed as fluids of different types. Both the *gaseous* (pneumatic) and the *liquid* (hydraulic) type are used in thousands of practical and industrial applications.

Pneumatics, literally "pertaining to air" (the atmosphere enveloping the earth), has one set of fundamental laws governing the behavior of gaseous fluids. *Hydraulics*, literally "pertaining to water", relates also to other liquids, especially oils, and has a different set of fundamental laws beyond the scope of this text. To some extent the two subjects are interrelated, but these instances will be minimized and limited to applications where pneumatics is the primary system and hydraulics is the secondary system.

The term "fluid power" is fairly recent in man's history, and relates to the employment of fluid media under controlled conditions to perform useful work. The power itself, however, is very ancient. In fact, it has been in existence on this planet since there has been water and an atmosphere.

When we mention fluid power in general, we think of two main media capable of transmitting force in any direction. These media are the atmosphere surrounding the earth and the water found in abundance in most parts of the earth. These media have no inherent source of energy in themselves. They are therefore useful for performing work only as they are permitted to be influenced by a force.

Taking a well known example from nature, a surface may be heated by the rays of the sun faster than the surrounding areas, causing the air above it to rise, because air becomes lighter when expanded by the heat. This will cause an inrush of air from other directions. Under certain conditions, if two or more turbulent currents of air meet, a tornado is started. This is a rotating funnel cloud resulting from condensation of moisture by cooling and expansion, thus lifting the air. This rotating cloud, using the primary medium of air, may transmit an enormous force. If it passes over water, this cloud may also use the water as a secondary medium for transmitting force.

Notable Discoveries

For a long period of time gradual progress has been made in the development of laws and theories for fluid mechanics, and most of these have remained as they were in the beginning. Some of the statements of separate discoveries have been combined into one useful law, but progress is generally the result of using and improving earlier discoveries rather than completely discarding them. Of the notable discoveries made through the centuries, many have been concerned with the behavior of liquids. Only a few of these will be mentioned in this book, because our present concerns are the behavior and uses of gaseous media, particularly air.

We have no historical record of scientific statements concerning the laws of fluid behavior before the Greek scientist Archimedes (287–212 B.C.). He invented a spiral water screw enclosed in a cylinder. When this screw was revolved, it was intended to be capable of moving or pumping water to a higher level. See Fig. 1–1. This discovery or invention is mentioned here, even though it concerns liquid, for two reasons: first, its great antiquity, and second, because it shows the long time span sometimes required between the conception of an original idea and its ultimate use.

Fig. 1–1. Sectional drawing of the Archimedes water screw for raising water to a higher level by manual operation. Efficiency of this device without a mechanical power source is so low that it was worthless for industrial use, but with suitable power readily available, devices based on this principle are used in some hydraulic applications today. The ancient water screw shown here is still used by some Egyptian farmers.

Unfortunately, many inventions such as this one are dependent on other engineering developments for a successful and profitable application. Because the water screw could not be operated efficiently without an adequate source of power to turn it, for many centuries it was not considered of much practical value.

There is no record of a really practical

Fig. 1–2. The windmill was first introduced to Central Europe about 1100 AD and is still one of the simplest forms of fluid power drive in common use. (Courtesy of Netherlands National Travel Office)

power drive until the windmill was introduced to Central Europe about 1100 A.D. See Fig. 1–2. Much later, starting with the steam engine about 1700, the internal combustion engine about 1800, and still later the electric motor, the ancient water screw of Archimedes finally came into practical use. Today, exact duplicates or very similar designs are found in industry because now so many means of efficient propulsion are available.

A close parallel to this line of reasoning is seen in a recent revolutionary invention, the German Wankel internal combustion engine. The combustion chamber for this engine was unprofitable to put into high quality mass production with available standard production machinery. Later, with the development of very accurate, high-quality production machines, it is successfully produced.

The French philosopher and mathematician Blaise Pascal (1623–1662) made the discovery that fluid in a closed system exerts pressure equally in all directions. This discovery is of supreme importance in fluid mechanics. Around the same time, the Italian scientist Torricelli

(1608–1647) invented the mercury barometer, in 1643. He was the first to measure the pressure of the atmosphere, and he also formed a vacuum by inverting a tube filled with mercury. Soon afterward, the German physicist Otto von Guericke (1602–1686) invented the first vacuum pump.

The Irish scientist Robert Boyle (1627–1691) discovered that for a gaseous substance at constant temperature the volume is inversely proportional to the pressure. This discovery, of great theoretical and practical importance in *pneumatics*, must be used cautiously because it is not perfectly accurate at extreme temperatures. The French physicist Edme Mariotte (1620–1684), a contemporary of Boyle, formulated the statement now known as *Boyle's Law.*

Another French physicist, Jacques Charles (1746–1823), discovered that the volume of a given mass of gaseous substance increases or decreases 1/273 for each degree Centigrade of temperature change. Charles was the first to use hydrogen in balloons. And the French physicist Gay Lussac (1778–1850) discovered the law of expansion of gases when heated. He devised the hydrometer and, in 1809, determined that the volume of a gaseous *compound* is equal to or (in a simple ratio) is less than the sum of the volumes of the gases which are combined. At about this time important contributions to the calculation of heat conduction were made by the French mathematician Jean Baptiste Joseph Fourier (1768–1830).

Another important discovery about gases was made by the British chemist and atomic physicist John Dalton (1766–1844). He discovered that for a mixture of gases which do not react chemically, each gas exerts its own pressure independently, as if no other gas were present.

In 1811, the Italian physicist Amadeo Avogadro (1776–1856) advanced the theory that at the same temperature and pressure, equal volumes of different gases contain equal numbers of molecules. In the United States, around 1839, Swedish-born John Ericsson, an engineer and inventor, made many noteworthy contributions to the science of fluid mechanics.

The German physicist Julius Robert von Mayer (1814–1878) was the first to formulate clearly the principle of the conservation of energy. This principle is now basic in all physical sciences.

The British physicist James Prescott Joule (1818–1889) determined the mechanical equivalent of heat, which he produced by passing an electric current through a conductor. He also established that a perfect gas has no latent heat. A British chemist, Sir James Dewar (1842–1923), was the first to liquefy hydrogen, in 1889, and to solidify it, in 1899. He also devised the insulated *dewar flask*, a forerunner of the modern thermos bottle.

About this time three German chemists, working separately, made important discoveries in processes. Fritz Haber (1868–1934) developed a synthetic process for the production of ammonia by direct combination of nitrogen and hydrogen. Karl Bosch (1874–1940) developed a method for production of hydrogen by a combination of carbon monoxide obtained catalytically, passing steam at 500°C through a hydrocarbonous substance and water gas. He also adopted Haber's method for fixing nitrogen in the synthetic production of ammonia. Friedrich Bergius (1884–1949) developed a method of producing crude mineral oil by combining coal dust and hydrogen under high pressure. This was a notable discovery, of special value at this time when an abundance of coal and hydrogen makes the process practical and high pressures are easily obtained, as later chapters in this book will show. The full potential impor-tance of the method is becoming apparent in view of the increasing shortage of mineral oil.

Pneumatic and Hydraulic Media for Transmitting Force

In industry, the *pneumatic* or gaseous medium generally used for transmitting a force is air, the earth's atmosphere. Other gases may also be used, but they are usually classified as auxiliary media. In its simplest form, the air medium is used to drive a windmill, which in turn may do other useful work such as pumping water to a higher level where it may be stored in a tank or reservoir for future use. The air, then, is only a medium, because it has been set in motion by another or other forces.

There are many cases where the two media inadvertently have been mixed and if not properly dealt with can be a major source of trouble, as in the case of excessive water vapor in air lines operating machine parts or in the case of air in oil lines, also operating machine parts.

On the other hand, there are many cases where the two media can be used effectively in the same system due to their different behavior. For instance, gaseous substances are compressible with increase in pressure, in proportion to reduc-

Fig. 1–3. The Princess Anne Seaspeed hovercraft leaving the chalk cliffs of Dover on the southeast coast of England on its way to France across the English Channel. (Courtesy of British Rail Hovercraft Ltd.)

tion of their volume. The very slight compression rate of liquids due to changes in pressure has no practical value in engineering. However, it should be noted that liquids expand with increase in temperature, as gaseous substances do; therefore temperature control may have to be considered for best results in an application. Careful consideration should therefore be given at the conception of a fluid power project to determine which is the best medium for transmission of a force, or if the two media should be interlocked.

Since gaseous substances are compressible in ratios of reduction of volume to increase in pressure, a compressor is used as a source of energy, and the compressed gaseous substance is stored for future use in a pressure tank, also called a *receiver*. When the gaseous substance then is used as a medium for moving a part, the part does not start to move until the pressure has increased enough to overcome the resistance, and full pressure is not attained until the part reaches the end of its travel. This behavior of the gaseous substances may sometimes be an advantage, but it may also be a disadvantage.

The cushioning effect obtained by the compressibility of air as a medium is familiar to everyone in the form of automobile and bicycle tires. In recent years a much more spectacular application is seen in the fast passenger ships known as *hovercrafts*, which travel above the surface of the water suspended by compressed air beneath the hull and driven by airplane-type propellers. Fig. 1-3 shows the *Princess Anne* hovercraft just leaving the chalk cliffs of Dover on the southeast coast of England. This type of craft can ride over waves twelve feet high.

Review Questions

1. What phenomenon in nature is a good example of applied fluid power?

2. Describe the two main media used in industry for fluid power.

3. Must the two main media for fluid power be influenced by other forces to perform useful work?

4. What is the first fluid power drive on record?

5. What is a modern duplicate of the Archimedes spiral screw pump?

6. Describe the Pascal law.

7. Who was the first to measure the pressure of the atmosphere?

8. Who invented the first vacuum pump?

9. Who formulated Boyle's Law and what is this law?

10. Who was the first to establish a definite relationship between volume and temperature of a gaseous medium and what is this relationship?

11. Who discovered the law of expansion of gases?

12. Control of heat conduction is important in the development of fluid power for industrial use. Who was the first to make any noteworthy contribution to this branch of science?

13. For a mixture of gases, where the gases do not react chemically, what is to be noticed about the pressure?

14. What is important to remember about equal volumes of different gases at the same temperature and pressure, and who made this discovery?

15. Conservation of energy is an important scientific fact. Who first formulated this principle clearly?

16. Who determined the mechanical equivalent of heat?

17. Does a gas have latent heat?

18. Who was the first to liquefy and then solidify hydrogen?

19. Who discovered a synthetic process for the production of ammonia and what is this process?

20. Who fixed nitrogen by adopting the production method of ammonia?

21. What fluid power medium may be processed by combining coal dust and hydrogen under high pressure and who developed this method?

22. Name the principal gaseous medium used for transmitting a force in fluid power for industrial use.

23. For compressed gaseous media, what is another common name for a receiver?

24. What source of energy is used for a gaseous medium in fluid power for industrial use?

SEE END OF BOOK FOR ANSWERS TO QUESTIONS

Basic Laws and Behavior of Gaseous Media

Properties and Characteristics of Gases

Shape and Volume. The gaseous media are characterized by the fact that they have no fixed shape or volume. They do, however, completely fill and take the exact shape of the confinement they occupy.

Weight. The gaseous media are influenced by the gravitational forces of the earth, which may easily be proved by weighing a container filled with air; then, after pumping out the air and weighing the container again, it will be found to weigh less. According to physical tables of the Smithsonian Institution, the weight of pure air at 32°F and barometric pressure of 14.696 lbs per square inch is 0.0871 lbs per cubic foot. In the metric system, according to the French chemist and physicist Henri Victor Regnault (1810–1878), the weight of pure air at 0°C and 76 cm Hg pressure is 1.293 kilograms per cubic meter (which may be written as kg/m³).

The weight and volume of air changes for variations in temperature and pres-

sure. See Table 2–1 in the U.S. system and Table 2–2 in the metric system. These tables show the volume and weight for variations of temperature only at atmospheric pressure. Table 2–3 shows weight of air per cubic unit at various pressures and temperatures.

Pressure. As previously stated, the gaseous media completely fill and take the shape of the confinement they occupy, and the atmospheric pressure may be defined as the force the air exerts on every point which it contacts. Since the atmosphere fluctuates due to variations in temperature of the surface it contacts, the atmospheric pressure is not constant at any location, but a small change is continually taking place. This change is so small, however, that it has no practical value for most industrial cases. The pressure of the atmosphere is measured with a barometer, which is illustrated in its simplest form in Fig. 2–1, and given as inches of mercury barometer reading or as pressure in pounds per square inch. In

TABLE 2-1. VOLUME AND WEIGHT OF AIR AT ATMOSPHERIC PRESSURE FOR VARIOUS TEMPERATURES.
(U. S. MEASUREMENT)

TEMPERATURE DEGREES FAHRENHEIT	VOLUME OF 1 POUND OF AIR IN CUBIC FEET	WEIGHT PER CUBIC FOOT IN POUNDS	TEMPERATURE DEGREES FAHRENHEIT	VOLUME OF 1 POUND OF AIR IN CUBIC FEET	WEIGHT PER CUBIC FOOT IN POUNDS
0	11.57	0.0864	325	19.76	0.0506
12	11.88	.0842	350	20.41	.0490
22	12.14	.0824	375	20.96	.0477
32	12.39	.0807	400	21.69	.0461
42	12.64	.0791	450	22.94	.0436
52	12.89	0.0776	500	24.21	0.0413
62	13.14	.0761	600	26.60	.0376
72	13.39	.0747	700	29.59	.0338
82	13.64	.0733	800	31.75	.0315
92	13.89	.0720	900	34.25	.0292
102	14.14	0.0707	1000	37.31	0.0268
112	14.41	.0694	1100	39.37	.0254
122	14.66	.0682	1200	41.84	.0239
132	14.90	.0671	1300	44.44	.0225
142	15.17	.0659	1400	46.95	.0213
152	15.41	0.0649	1500	49.51	0.0202
162	15.67	.0638	1600	52.08	.0192
172	15.92	.0628	1700	54.64	.0183
182	16.18	.0618	1800	57.14	.0175
192	16.42	.0609	2000	62.11	.0161
202	16.67	0.0600	2200	67.11	0.0149
212	16.92	.0591	2400	72.46	.0138
230	17.39	.0575	2600	76.92	.0130
250	17.89	.0559	2800	82.64	.0121
275	18.52	.0540	3000	87.72	.0114
300	19.16	.0522	----	-----	-----

the metric system, barometric pressures are in kilograms per square centimeter (which may be written as kg/cm²). Standard or mean air pressure is 76 cm Hg or 1.0333 kg/cm² at sea level.

It has been demonstrated that air, like other substances, is attracted by gravitational forces, but unlike solid substances the molecules of the air are free to move as the air expands, permitting the expanded, lighter air to move to the top. Therefore the pressure of a column of air varies, decreasing with altitude.

The barometer, in the form invented by Torricelli, is still the most reliable instrument for measuring atmospheric pressures. The most accurate barometer is still a *comparator*; that is, it compares the known weight of a column of liquid to a column of air of the same cross-sectional area. The heaviest known liquid, mercury, which weighs 849 lbs per cubic foot at 32°F (in the metric system 13.59 grams per cubic centimeter at 0°C) at sea level has therefore been chosen. Another advantage of mercury is that it remains in a liquid state down to a temperature of −38.67°C or −37.8°F.

TABLE 2-2. VOLUME AND WEIGHT OF AIR AT ATMOSPHERIC PRESSURE FOR VARIOUS TEMPERATURES
(METRIC MEASUREMENT)

TEMPERATURE DEGREES CENTIGRADE	VOLUME OF 1 KILOGRAM OF AIR IN CUBIC METERS	WEIGHT PER CUBIC METER KILOGRMAS	TEMPERATURE DEGREES CENTIGRADE	VOLUME OF 1 KILOGRAM OF AIR IN CUBIC METERS	WEIGHT PER CUBIC METER KILOGRAMS
-17.3	0.72	1.38	163	1.23	0.81
-11.1	.74	1.35	176	1.27	.78
- 5.5	.76	1.32	190	1.31	.76
0	.77	1.29	204	1.35	.74
5.5	.79	1.27	232	1.43	.70
11.1	0.80	1.24	260	1.51	0.66
16.6	.82	1.22	315	1.66	.60
22.2	.84	1.20	370	1.84	.53
27.7	.85	1.17	426	1.98	.50
33.3	.87	1.15	482	2.14	.47
38.9	0.88	1.13	537	2.33	0.43
44.4	.90	1.11	593	2.49	.41
50.0	.91	1.09	648	2.61	.38
55.5	.93	1.07	704	2.77	.36
61.1	.95	1.05	760	2.93	.35
66.6	0.96	1.04	815	3.09	0.32
72.2	.98	1.02	870	3.24	.31
77.7	.99	1.00	925	3.40	.28
83.3	1.00	.99	980	3.56	.27
88.8	1.02	.97	1092	3.88	.26
94.4	1.04	0.96	1200	4.18	0.23
100.0	1.06	.95	1315	4.52	.22
110.0	1.09	.92	1325	4.80	.21
121.0	1.12	.89	1536	5.16	.19
135.0	1.16	.86	1647	5.47	.18
150.0	1.20	.84	----	----	----

TABLE 2-3 . WEIGHT OF AIR IN POUNDS PER CUBIC FOOT AT VARIOUS PRESSURES AND TEMPERATURES
(U.S. MEASUREMENT)

TEMPERATURE DEGREES FAHRENHEIT	PRESSURE, PSI												
	0	5	10	20	30	40	50	60	80	100	120	150	200
−20	0.090	0.121	0.152	0.213	0.274	0.336	0.397	0.458	0.580	0.702	0.825	1.010	1.318
−10	.088	.118	.149	.209	.268	.328	.388	.448	.567	.687	.807	.989	1.288
0	.086	.116	.146	.204	.263	.321	.380	.438	.555	.672	.790	.968	1.260
10	.085	.114	.143	.200	.257	.314	.372	.429	.543	.658	.774	.947	1.233
20	0.083	0.111	0.140	0.196	0.252	0.307	0.364	0.420	0.533	0.645	0.757	0.927	1.208
30	.081	.109	.137	.192	.246	.301	.357	.412	.522	.632	.742	.908	1.184
40	.080	.107	.134	.188	.241	.295	.350	.404	.511	.619	.727	.890	1.161
50	.078	.105	.131	.184	.237	.290	.343	.396	.501	.607	.713	.873	1.139
60	0.076	0.103	0.128	0.180	0.232	0.284	0.336	0.388	0.493	0.596	0.700	0.856	1.116
80	.074	.095	.124	.174	.224	.274	.324	.374	.473	.572	.673	.824	1.074
100	.071	.094	.120	.168	.215	.264	.312	.360	.455	.551	.648	.794	1.035
120	.069	.092	.116	.162	.208	.255	.302	.348	.440	.533	.626	.767	1.001
140	0.066	0.089	0.112	0.157	0.201	0.246	0.291	0.336	0.426	0.516	0.606	0.742	0.968
150	.065	.087	.110	.154	.198	.242	.286	.331	.419	.508	.596	.730	.953
175	.063	.084	.105	.148	.191	.233	.275	.318	.403	.488	.573	.701	.914
200	.060	.081	.101	.143	.184	.225	.265	.305	.388	.470	.552	.674	.879
225	0.058	0.078	0.098	0.137	0.177	0.216	0.255	0.295	0.374	0.452	0.531	0.649	0.846
250	.056	.075	.094	.132	.170	.208	.247	.284	.360	.436	.513	.627	.817
275	.054	.073	.091	.128	.164	.201	.238	.274	.348	.421	.494	.605	.789
300	.052	.071	.088	.124	.159	.194	.230	.265	.336	.407	.478	.585	.762
350	0.049	0.066	0.083	0.116	0.149	0.183	0.216	0.249	0.316	0.382	0.449	0.549	0.715
400	.046	.062	.078	.109	.140	.172	.203	.235	.297	.360	.423	.517	.674
450	.044	.059	.074	.103	.133	.163	.192	.222	.281	.340	.399	.488	.637
500	.041	.056	.070	.098	.126	.154	.182	.210	.266	.322	.379	.463	.604

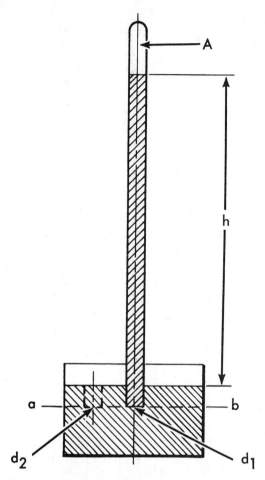

Fig. 2–1. Mercury barometer, consisting of a straight glass tube filled with mercury, closed at the top end, with open end at bottom immersed in pool of mercury in an open container.

d_1. The mercury would then have sunk, so we have a mercury column h above the surface of the mercury in the container. Since there is now no air under the closed end of tube A, we have a vacuum above the mercury column h, and this column is free to move up and down as influenced by variations in pressure.

The pressure on area d_1, the inside diameter of the glass tube at level $a-b$, is exactly the same on an equal area shown as d_2 from a column of air of that area as far up as the air extends, plus the pressure from a mercury column of the same area from the free surface of the mercury to level $a-b$. Therefore the pressure from the atmosphere on any portion $(d_2)^2 \times \pi/4$ or $0.785\ (d_2)^2$ of the free surface of the mercury in the container is equal to the pressure from a column of mercury d_1 diameter and h height.

The density of the air, and therefore also the pressure, remains constant for very short periods of time at the same location. It has been found, however, that the average height of column h is approximately 29.921 inches of mercury (76 cm Hg) at sea level. Since 1 cubic foot of mercury weighs 849 lbs, the pressure is therefore:

$$\frac{849 \times 29.921}{1728} = 14.7 \text{ psi}$$

(Remembering that 1 cu. ft = 1728 cu. in.)

Also, since 1 cubic centimeter of mercury weighs 13.59 grams or 0.01359 kg, the pressure may be expressed in the metric system as: $0.01359 \times 76 = 1.0333$ kg/cm², which is also one atmosphere.

The average barometric pressure at sea level has therefore been accepted as 14.7 psi or 29.921 inches of mercury, expressed as 76 cm Hg in the metric system. (Recall here that Hg is the chemical symbol for

In Fig. 2–1, assume that glass tube A has a uniform inside diameter d_1 of not less than 1/4 inch (6 mm) and one meter (39.37 inches) long. As shown in the drawing, this tube is closed at one end and filled with mercury. If held in an upright position, with the open end up, the air will be driven out from the closed bottom of the tube. Now close the open end of the tube temporarily, submerge this end in a container partially filled with mercury, and again open the end at

TABLE 2-4. ATMOSPHERIC PRESSURE AND BAROMETER READINGS FOR VARIOUS ALTITUDES
(U. S. MEASUREMENT)

ALTITUDE IN FEET ABOVE SEA LEVEL	PRESSURE IN LBS PER SQUARE INCH	BAROMETER READING INCHES OF MERCURY
0	14.69	29.92
500	14.42	29.38
1,000	14.16	28.86
1,500	13.91	28.33
2,000	13.66	27.82
2,500	13.41	27.31
3,000	13.16	26.81
3,500	12.92	26.32
4,000	12.68	25.84
4,500	12.45	25.36
5,000	12.22	24.89
5,500	11.99	24.43
6,000	11.77	23.98
6,500	11.55	23.53
7,000	11.33	23.09
7,500	11.12	22.65
8,000	10.91	22.22
8,500	10.70	21.80
9,000	10.50	21.38
9,500	10.30	20.98
10,000	10.10	20.58
10,500	9.90	20.18
11,000	9.71	19.75
11,500	9.52	19.40
12,000	9.34	19.03
12,500	9.15	18.65
13,000	8.97	18.29
13,500	8.80	17.93
14,000	8.62	17.57
14,500	8.45	17.22
15,000	8.28	16.88

mercury.) These figures, somewhat less than exact, are close enough for most engineering calculations. The standard pressure (29.921 inches of mercury or 14.7 lbs per square inch at sea level) decreases approximately one half pound for every 1,000 feet in altitude, as shown in Table 2-4, in U.S. measurements, and in Table 2-5, in metric measurements.

Absolute Zero Pressure. The complete absence of pressure, or absolute zero pressure, is vacuum, designated as zero *psia*. (Here *a* stands for "absolute.")

Gage Pressure. Most engineering calculations for industrial uses are, however, based on gage pressure, *psig* (expressed as kg/cm² in the metric system). This is the actual pressure above atmospheric pressure. (The final *g* in psig stands for "gage".)

The reason for this is that a container filled with a gaseous substance, while exerting a certain pressure on the inside wall, is also being influenced by the atmospheric pressure on the outside wall. The walls of the container are therefore sub-

TABLE 2-5. ATMOSPHERIC PRESSURE AND BAROMETER READINGS FOR VARIOUS ALTITUDES
(METRIC MEASUREMENT)

ALTITUDE IN METERS ABOVE SEA LEVEL	PRESSURE IN KGS PER SQUARE cm	BAROMETER READINGS cm OF MERCURY
0	1.0333	76.0
150	1.0137	74.6
300	0.9954	73.3
450	.9779	72.0
600	.9603	70.7
750	.9427	69.4
900	0.9251	68.1
1,050	.9073	66.8
1,200	.8914	65.5
1,350	.8752	64.4
1,500	0.8590	63.2
1,650	.8429	62.0
1,800	.8274	60.9
1,950	.8120	59.7
2,100	0.7965	58.6
2,250	.7817	57.5
2,400	.7670	56.4
2,550	.7522	55.4
2,700	0.7382	54.3
2,850	.7241	53.3
3,000	.7100	52.3
3,150	.6960	51.3
3,300	0.6826	50.2
3,450	.6693	49.3
3,600	.6566	48.3
3,750	.6432	47.3
3,900	0.6306	46.4
4,050	.6186	45.5
4,200	.6060	44.6
4,350	.5940	43.7
4,500	0.5820	42.8

ject only to the *difference* between inside and outside pressure, which is gage pressure. Therefore the gage used for pressure measurements in engineering is set at zero for the altitude where it is used, which would be 14.7 psia at sea level and 12.22 psia at 5,000 feet altitude. If the pressure is 1 atmosphere (or 1.0333 kg/cm² at sea level, in the metric system) it would fall to 0.859 atmosphere at 1,500 meters altitude.

Vacuum. When all gaseous substances are removed from the inside of a container, the walls of the container are exposed only to the pressure of the atmosphere. An example of this is the electric light bulb, where most of the air has been evacuated to prevent combustion of the filament. In this case the walls should be strong enough to withstand the full outside pressure. This pressure can be considerable. The German physicist Guericke, who was also mayor of Magdeburg, demonstrated that two large, hollow metal hemispheres which had been put together and evacuated could not be pulled apart by opposing teams of horses.

One inch of mercury is equivalent to $14.696 \div 29.921 = 0.49116$ lbs per square inch, or 0.491 lbs per square inch for ordinary calculations. Assume now that the inside of a container has been evacuated to 12 inches of mercury. Since one inch of mercury is approximately 0.491 lbs per square inch, the absolute pressure is: $(29.9 - 12.0) \times 0.491 = 8.80$ psia (approx.). See Fig. 2–2 illustrating a partial vacuum. In the metric system 1 cm of mercury would exert a pressure of 1/76 times the standard pressure of 1.0333 kg/cm² because this is the pressure of 76 cm Hg. So the pressure of 1 centimeter of mercury would be 1.0333 kg/cm² ÷ 76 = 0.0136 kg/cm². Therefore, if the inside of a container has been evacuated to 30 cm of mercury, the pressure would be: $(76 - 30) \times 0.0136 = 0.6256$ kg/cm².

Assume, in Fig. 2–2, a glass U-tube F of approximately the same general dimensions as the tube previously shown in Fig. 2–1. After the U-tube is immersed in mercury and withdrawn in a vertical position, the mercury in the tube would fall to surface d_1, creating a vacuum at A. Height h, the vertical distance from surface d to d_1, would then be the atmospheric barometer reading of, let us say, 29.921 inches of mercury.

If the glass tube is now secured to tube G of tank B, and some of the air is evacuated from tank B with pump C until the mercury falls to surface d_2, the barometer reading in the tank would then be h_1.

Before evacuation, the pressure on the inside of the tank would oppose an equal pressure on the outside, and we would have equilibrium. After evacuation, the walls of the tank would be subject to a pressure of $h - h_1 = h_2$ inches of mercury, or h_2 cm Hg in the metric system.

Avogadro's Law, a very important discovery for vacuum calculations, established a definite relationship between the number of molecules in a gaseous medium and the pressure exerted by this gaseous medium. Because the number of molecules in even a very small amount of

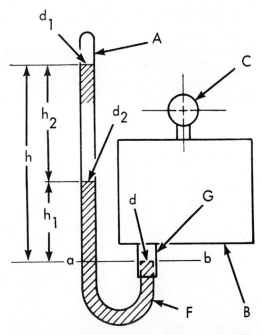

Fig. 2–2. Measuring partial vacuum with simple apparatus consisting of a glass U-tube *F* filled with mercury, tank *B*, connecting tube *G*, and pump *C* to partially evacuate the tank of air.

a gaseous medium has been found to be enormously high, the *mole* has been established as a unit of measurement. One mole of any gas is roughly 6×10^{23} (that is, 6 followed by 23 zeros) molecules, and occupies a space of 0.791 cubic feet at a temperature of 32°F and a pressure of 14.7 psia. From this it is obvious that the molecular density of any gas constituent can easily be found if its pressure and temperature are known.

Thus, one cubic foot of air at 32°F and 14.7 psia contains:

$$\frac{6 \times 10^{23}}{0.791} = \frac{6 \times 10^{23}}{7.91 \times 10^{-1}} = \frac{6}{7.91} \times 10^{24}$$

$$= 0.758 \times 10^{24} = 7.58 \times 10^{23}$$

molecules.

In most calculations for vacuum work in industry, the temperature and volume remain constant as the gas is evacuated. Removing gas will therefore reduce the pressure as expressed in the following equation:

$$\frac{p_1}{n_1} = \frac{p_2}{n_2}, \text{ where:}$$

p_1 = the initial pressure

p_2 = the pressure after evacuation

n_1 = the number of molecules before evacuation

n_2 = the number of molecules after evacuation

Now assume that an enclosed vessel contains 2 moles of a gaseous medium at a pressure of 14.7 psia and it is required to reduce the pressure to 1 *torr* at constant temperature. (A torr is a unit absolute pressure equivalent to 1 millimeter of mercury.) How many moles must be evacuated to obtain this pressure?

The given data are:

p_1 = 14.7 psia = 760 torr

p_2 = 1 torr

n_1 = 2 moles

The unknown quantity in this case is n_2, the number of moles after evacuation, which is the number of moles remaining in the vessel. Solving first for n_2 gives:

$$n_2 = \frac{p_2 \times n_1}{p_1} = \frac{1 \times 2}{760} = 0.0026 \text{ moles.}$$

The number of moles that must be evacuated is obviously the original number less the number remaining in the vessel after partial evacuation—a simple subtraction:

$n_1 - n_2 = 2.0000 - 0.0026 = 1.9974$ moles, which must be evacuated to obtain a final pressure of 1 torr.

Devices Operated on Atmospheric Pressure

Many instruments in ordinary use are dependent on atmospheric pressure for operation. The syringe shown in Fig. 2–3 is a simple illustration.

A rubber syringe such as the one shown in Fig. 2–3 may be flattened to expel most of the air from the inside. Then, if the syringe is immersed in a container filled with water to level $g–h$, the atmospheric pressure will force the water into the syringe to level $l–m$ until the pressure of the water column from surface $a–b$ to surface $l–m$ plus the partial vacuum at A is equal to the pressure on d_2, of the same area as opening d_1. The water in the container will then have sunk to level $c–e$.

If the syringe is now withdrawn slowly, the water level in the container will gradually rise to level $j–k$ and the level in the syringe will fall to level $n–o$. This is because the pressure of the water in column d_2 is gradually diminished to zero. The water will, however, remain in the syringe due to the atmospheric pressure, which is equal to the pressure from the water column d_1 to surface $n–o$ plus partial pressure in the syringe.

Fig. 2–4 shows a siphon, which also depends on atmospheric pressure for operation. The purpose of the siphon is to empty liquid out of a container without a pump or other mechanical device.

Using the siphon shown in Fig. 2–4, flow may be started by inverting the tube A, closing end d_1, filling the tube with the

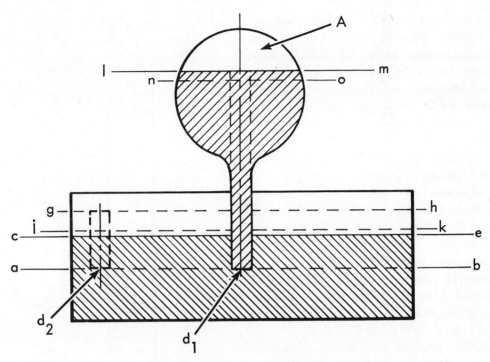

Fig. 2–3. Rubber syringe immersed in water in an open tank.

liquid to be pumped out, closing end d_3 also, and immersing the short end in the liquid while both ends are closed.

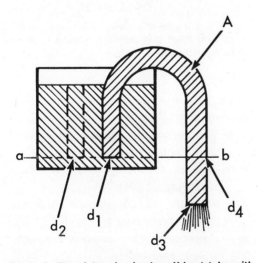

Fig. 2–4. The siphon is simply a U-bent tube with the short end immersed in liquid in an open container. After once it is started, the liquid pours out of the long end at d_3 until level $a-b$ is reached.

The liquid will start to flow as soon as both ends of the tube are opened and will continue to flow until level $a-b$ is reached. A balanced condition will then exist when liquid between d_3 and d_4 has been emptied out and atmospheric pressure is exerted on areas d_1, d_2, and d_4.

Mariotte's Law. If a U-formed tube, such as shown in Fig. 2–5, open to the atmosphere in the long end B and closed in the short end A is filled with mercury so that the height in both branches of the tube is the same (level $a-b$) this would prove that the pressure inside the enclosed end A is the same as the atmospheric pressure at the open end because the liquid is in balance.

If more mercury is now added to the open end B, mercury will also rise at enclosed end A, thus compressing the enclosed air. If so much mercury has been added to the open end B that the difference in height between the two surfaces of mercury shown is Fig. 2–5 is equal to the existing mercury reading of 29.921 inches (76 cm Hg in the metric system) at sea level, the pressure of the air in the enclosed end at *A* has been raised to twice the existing atmospheric pressure. At the same time, it is found that the volume of the enclosed air at *A* has been compressed to half its original volume.

If the open tube were long enough, we would find that by increasing the distance between the two mercury surfaces by adding mercury into the open end *B*, the difference *h* would be increased 3, 4, or 5 times the existing atmospheric mercury reading. Also, the volume in the enclosed end *A* would be decreased to 1/3, 1/4, or 1/5 of its original volume.

If the pressure were decreased by removing mercury from the open end *B*, the enclosed air volume would *increase* in proportion. It is therefore easily discovered that the weight of air per cubic foot is changing under compression as well as expansion. If, for instance, the volume were decreased to half its original size, then every cubic foot would contain twice as much air and consequently weigh twice as much per cubic foot as originally.

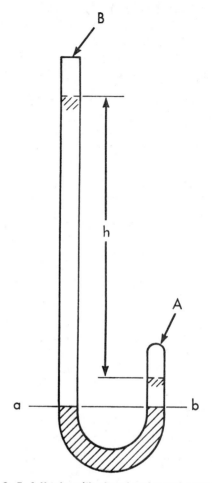

Fig. 2–5. A U-tube with closed end *A* and open end *B*, partially filled with mercury, is used to demonstrate Mariotte's Law.

Effect of Compression and Expansion

This behavior of the air under compression and expansion was discovered simultaneously by Mariotte and Boyle and may be expressed by the following statement: *If a gaseous medium is compressed or expanded under constant temperature,*

1. The volume is inversely proportional to the absolute pressure.
2. The weight per cubic unit is inversely proportional to the volume.
3. The weight per cubic unit is directly proportional to the pressure.

Assume then:

V_1 = Volume of the gaseous medium before compression

V_2 = Volume of the gaseous medium after compression

p_1 = Pressure of the gaseous medium before compression

p_2 = Pressure of the gaseous medium after compression

ρ_1 = Density, weight per cubic unit of the gaseous medium before compression

$\rho_2 =$ Density, weight per cubic unit of the gaseous medium after compression

Under compression or expansion the product of volume and pressure is constant and may be expressed as follows:

$$\frac{V_1}{V_2} = \frac{p_1}{p_2} \text{ or } V_1 \times p_1 = V_2 \times p_2$$

Under compression or expansion the product of volume and weight per cubic unit (or density) is constant and may be expressed as follows:

$$\frac{V_1}{V_2} = \frac{\rho_2}{\rho_1} \text{ or } V_1 \times \rho_1 = V_2 \times \rho_2$$

Under compression or expansion the pressure and weight per cubic unit is directly proportional and may be expressed as follows:

$$\frac{p_1}{p_2} = \frac{\rho_1}{\rho_2} \text{ or } p_1 \times \rho_2 = p_2 \times \rho_1$$

Characteristics of Air

Composition. Dry air at sea level is composed of 78.03% nitrogen, 20.99% oxygen and 0.98% argon. By molecular weight this would be, 28.016 nitrogen, 32.000 oxygen and 39.944 argon. These figures are sufficiently accurate for engineering calculations, and are independent of location at sea level, but vary somewhat with altitude. The small percentage of carbon dioxide and hydrogen in the atmosphere are combined with the rare gases and given as argon.

Absolute Humidity. Some water vapor is always present in the common atmosphere, and the amount may vary from a very small amount up to the point of saturation. The water vapor in the atmosphere is in the form of superheated steam. When the atmosphere has reached the point of saturation, it is understood that the steam present in the air is in the saturated condition. The absolute humidity then is the actual quantity of water, most often referred to as "steam" or "vapor", present in the air, or the actual weight in milligrams per liter or in grains per cubic foot of air. (One grain is 1/7,000 part of a pound or 64.8 milligrams.) When calculating the amount of water vapor in the air, it is important to remember that the *volume* of the vapor is exactly the same as the volume of the air, since both of these fluids take exactly the shape of the confinement they occupy.

The amount of water vapor carried in a certain volume of air depends largely on the temperature of the air. The amount of water vapor in free air, which is the atmospheric constituent where the air is used for an industrial purpose, is only slightly influenced by pressure. It may, however, be of interest to notice that it takes between 8 and 10 cubic feet (226 to 283 liters) of free air at sea level to make 1 cubic foot of compressed air at 100 psi. (One cubic foot = 28.3 liters, approx.) Calculated theoretically from Boyle's Law, $V_1 \times P_1 = V_2 \times P_2$, we would have:

$$V_1 = \frac{1 \times 114.7}{14.7} = 7.8 \text{ cubic feet}$$

(or 220 liters), approx.

Due to low volumetric efficiency in many practical cases, between 8 and 13 cubic feet (226 to 368 liters) is a more practical figure. This low efficiency is caused by heating of air during admission, leakage past valves and pistons, and the re-expansion of the clearance air in the com-

TABLE 2-6. RELATIVE HUMIDITY FOR VARIOUS TEMPERATURES AND 29 INCHES BAROMETER PRESSURE

READING OF DRY BULB THEROMETERS IN DEGREE F	DIFFERENCE IN DEGREES FAHRENHEIT BETWEEN DRY & WET BULB THERMOMETERS																
	1	2	3	4	5	6	7	8	9	10	11	12	13	14	15	16	17
50	93	87	81	74	68	62	56	50	44	39	33	28	22	17	12	7	2
51	94	87	81	75	69	63	57	51	45	40	35	29	24	19	14	9	4
52	94	88	81	75	69	63	58	52	46	41	36	30	25	20	15	10	6
53	94	88	82	75	70	64	58	53	47	42	37	32	27	22	17	12	7
54	94	88	82	76	70	65	59	54	48	43	38	33	28	23	18	14	9
55	94	88	82	76	71	65	60	55	49	44	39	34	29	25	20	15	11
56	94	88	82	77	71	66	61	55	50	45	40	35	31	26	21	17	12
57	94	88	83	77	72	66	61	56	51	46	41	36	32	27	23	18	14
58	94	89	83	77	72	67	62	57	52	47	42	38	33	28	24	20	15
59	94	89	83	78	73	68	63	58	53	48	43	39	34	30	25	21	17
60	94	89	84	78	73	68	63	58	53	49	44	40	35	31	27	22	18
61	94	89	84	79	74	68	64	59	54	50	45	40	36	32	28	24	20
62	94	89	84	79	74	69	64	60	55	50	46	41	37	33	29	25	21
63	95	90	84	79	74	70	65	60	56	51	47	42	38	34	30	26	22
64	95	90	85	79	75	70	66	61	56	52	48	43	39	35	31	27	23
65	95	90	85	80	75	70	66	62	57	53	48	44	40	36	32	28	25
66	95	90	85	80	76	71	66	62	58	53	49	45	41	37	33	29	26
67	95	90	85	80	76	71	67	62	58	54	50	46	42	38	34	30	27
68	95	90	85	81	76	72	67	63	59	55	51	47	43	39	35	31	28
69	95	90	86	81	77	72	68	64	59	55	51	47	44	40	36	32	29
70	95	90	86	81	77	72	68	64	60	56	52	48	44	40	37	33	30
71	95	90	86	82	77	73	69	64	60	56	53	49	45	41	38	34	31
72	95	91	86	82	78	73	69	65	61	57	53	49	46	42	39	35	32
73	95	91	86	82	78	73	69	65	61	58	54	50	46	43	40	36	32
74	95	91	86	82	78	74	70	66	62	58	54	51	47	44	40	37	34
75	96	91	87	82	78	74	70	66	63	59	55	51	48	44	41	38	34
76	96	91	87	83	78	74	70	67	63	59	55	52	48	45	42	38	35
77	96	91	87	83	79	75	71	67	63	60	56	52	49	46	42	39	36
78	96	91	87	83	79	75	71	67	64	60	57	53	50	46	43	40	37
79	96	91	87	83	79	75	71	68	64	60	57	54	50	47	44	41	37
80	96	91	87	83	79	76	72	68	64	61	57	54	51	47	44	41	38
81	96	92	88	84	80	76	72	69	65	62	58	55	52	49	46	43	40
82	96	92	88	84	80	76	72	69	65	62	58	55	52	49	46	43	40
83	96	92	88	84	80	77	73	70	66	63	59	56	53	50	47	44	41
84	96	92	88	84	80	77	73	70	66	63	59	56	53	50	47	44	41
85	96	92	88	85	81	77	74	70	67	63	60	57	54	51	48	45	42
86	96	92	88	85	81	77	74	70	67	63	60	57	54	51	48	45	43
87	96	92	88	85	81	78	74	71	67	63	61	58	55	52	48	46	43
88	96	92	88	85	81	78	74	71	67	64	61	58	55	52	49	46	43
89	96	92	89	85	81	78	75	71	68	64	62	59	56	53	50	47	44
90	96	92	89	85	81	78	75	71	68	65	62	59	56	53	50	47	44
91	96	92	89	85	82	78	75	72	69	65	62	59	57	54	51	48	45
92	96	92	89	85	82	78	75	72	69	65	62	59	57	54	51	48	45
93	96	93	89	86	82	79	75	72	69	66	63	60	57	54	52	49	46
94	96	93	89	86	82	79	75	72	69	66	63	60	57	54	52	49	46
95	96	93	89	86	82	79	76	73	70	67	64	61	58	55	53	50	47
96	96	93	89	86	82	79	76	73	70	67	64	61	58	55	53	50	47
97	96	93	89	86	83	79	76	73	70	67	64	61	59	56	53	51	48
98	96	93	89	86	83	79	76	73	70	67	64	61	59	56	53	51	48
99	96	93	90	86	83	80	77	74	71	68	65	62	59	57	54	52	49
100	96	93	90	86	83	80	77	74	71	68	65	62	59	57	54	52	49

pressor. These factors will be explained in a more detailed way in the next chapter. There is also a considerable difference in volumetric efficiency depending on the type of compressor used.

Relative Humidity. The amount of water vapor that is carried by a volume of air is given as *relative humidity*, and is the relation between the actual amount of water in the air and the maximum amount it is possible for the air to hold at the given temperature. At a high temperature the air will carry a larger amount of water vapor than at a lower temperature. The amount of water vapor the air will carry at 100% relative humidity, which is saturated air, approximately doubles for every 20°F (or 11.1°C) temperature rise. When the relative humidity reaches a point of saturation (100%), the water vapor is released as a liquid. *Dew point* may be defined as the temperature at which the air becomes saturated with water vapor.

The *hygrometer*, a stationary dry and wet bulb instrument, is used to find the approximate relative humidity. It is, however, not a reliable instrument and is often subject to large errors.

The relative humidity may be measured more accurately with a *wet bulb thermometer*, the bulb being covered closely with a clean fabric, thoroughly saturated with water (preferably distilled). This thermometer should be whirled around rapidly for some time so the bulb is cooled to the minimum. The observation should be made outdoors, away from heat sources, if ever so small, and away from direct sunlight.

The reading of the wet bulb thermometer should be recorded quickly, without touching the bulb. Then the reading of the dry bulb thermometer should be recorded and the wet bulb reading should be subtracted from this. With this difference and the dry thermometer temperature find the relative humidity from Table 2-6.

Air below 100% humidity is, as a rule, considered satisfactory for most industrial applications, and is considered dry air. An adequate margin of safety must, however, be maintained to ensure no condensation in the operation of tools susceptible to corrosion. For most industrial applications, air filters installed at the intakes of the pneumatic appliances are adequate. These filters will automatically remove water vapor caused by lowering the supply line from ceiling level, where the temperature may be extremely high on a hot summer day, to the intake level of the pneumatic appliance, which is close to the floor level.

There are, of course, also industrial processes where excessive moisture would be harmful to the material being processed. In such cases dryers should be used.

Review Questions

1. How is the pressure of the atmosphere most commonly measured?

2. What is another definition for vacuum?

3. Describe the definition of gage pressure.

4. What is a barometer?

5. What is the average barometric pressure at sea level?

6. What is the unit measurement for molecules in gaseous media?

7. What is the scientific term *torr*?

8. What is known as Mariotte's Law?

9. What is the composition of dry air at sea level?

10. What is known as free air?

11. Describe absolute humidity.

12. Describe relative humidity.

13. What is known as the dew point?

14. Describe the most accurate way to determine relative humidity.

SEE END OF BOOK FOR ANSWERS TO QUESTIONS

Compression, Expansion, and Compressors

Chapter

3

Fundamental Principles Governing Compression and Expansion of Gaseous Media

All engineering materials are compressible. The most compressible of these are the gaseous media. They are very useful in engineering work for storing up energy for future use. For this purpose, the air enveloping the earth is the most commonly used gas. Most industrial plants today take advantage of this common commodity in one way or another to perform useful work. For successful use of the gaseous media a good understanding of the basic laws governing their behavior is therefore necessary.

One of the most fundamental laws of nature is that energy can neither be created or destroyed, but is the force required to overcome resistance in transmitting a motion from one place to another or storing up this energy for potential use. This is exactly what is done in compressing the gaseous medium. As stated in the previous chapter, a gaseous medium for performing work has the inherent characteristic of taking the exact shape of the confinement it occupies. Another important characteristic of the medium is that the unit pressure within one confinement is exactly the same on all walls of the confinement. This is Pascal's Law. In this connection see Fig. 3–1.

Notice that in the extremely irregular container illustrated in Fig. 3–1 the same unit pressure is exerted equally on all points regardless of their direction or distance from one another.

In the process of compressing or expanding a gaseous medium, energy is

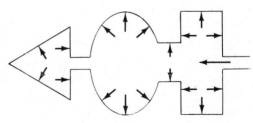

Fig. 3–1. Pressure is equal at all points in this irregular shaped container. This illustrates Pascal's Law.

transformed, since it cannot be destroyed. The effect of this transformation is that heat is generated during compression and refrigeration takes place during expansion. And, as shown by the British physicist Joule, a perfect gas has no latent heat capacity.

It was formerly believed that many gases such as air, oxygen, nitrogen, and hydrogen could not be liquefied at any temperature. These gases were given the name of *permanent gases*. All gases now known have, however, been liquefied.

A *perfect gas* is a hypothetical gas which will follow the simple laws in this chapter exactly.

Basically the gaseous media, of which air is the most commonly used, can be compressed or expanded according to two different laws, *adiabatic* or *isothermal*, since the temperature rises under compression and falls under expansion. This is expressed by Charles' Law, expressed in two basic ways.

Before we go into these two basic ways of compression and expansion of a gaseous medium in detail, however, it is well to fix in our minds that 100% adiabatic or isothermal compressions and expansions are impossible in practical cases.

Pure adiabatic compression requires that compression or expansion take place without removing any heat whatsoever during compression or adding any heat whatsoever during expansion.

Inversely, pure isothermal compression requires that heat be removed or added at exactly the same rate as heat is generated during compression or removed during expansion.

These 100% conditions are impossible in practical cases, because we can learn from the theory of heat transfer in thermodynamics that all known materials will conduct heat.

1. At *constant pressure*, the volume of a gaseous medium is proportional to its absolute temperature. Mathematically this is:

$$\frac{V_1}{T_1} = \frac{V_2}{T_2}; \quad T_2 = \frac{T_1 \times V_2}{V_1}; \quad V_2 = \frac{V_1 \times T_2}{T_1},$$

where:

V_1 = initial volume of the gaseous medium

V_2 = final volume of the gaseous medium

T_1 = initial absolute temperature of the gaseous medium

T_2 = final absolute temperature of the gaseous medium

Note that for these formulas to work, both temperatures must be in *absolute* values, *not* in degrees C or degrees F. Also, the constant pressure is absolute: *psia*, not *psig*. More will be said about absolute values later on.

See Fig. 3–2, a cross-sectional view of an apparatus illustrating this part of

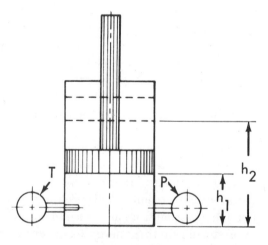

Fig. 3–2. Schematic illustration of cylinder and close-fitting piston showing that at *constant pressure* volume of gas is proportional to its absolute temperature. Gages shown are T, calibrated to absolute temperature and P, calibrated to absolute pressure.

Charles' Law. What we have here is a cylinder with a close-fitting piston of substantial weight. The air in the cylinder below this piston is the medium being investigated. Assume that the piston is free to move up and down, being held to a given height only by the air beneath it. For simplicity, further assume that T is a temperature gage calibrated in absolute degrees and P is a pressure gage calibrated to units of absolute pressure rather than ordinary gage pressure.

Now assume that the pressure gage P shows a pressure of 20 psia, the pressure necessary to hold the piston at the vertical height h_1, and that no air can escape from the cylinder. As long as the absolute temperature of the air registered by the temperature gage T remains the same (T_1 of the equation), the piston will remain at height h_1. This initial volume (V_1 of the equation) will be V_1 = piston area $\times h_1$.

If, however, the air in the cylinder is heated, while the resistance of the piston remains unchanged, the pressure registered on gage P will also remain stationary during the heating process. But when a new temperature T_2 has been reached, the piston has moved to a new position h_2 while the pressure has remained constant. At this point we have an expanded volume of air under the piston. This will be V_2 = piston area $\times h_2$.

To make the apparatus shown in Fig. 3–2 really practical would require a precise method of measuring heights h_1 and h_2. This could easily be done using a suitable height gage outside the cylinder, measuring from the bottom of the cylinder wall to the top of the piston rod extending above the cylinder. The height of the rod, plus the thickness of the piston itself, plus the bottom wall thickness of the cylinder, could be subtracted from height gage readings to obtain the heights h_1 and h_2. For simplicity, a measuring device was not included in the illustration.

In this example we have seen how the gaseous medium behaves when the pressure is held constant while the volume is allowed to change proportionately to a change in absolute temperature. The second aspect of Charles' Law, of at least equal importance, follows.

2. At *constant volume*, the pressure is proportional to its absolute temperature. Mathematically this is:

$$\frac{p_1}{T_1} = \frac{p_2}{T_2}; \ T_2 = \frac{T_1 \times p_2}{p_1}; \ p_2 = \frac{p_1 \times T_2}{T_1},$$

where:

p_1 = initial absolute pressure of the gaseous medium

p_2 = final absolute pressure of the gaseous medium

T_1 = initial absolute temperature of the gaseous medium

T_2 = final absolute temperature of gas the gaseous medium

This is the adiabatic form, in which the temperature is not controlled but allowed to increase or decrease to a maximum with increase or decrease of pressure. Adiabatic compression or expansion takes place when the gaseous medium is compressed or expanded without transmission of heat from it or to it. This can, of course, only happen if the gaseous medium is compressed or expanded in a cylinder made of material which will not transmit any heat from or to the enclosed area while the process is in progress. In practice, no known material fully meets this requirement.

Fluid Power: Pneumatics

See Fig. 3–3 showing an apparatus similar, but not identical, to the apparatus shown in Fig. 3–2. In Fig. 3–3 the piston is locked at a vertical height h so that the volume cannot change.

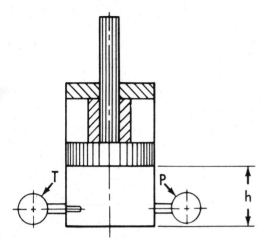

Fig. 3–3. In this cylinder and piston apparatus the piston is prevented from moving, to illustrate that at *constant volume* the absolute pressure of a gas is proportional to its absolute temperature.

Assume that the air in the cylinder below the piston is heated from absolute temperature T_1 to absolute temperature T_2, as shown on temperature gage T. The air in the cylinder cannot expand, so the absolute pressure will rise from p_1 to p_2, as shown on gage P. It has been found that the absolute pressure increases in direct proportion to the increase in absolute temperature.

Boyle's Law, however states: At *constant temperature* the absolute pressure of a gaseous medium is inversely proportional to its volume. Mathematically this is:

$$\frac{p_1}{p_2} = \frac{V_2}{V_1}; \quad p_2 = \frac{p_1 \times V_1}{V_2}; \quad V_2 = \frac{p_1 \times V_1}{p_2},$$

where:

p_1 = initial absolute pressure of the gaseous medium

p_2 = final absolute pressure of the gaseous medium

V_1 = initial volume of the gaseous medium

V_2 = final volume of the gaseous medium

Fig. 3–4 illustrates this law schematically, using an apparatus identical to the one previously shown in Fig. 3–2 but operated differently.

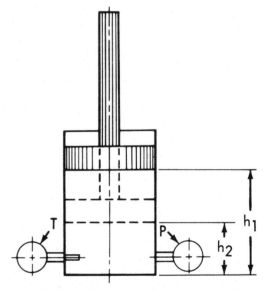

Fig. 3–4. Here the cylinder and piston apparatus is set up to move the piston by pushing the piston rod, to illustrate Boyle's Law that at *constant temperature* the absolute pressure of gas is inversely proportional to its volume.

Assume that the piston has been pushed from a height of h_1 to h_2 and that the absolute temperature T has been held constant during the process. Further assume that as a result of pushing the piston we find the two volumes beneath the piston to be:

V_1 = piston area $\times h_1 = 2$ cubic units

V_2 = piston area $\times h_2 = 1$ cubic unit (because the original height has been reduced one half)

Then, with the initial pressure of 14.7 psia, or 1.033 kg/cm² absolute in the metric system, the final pressure P_2 would be:

$$\frac{14.7 \times 2}{1} = 29.4 \text{ psia, or } \frac{1.033 \times 2}{1}$$

$$2.066 \text{ kg/cm}^2 \text{ absolute.}$$

The calculation can be verified by absolute pressure gage P.

This behavior of a gaseous medium was discovered simultaneously by Mariotte and Boyle.

When compressing or expanding a gaseous medium, a certain relationship must be considered between pressure, volume, and temperature. This relationship can be determined by combining the two experimental laws, Boyle's and Charles', as was done by Gay-Lussac. This may be expressed as follows:

$$\frac{p_1 V_1}{T_1} = \frac{p_2 V_2}{T_2} \text{ (The General Gas Law)}$$

Also,

$$p_1 V_1 = p_2 V_2 = M \text{ (a constant), where:}$$

$p_x =$ pressure at any points; $V_x =$ volume at that point:

$$p_x = \frac{p_1 V_1}{V_x}$$

Absolute Pressure and Gage Pressure

Absolute pressure is used in calculations pertaining to the performance of a compressor, as we have seen in previous examples. As a rule, however, *gage pressure* is used in calculations concerning the performance and safety of components operated by the gaseous media after leaving the compressor. At this point, therefore, a simple clarification of these two expressions would be helpful.

See Fig. 3–5, a schematic illustration of gage pressure and absolute pressure. Assume a tank A has a glass tube on one side, open to the atmosphere at B. On the other side this tank has a U-shaped glass tube filled with mercury to a height $a-b$. The mercury will then be at exactly the same height in both branches of the tube, C and D, because the atmosphere exerts the same pressure at both surfaces of the mercury. There is balance, and the pressure is atmospheric, or 29.921 inches of mercury (or 76 cm Hg) at sea level.

Now assume that a check valve is fastened to tube B and a higher pressure is forced into tank A. The mercury in branch C will fall to d, and in branch D it will rise an equal amount, to point e.

We now have an indication of the pressure by h. This pressure in h is actually the pressure above the prevailing atmospheric pressure and is called the *gage pressure, psig,* or *kg/cm² gage.* This pressure is the actual pressure that the walls of tank A are exposed to. If then the height of mercury h is 50 inches, or 127 cm, we can easily figure it with a little arithmetic: $50 \times 0.4912 = 24.56$ psig, or $127 \times 0.136 = 1.727$ kg/cm² gage.

The absolute pressure, however, is the actual pressure exerted on surface d of mercury column C from tank A, and is equal to the pressure of the atmosphere (29.921 inches of mercury or 76 cm Hg) plus the mercury height h, times the pressure of this mercury, figuring this pressure as 0.4912 psia per inch of height or as 0.0136 kg/cm² absolute per centimeter of height.

The absolute pressure in this case can be easily calculated: $(29.921 + 50) \times 0.4912 = 39.26$ psia. In the metric system

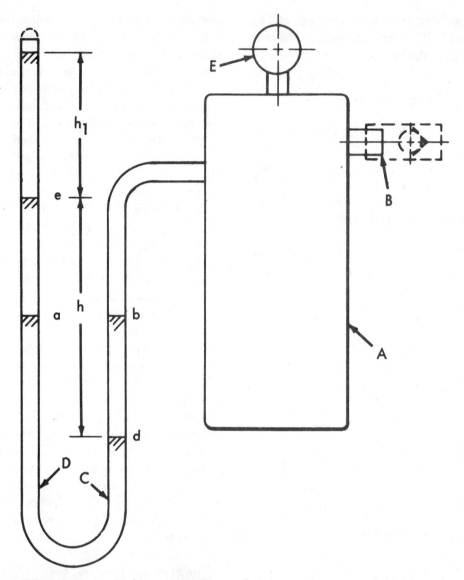

Fig. 3–5. This apparatus, used to illustrate the difference between gage pressure and absolute pressure, consists of tank *A*, bent glass tube *D* and *C*, straight tube *B*, and pressure gage *E*. The bent glass tube is partially filled with mercury.

this would be: $(76 + 127) \times 0.0136 = 2.76$ kg/cm² absolute.

If branch *D* in the glass tube were closed at its end and the gaseous medium above surface *e* of the mercury column were evacuated, the mercury would have risen a height corresponding to the prevailing mercury reading of the atmosphere, 29.921 inches of mercury or 76 cm Hg. This pressure is then equal to the gage, 50 inches of mercury or 127 cm Hg, plus the pressure of the atmosphere assumed to be 29.921 inches of mercury or 76 cm Hg, which again is 39.26 psia or 203 cm Hg equal to 2.76 kg/cm², the absolute pressure in tank *A*.

For industrial use the gage is always set at zero for the prevailing atmospheric pressure. The notation *psi* or *kg/cm²* is always considered as pressure above the atmospheric pressure, and this is the gage pressure. Absolute pressure must, however, always be indicated as *psia* or *kg/cm² absolute*. If the gage pressure for one component shows 100 psi or 7.03 kg/cm² and for another component shows 50 psi or 3.515 kg/cm², the pressure in the first component is twice as much as in the second component.

If absolute pressures were used instead of gage pressures, the pressure in the first component would be 114.7 psia or 8.036 kg/cm² absolute, and in the second component 64.7 psia or 4.548 kg/cm² absolute. Since $64.7 \times 2 = 129.4$, or $4.548 \times 2 = 9.096$, much more than 114.7 in the U.S. system or 8.063 in the metric system, misleading results would be obtained in calculating strength and performance of components.

Calculations for behavior of the gaseous media generally involve *proportions* in volumes, absolute pressures, and absolute temperatures. In such cases the absolute pressure is always used and is properly designated either as *psia* or as *kg/cm² absolute*.

Vacuum

Theoretically, vacuum may be defined as an enclosure devoid of all matter. This condition is impossible to obtain in industrial plants. *Partial vacuum* has, however, widespread applications in many industrial processes.

Torr

In vacuum technology, where the pressures are very low, a technical term has been established for a unit of pressure. This is the *torr*, which is 1/760 of atmospheric pressure. As standard atmospheric pressure at sea level is 76 cm or 760 mm Hg in the metric system, 1 torr equals 1 mm of mercury. It is readily seen that the atmosphere under standard conditions exerts 760 torr on a container open to the atmosphere, and is equivalent to 14.7 psia. An equivalent expression in the metric system is 76 cm Hg. (Hg is the chemical symbol for mercury.) The expression *torr* is in honor of the Italian scientist Torricelli.

Microns

Extremely low pressures are also sometimes given as *microns*, a micron being 1/1,000 of a torr.

Absolute or perfect vacuum is never practical, so various stages of vacuum have been designated:

1. Rough Vacuum = 760 torr to 1 torr
2. Low Vacuum = 1 torr to 10^{-3} torr (that is, .001 torr or 1 micron)
3. High Vacuum = 10^{-3} torr to 10^{-6} torr
4. Very High Vacuum = 10^{-6} torr to 10^{-9} torr
5. Ultra High Vacuum = 10^{-9} torr and less

Partial Pressure

This expression is generally used where more than one gaseous medium is contained in an enclosure. The expression is derived from the Dalton Law, which may be defined in this way: *the pressure one gas exerts on an enclosure is not affected by the pressure that another or other gases in the same container exert on the same enclosure.*

If, for instance, a container is filled with oxygen to a pressure of 100 torr and nitrogen to a pressure of 150 torr, the total pressure exerted on the walls of the container would be:

$p = p_1 + p_2 = 100 \text{ torr} + 150 \text{ torr}$
$= 250 \text{ torr.}$

where:
p = total pressure
p_1 = pressure of oxygen
p_2 = pressure of nitrogen

Therefore, a mixture of a number of gases has a total pressure p, or the sum of the constituent gases:

$p = p_1 + p_2 + p_3 \ldots + p_n$, where p_n is the pressure of the last constituent.

As stated previously, in vacuum technology a perfect vacuum is never obtainable, so the pressure is therefore partial. Partial vacuum has widespread applications in industrial processes. These processes are very specialized fields, so they will merely be mentioned briefly. Some of these are:

1. **Coating.** A process of depositing both metallic and nonmetallic substances to objects in a high-vacuum enclosure, using sufficiently high temperature for evaporation to take place at an economical rate.

   This method is widely used for decorative purposes, where a very thin, uniform metallic coating may be applied to plastics. The method has also been used for coating materials that are subject to corrosion.

2. **Drying and Impregnation.** Insulating oils are used in the manufacture of many electrical components. A small amount of water is, however, always present in commercial oils. It has been found that removing even a very minute amount of water from the impregnating oil, using a partial vacuum, will increase its insulating resistivity by a considerable amount.

3. **Freeze-Drying.** This method of processing food under vacuum for the purpose of preservation. After the foods have been freeze-dehydrated it is possible to store them at room temperature for a long period of time.

4. **Vacuum Distillation.** This is a process of vaporizing and condensing a liquid mixture simultaneously in a vacuum enclosure. This method of distillation is distinguished by the fact that it can be carried out at a lower temperature than ordinary distillation.

5. **Cryogenic Insulation.** The thermos bottle is a well known example of this method of thermal insulation, which is used extensively for storing refrigerated mixtures. The method is also useful for keeping liquids hot for a considerable length of time. The thermal conductivity of air in the range of atmospheric pressure, 760 torr down to a pressure of about 10 torr, is relatively constant. For lower pressures, however, the thermal conductivity takes a sharp drop to a pressure of about 10^{-3} torr. Any further reduction in pressure shows no detectable drop in conductivity. The decrease in heat transfer from a pressure to 10 torr to 10^{-3} torr may be as high as a ratio of 20:1.

6. **Space Environment Simulation.** This field is important when dealing with interplanetary travel. Temperatures in the range of $-320°$ to $-400°$ F (or $-196°$ to $-240°$C) are estimated. The pressure in interplanetary space is estimated as 10^{-16} torr.

Absolute Temperature

The instruments found in general use for registering temperature were originated in the same time period by three different scientists. The two instruments most widely used are the one using the centigrade scale (called *Celsius* in the European countries) originated by Anders Celsius (1701–1744), a Swedish physicist, and the one using the Fahrenheit scale, which was originated by the German physicist Gabriel Fahrenheit (1686–1736). The less used Réaumur scale was originated by René Réaumur, a French physicist. These scales are all based on the two principal temperatures of pure water: the freezing point and boiling point at atmospheric pressure at sea level — a barometric reading of 76 cm Hg, 29.921 inches of mercury, 14.7 psia, or 1.0333 kg/cm².

The freezing point on the centigrade (or Celsius) and the Réaumur scales is 0°, and on the Fahrenheit scale it is 32°. The boiling point on the centigrade scale is 100°, and on the Réaumur scale it is 80°. On the Fahrenheit scale it is 212°. This temperature range, from freezing to boiling points, is divided into equal parts on the centigrade scale, each division being 1°C. On the Réaumur scale it is divided into 80 equal parts, each division being 1°R. On the Fahrenheit scale it is divided into $212 - 32 = 180$ equal parts, each division being 1°F. These graduations are continued in increments above and below the boiling and freezing points on all scales. From this comparison we can set up the following equations:

$$\frac{C°}{100} = \frac{R°}{80} = \frac{F° - 32}{180}$$

$$C° = \frac{5}{4} R° = \frac{5}{9} (F° - 32)$$

$$R° = \frac{4}{5} C° = \frac{4}{9} (F° - 32)$$

$$F° = \frac{9}{4} R° + 32 = \frac{9}{5} C° + 32$$

Now examine Fig. 3–6, showing the comparison between these scales. From a careful examination it is easily seen that 40°C is *not* twice as hot as 20°C or that 104°F is *not* twice as hot as 68°F or that 32°R is *not* twice as hot as 16°R, as many people erroneously believe. Notice, for example, that at the boiling point of water the Fahrenheit scale shows 112° higher than the centigrade scale, at the freezing point of water the Fahrenheit scale is 32° higher, and at −40°F is nearly the same as the centigrade scale.

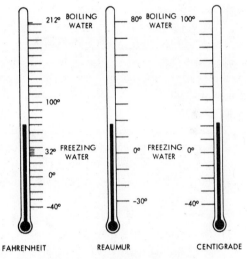

Fig. 3–6. **Comparison of thermometer scales.**

For your convenience, Table 3–1, showing conversions of centigrade and Fahrenheit temperatures over a wide range, is included in this chapter.

Since most calculations for the behavior of gaseous media involving temperature changes are based on proportions, zero temperature for these calculations has been set at a point where no further cooling is considered possible. Charles proved that the volume of a confined gaseous medium would increase or decrease 1/273.2 of its original volume for every one degree centigrade change in tempera-

TABLE 3-1. TEMPERATURE CONVERSION FROM CENTIGRADE TO FAHRENHEIT OR FAHRENHEIT TO CENTIGRADE

LOOK FOR THE NUMBER OF DEGREES YOU WISH (EITHER FAHRENHEIT OR CENTIGRADE) IN THE MIDDLE COLUMN MARKED TEMP. THEN FIND ° C IMMEDIATELY TO THE LEFT OR THE ° F IMMEDIATLEY TO THE RIGHT.

° C	TEMP	° F	° C	TEMP	° F	° C	TEMP	° F	° C	TEMP	° F
-273.2	-459.7		-17.2	1	33.8	9.3	49	120.2	36.1	97	206.6
-268	-450		-16.6	2	35.6	9.9	50	122.0	36.6	98	208.4
-262	-440		-16.1	3	37.4	10.4	51	123.8	37.1	99	210.2
-257	-430		-15.5	4	39.2	11.1	52	125.6	37.7	100	212.0
-251	-420		-15.0	5	41.0	11.5	53	127.4	43.0	110	230.0
-246	-410		-14.4	6	42.8	12.1	54	129.2	49.0	120	248.0
-240	-400		-13.9	7	44.6	12.6	55	131.0	54.0	130	266.0
-234	-390		-13.3	8	46.4	13.2	56	132.8	60.0	140	284.0
-229	-380		-12.7	9	48.2	13.7	57	134.6	65.0	150	302.0
-223	-370		-12.2	10	50.0	14.3	58	136.4	71.0	160	320.0
-218	-360		-11.6	11	51.8	14.8	59	138.2	76.0	170	338.0
-212	-350		-11.1	12	53.6	15.6	60	140.0	83.0	180	356.0
-207	-340		-10.5	13	55.4	16.1	61	141.8	88.0	190	374.0
-201	-330		-10.0	14	57.2	16.6	62	143.6	93.0	200	392.0
-196	-320		- 9.4	15	59.0	17.1	63	145.4	99.0	210	410.0
-190	-310		- 8.8	16	61.8	17.7	64	147.2	100.0	212	413.0
-184	-300		- 8.3	17	63.6	18.2	65	149.0	104.0	220	428.0
-179	-290		- 7.7	18	65.4	18.8	66	150.8	110.0	230	446.0
-173	-280		- 7.2	19	67.2	19.3	67	152.6	115.0	240	464.0
-169	-273.2	-459.7	- 6.6	20	68.0	19.9	68	154.4	121.0	250	482.0
-168	-270	-454.0	- 6.1	21	69.8	20.4	69	156.2	127.0	260	500.0
-162	-260	-436.0	- 5.5	22	71.6	21.0	70	158.0	132.0	270	518.0
-157	-250	-418.0	- 5.0	23	73.4	21.5	71	159.8	138.0	280	536.0
-151	-240	-400.0	- 4.4	24	75.2	22.2	72	161.6	143.0	290	554.0
-146	-230	-382.0	- 3.9	25	77.0	22.7	73	163.4	149.0	300	572.0
-140	-220	-364.0	- 3.3	26	78.8	23.3	74	165.2	154.0	310	590.0
-134	-210	-346.0	- 2.8	27	80.6	23.8	75	167.0	160.0	320	608.0
-129	-200	-328.0	- 2.2	28	82.4	24.4	76	168.8	165.0	330	626.0
-123	-190	-310.0	- 1.6	29	84.2	25.0	77	170.6	171.0	340	644.0
-118	-180	-292.0	- 1.1	30	86.0	25.5	78	172.4	177.0	350	662.0
-112	-170	-474.0	- 0.6	31	87.8	26.2	79	174.2	182.0	360	680.0
-107	-160	-256.0	.0	32	89.6	26.8	80	176.0	188.0	370	698.0
-101	-150	-238.0	+ 0.5	33	91.4	27.3	81	177.8	193.0	380	716.0
- 96	-140	-220.0	1.1	34	93.2	27.7	82	179.6	199.0	390	734.0
- 90	-130	-202.0	1.6	35	95.0	28.2	83	181.4	204.0	400	752.0
- 84	-120	-184.0	2.2	36	96.8	28.8	84	183.2	210.0	410	770.0
- 79	-110	-166.0	2.7	37	98.6	29.3	85	185.0	215.0	420	788.0
- 73	-100	-148.0	3.3	38	100.4	29.9	86	186.8	221.0	430	806.0
- 68	- 90	-130.0	3.8	39	102.2	30.4	87	188.6	226.0	440	824.0
- 62	- 80	-112.0	4.4	40	104.0	31.0	88	190.4	232.0	450	842.0
- 57	- 70	- 94.0	4.9	41	105.8	31.5	89	192.2	238.0	460	860.0
- 51	- 60	- 76.0	5.5	42	107.6	32.1	90	194.0	243.0	470	878.0
- 46	- 50	- 58.0	6.0	43	109.4	32.6	91	195.8	249.0	480	896.0
- 40	- 40	- 40.0	6.6	44	111.2	33.3	92	197.6	254.0	490	914.0
- 34	- 30	- 22.0	7.1	45	113.0	33.8	93	199.4	260.0	500	932.0
- 29	- 20	- 4.0	7.7	46	114.0	34.4	94	201.2	265.0	510	950.0
- 23	- 10	+ 14.0	8.2	47	116.6	34.9	95	203.0	271.0	520	968.0
- 17.7	- 0	32.0	8.8	48	118.4	35.5	96	204.8	276.0	530	986.0

ture. This would be an increase or de-crease of 1/459.7 of its original volume for every degree Fahrenheit change in temperature.

According to the experimental laws of Boyle and Charles or Gay-Lussac, the absolute temperature is directly proportional to the product of absolute pressure and volume, as previously stated. Two scales for absolute temperature are in general use in industry, both scales having a common zero point beyond which no further cooling is possible. In practice, of course, this zero point can never be reached.

The Kelvin (K) scale is the *centigrade* absolute scale. The Rankine scale is the *Fahrenheit* absolute scale. See Fig. 3-7.

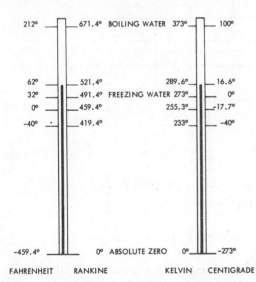

Fig. 3-7. Comparison of Rankine and Kelvin absolute temperatures to Fahrenheit and centigrade (Celsius) temperatures.

To convert centigrade to Kelvin, add 273.2°: $K° = C° + 273.2$.

To convert Fahrenheit to Rankine, add 459.4°: $Rankine° = F° + 459.7$.

To avoid confusion, it may sometimes be necessary to designate Kelvin degrees as K_c, indicating that it belongs to the centigrade scale, and Rankine degrees as R_f, indicating that it belongs to the Fahrenheit scale. This practice is particularly useful in the case of the Rankine scale, to avoid confusion with the Réaumur scale, which is abbreviated as R. Many writers prefer to spell out the word Rankine in full.

Gas Constant

In all branches of engineering, the various materials are known by some distinguishing characteristics. Assume that we have several wires of exactly the same diameters but made of a number of different materials. These wires would offer a great variation of resistance to identical values of an electric current sent through them at the same temperature. We do not know exactly what takes place in these wires when we send an electric current through them, but we can measure the results very accurately, because heat is produced in direct proportion to the current and the resistance of the material. It is a known and proven fact that the resistance of any one material is always the same at the same temperature. What really takes place in these various materials as the electric current is sent through them is highly hypothetical, but we do not have to know what actually takes place so long as we can measure the results accurately. In this case the resistance of the material, which determines the work performed on the material, has been found experimentally and it is always the same at the same temperature. We can therefore call the resistance a *constant* peculiar to each material.

In the gaseous media we have an analogous condition. The molecular weights of various gaseous media vary widely, as

TABLE 3-2. PERFECT GASES - DISTINQUISHING CHARACTERISTICS

NAME OF GAS	CHEMICAL SYMBOL	NUMBER OF ATOMS	MOLECULAR WEIGHT APPROX. (M)	GAS CONSTANT (R)
AIR	------	------	29	53.34
AMMONIA	NH_3	4	17	90.50
CARBON DIOXIDE	CO_2	3	44	35.09
CARBON MONOXIDE	CO	2	28	35.14
HELIUM	He	1	4	386.00
HYDROGEN	H_2	2	2.016	765.87
METHANE	CH_4	5	16	95.87
METHYL CHLORIDE	CH_3Cl	5	50.5	30.57
NITROGEN	N_2	2	28	55.14
OXYGEN	O_2	2	32	48.25
SULFUR DIOXIDE	SO_2	3	64	24.12

shown in Table 3-2. Through a number of experiments, however, it has been established that a certain constant relationship exists between the molecular weight *m* of a gaseous medium and a number slightly more than 1544. This relationship is known as the *gas constant* R = 1544/m This relationship is not absolutely exact, because sometimes we may see it as 1544/m and at other times as 1545/m. Either one is close enough for any engineering calculation.

Based on this relationship we may then set up the following formula according to the laws of Charles and Boyle. This is valuable in the calculation of volume and weights for gaseous media at given temperatures:

$$p V = R W T$$

Remember that whether the U.S. system or the metric system of measurement is used, all measurements must be converted to the same units.

p = Pressure in weight W per cubic unit

V = Volume in cubic units occupied by W weight of the gaseous medium at T°

W = Weight of the gaseous medium

T = Absolute temperature

R = Gas constant, see Table 3 – 2

Examples:

1. What is the weight per cubic foot of air at 800 lbs/in² absolute (800 psia) and 70°F?

From Table 3 – 1 we see that the absolute temperature for 70°F would be 70 + 459.7 = 529.7. Transforming the basic equation to solve for W, we get:

$$W = pV/RT = \frac{800 \times 144 \times 1}{53.34 \times 529.7} = 4.08 \text{ lbs}$$

2. What volume does 1 pound of nitrogen occupy when the barometric pressure is 14.7 lbs/in² (14.7 psia) and the temperature is 60°F?

R = 55.14 for nitrogen, from Table 3 – 2. Transforming the basic equation to solve for V, we get:

$$V = \frac{RWT}{p} = \frac{55.14 \times 1 \times 519.4}{14.7 \times 144}$$

= 13.53 cubic feet

3. In the metric system of measuring what would be the weight of air per liter at 60 kg/cm² and 20°C?

p = 60 kg/cm²

T = 20 + 273 = 293° absolute or degrees Kelvin. Solving for W, we get:

$$W = pV/RT = \frac{60 \times 1 \times 10^3}{53.34 \times 293}$$

= 0.384 kg or 384 grams

4. What volume does 1 kg of nitrogen occupy when the barometric pressure is 1.33 kg/cm² and the temperature is 18°C?

$$V = \frac{RWT}{p} = \frac{55.14 \times 1 \times 291}{1.033}$$

= 15.53 liters

In the above examples we should remember that 1 liter, which actually is 1 cubic decimeter, also is equal to 1,000 cubic centimeters. 1 decimeter is equal to 10 centimeters in length measurements, Therefore, in cubic measurements, 1 cubic decimeter is equal to $10 \times 10 \times 10$ = 1,000 cubic centimeters.

Compressors

Many engines such as steam and internal combustion engines may be classified as compressors. Also many types of jet engines, which expand a gaseous medium to do useful work, may be put in the category of compressors. Such engines, however, are in specialized fields of their own outside the scope of this book.

Energy is required to compress a gaseous medium, and since energy is the force necessary to overcome resistance in doing this work, it is very important to consider some of the undesirable effects in this process.

Consider, for instance, the simple job of bending a soft steel wire. The bending is the task to be performed, and may therefore be classed as useful work. To do this requires energy, but not all of this energy goes into the useful work of bending the wire; some of it is used in generating heat induced by the physical resistance of the wire to the bending operation. If the bending is slow the heat generated will be dissipated by conduction, convection, and radiation, without being detected. If, however, the wire is bent rapidly it will become hot to the touch. The heat in both cases is wasted energy. In the first case the waste is small, in the second case it is greater.

Assume that in some way the wire could be kept at a constant temperature while the bending was in progress. Then all the energy expended would go to the useful work of bending the wire. There would be no waste in generating unwanted heat.

In the process of compressing a gaseous medium we have the same effects. Some of the energy is expended in reducing the volume of the gaseous medium, thus increasing the pressure for potential future use. This is the useful work. Some of the energy expended is, however, also wasted in the heat induced by the resistance to compression. There are, of course, also some other unavoidable wastes of energy resulting from friction in the moving components of the compressor and friction caused by moving the compressed gaseous medium. All these undesirable side-effects must be considered in calculating the output of a compressor and selecting the right compressor for the job being considered.

Theoretically, adiabatic compression of a gaseous medium is the most wasteful. In this form of compression the temperature is not, or cannot be, controlled. Therefore the pressure must be raised to a higher level than required, because when the gaseous medium leaves the compressor it will gradually cool to ambient temperature and thus lower the pressure. The energy expended in raising the pressure above that which is required is a waste of energy. There are, however, many cases where compression close to adiabatic conditions would not be objectionable, for instance a compressor for intermittent duty, where low pressures are required.

Fortunately, however, there are several ways of obtaining compression closer to the isothermal (uniform temperature) condition. These are:

1. Air cooled compressors depending on large surface areas to dissipate the heat.

2. Water-cooled compressors, usually with a jacket circulating cold water around the outside of the cylinder.

3. It may be desirable to use multistage compressors with intercoolers when the required pressure is in the higher ranges.

Positive Displacement Compressors

The distinctive feature of a positive displacement compressor is that the gaseous medium is compressed to a higher pressure by being positively and gradually confined in a decreasing space.

Fig. 3–8 shows the three compression curves to be considered:
1. The undesirable adiabatic curve.
2. The idealistic isothermal curve.
3. The practical curve, obtained by careful planning, design, and operation.

We have previously found from combining the Boyle's and Charles' or Gay-Lussac Laws that when the temperature

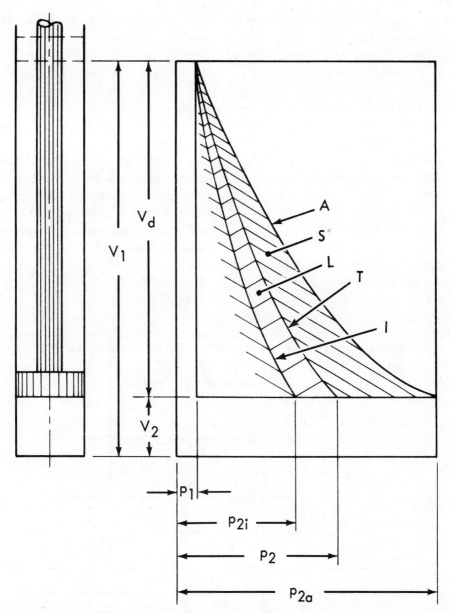

Fig. 3—8. Adiabatic, isothermal, and actual curves for compression of gaseous media. Symbols used and their meanings are:

A = Adiabatic Curve
I = Isothermal Curve
T = Tangible or Produced Curve
S = Saved during Compression
L = Lost during Compression
V_i = Initial Volume

V_d = Displacement
V_2 = Discharge Volume (Clearance)
p_1 = Intake Pressure
p_{2i} = Isothermal Discharge Pressure
p_2 = Tangible or Actual Discharge Pressure
p_{2a} = Adiabatic Discharge Pressure

is constant, the product of pressure and volume is also constant:

$$p_1 \times V_1 = p_2 \times V_2, \text{ or } p \times V_n^k = \text{constant}$$

This is isothermal compression where $k = 1$. The subscript n only signifies that this V^k term is the last one in a series of terms, such as $V_1^k, V_2^k, V_3^k \ldots V_n^k$, with n designating the nth term.

$$p_2 = \frac{p_1 \times V_1^1}{V_2}, \text{ or simply } p_2 = \frac{p_1 V_1}{V_2}$$

For adiabatic compression, however, k becomes a greater value than 1, because it is the ratio of specific heat at constant pressure to specific heat at constant volume, given as:

$$k = \frac{c_p}{c_v},$$

where:

k = a constant ratio for each gaseous medium

c_p = specific heat at constant pressure

c_v = specific heat at constant volume

In Table 3–3 we find that the specific heat at constant pressure and the specific heat at constant volume for dry air between 32°F and 212°F (14.8°C and 100°C) are:

$c_p = 0.238$

$c_v = 0.169$

TABLE 3-3. SPECIFIC HEAT OF GASES, 32° F to 212° F (unless indicated with *)

NAME OF GAS	CHEMICAL SYMBOL	SPECIFIC HEAT AT CONSTANT PRESSURE c_p	SPECIFIC HEAT AT CONSTANT VOLUME c_v	$k = \dfrac{c_p}{c_v}$
AIR	------	0.238	0.169	1.41
AMMONIA	NH_3	0.520	0.391	1.33
CARBON DIOXIDE*	CO_2	0.210	0.160	1.31
CARBON MONOXIDE	CO	0.243	0.173	1.41
HELIUM	He	1.250	0.750	1.66
HYDROGEN	H_2	3.410	2.420	1.41
METHANE	CH_4	0.593	0.450	1.32
METHYL CHLORIDE	CH_3Cl	0.240	0.200	1.20
NITROGEN	N_2	0.244	0.173	1.41
OXYGEN	O_2	0.218	0.155	1.41
SULFUR DIOXIDE	$SO2$	0.154	0.123	1.25

* 59° F TO 212° F, or 14.8° C TO 100° C

For adiabatic compression of dry air we therefore have:

$$k = \frac{c_p}{c_v} = \frac{0.238}{0.169} = 1.41$$

The values of k for various gaseous media may be found in Table 3–3. The practical value for k does, however, vary considerably, depending on design and operation of the compressor. Some authorities give the value of k as low as 1.15 for multi-stage compression and as high as 1.3 for a single cylinder dry compressor.

For adiabatic compression the equation for pressures then becomes:

$$p_2 = p_1 \left(\frac{V_1}{V_2} \right)^k$$

We can compare actual conditions to theoretical conditions by referring to Fig. 3–8, which shows a long cylinder and a piston of relatively small diameter.

Assume that the compression ratio for this cylinder is 7 to 1 and that the piston diameter is 5 inches (or 12.7 cm) with a stroke of 3-1/2 inches (or 8.89 cm), with a piston displacement of 20 cubic inches per inch of stroke (or 127 cm³ per cm of stroke). The total displacement is then $20 \times 3.5 = 70$ cubic inches (or $127 \times 8.89 = 1126$ cm³) $= V_d$. To find the final volume, V_2, we subtract the total displacement, V_d, from the initial volume, V_1.

$$\frac{V_1}{V_2} = \frac{7}{1} \text{ ratio}; V_2 = \frac{V_1}{7} = V_1 - V_d$$

$$V_1 - V_d = \frac{V_1}{7}; V_1 = 7(V_1 - V_d)$$

$$= 7(V_1 - 70)$$

$$V_1 = 7V_1 - 490; 7 V_1 - V_1 = 490;$$

$$6 V_1 = 490$$

$$V_1 = 81.66 \text{ cubic inches}$$

$$V_2 = 81.66 - 70 = 11.66 \text{ cubic inches}$$

In the metric system we would then have:

$$V_1 = 7(V_1 - 1126) = 7 V_1 - 7882$$

$$6 V_1 = 7882$$

$$V_1 = \frac{7882}{6} = 1313 \text{ cm}^3$$

$$V_2 = V_1 - V_d = 1313 - 1126 = 187 \text{ cm}^3$$

To find the final pressures for isothermal, adiabatic, and practical conditions, based on this example and the general equation $p_2 = p_1 \left(\frac{V_1}{V_2} \right)^k$, we substitute the actual numbers. This is done in the following paragraphs.

(In all cases assume that $p_1 = 14.7$ pounds per square inch and that p_{2i} designates p_2 under isothermal conditions, while p_{2a} designates p_2 under adiabatic or partially adiabatic conditions.)

For *isothermal compression* we find:

$$p_{2i} = \frac{14.7 \times 81.66}{11.66} = 103 \text{ psi}$$

(In this case $k = 1$ and does not enter into the calculation) For *adiabatic compression* we find:

$$p_{2a} = 14.7 \left(\frac{81.66}{11.66} \right)^{1.41} = 228 \text{ psi}$$

For the most *practical compression* obtained by compressors, using a k value of 1.15, we find:

$$p_{2a} = 14.7 \left(\frac{81.66}{11.66} \right)^{1.15} = 138 \text{ psi}$$

Fluid Power: Pneumatics

To work with these equations with partly fractional exponents you will have to use logarithms or the slide rule. Here is an example, in easy steps:

Let $N = \left(\dfrac{81.66}{11.66}\right)^{1.41}$; $N = (7.003+)^{1.41}$, or

for practical purposes, $N = (7)^{1.41}$.

Taking logs of both sides of this equation:

$\log N = 1.41 \times \log 7$; $\log 7 = 0.845$ (correct to 3 significant figures), from tables of common logarithms or slide rule.

$\log N = 1.41 \times 0.845 = 1.19145 = 1.191$ (approx.)

$N = $ antilog $1.191 = 15.54$

The rest is simple arithmetic:

$p_{2a} = 14.7 \times 15.54 = 228.438 = 228$ psi, rounded off to three significant figures). (Such a calculation as $N = (7.00)^{1.41}$ can be made in one continuous step on the log-log type of slide rule.)

By following examples previously given in the metric system and by referring to the metric system appendix at the end of the book, these examples may be easily converted to metric measurements.

Compression Diagrams. Two of the main diagrams are:
1. Diagram for Pressure Changes
2. Diagram for Work in Compression

A theoretical diagram may be expressed graphically to represent the pressure changes a gaseous medium is exposed to as it is compressed or expanded according to Boyle's Law as formulated by Mariotte, assuming that the temperature

is constant during compression. This is strictly a theoretical assumption shown in Fig. 3–9.

Such a condition is, of course, never possible in practice, because it is not practical to make a compressor without clearance, which is the volume of air left in the cylinder at the end of the stroke. Also it has been found that this clearance causes the compression curve to be lower than the theoretical curve shown in Fig. 3–9. This reduces the power requirement and the volumetric delivery of air from the cylinder in almost direct proportion.

Furthermore, the air left in the cylinder at the end of the stroke of the piston expands on the return stroke, thus lowering the pressure below the prevailing ambient pressure. This, of course, is a necessary requirement for the functioning of the compressor, since a differential pressure caused by expansion of a gaseous medium is necessary to move the gaseous medium. This differential in pressure must, of course, be great enough to overcome the resistance offered in the intake components of the compressor.

Fig. 3–10 shows an isothermal compression curve constructed from actual data. It shows clearly that the product of volume and pressure remains constant during isothermal compression or expansion. The given data and calculations to construct this curve are listed:

$p_1 = 14.7$ psia, initial pressure

$V_1 = 8$ cubic feet, initial volume

Assume then that:

$V_2 = \dfrac{3}{4}$ of V_1 or 6 cubic feet

$p_2 = \dfrac{p_1 \times V_1}{V_2} = \dfrac{14.7 \times 8}{6} = 19.6$ psia

$V_3 = \frac{1}{2}$ or V_1 or 4 cubic feet

$p_3 = \frac{p_1 \times V_1}{V_3} = \frac{14.7 \times 8}{4} = 29.4$ psia

$V_4 = \frac{1}{4}$ of V_1 or 2 cubic feet

$p_4 = \frac{p_1 \times V_1}{V_4} = \frac{14.7 \times 8}{2} = 58.8$ psia

$V_5 = 1.5$ cubic feet

$p_5 = \frac{14.7 \times 8}{1.5} = 78.4$ psia

$V_6 = 1$ cubic foot, discharge volume, (clearance volume)

$p_6 = \frac{14.7 \times 8}{1} = 117.6$ psia

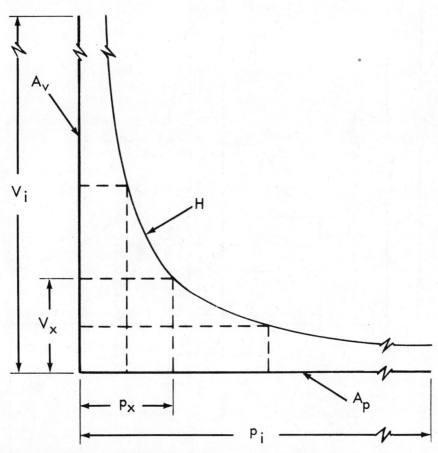

Fig. 3–9. Theoretical compressor diagram. Symbols used and their meanings are:

V_i = Infinite Volume
p_i = Infinite Pressure
V_x = Volume in Progress of Compression
p_x = Pressure in Progress of Compression
H = Pressure Curve, a true Hyperbola
A_v = Volume Asymptote, a straight line along the Volumetric Displacement that never will meet the Hyperbolic Curve
A_p = Pressure Asymptote, a straight line along the pressure measurements that never will meet the Hyperbolic Curve

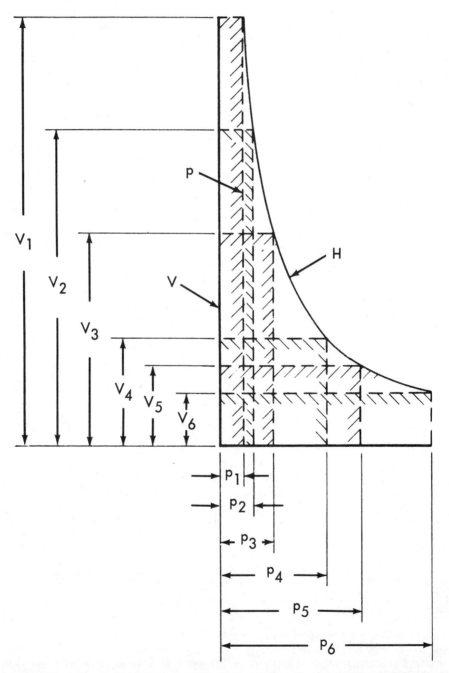

Fig. 3–10. Chart illustrating isothermal compression and expansion, showing that the product of volume and pressure remains constant during isothermal compression or expansion. The isothermal pressure curve *H* is a true hyperbola.

$$p_1 \times V_1 = p_2 \times V_2 = p_3 \times V_3 = p_4 \times V_4$$
$$= p_5 \times V_5 = p_6 \times V_6 = 117.6 \text{ psia}$$

The area of all shaded rectangles are equal

V = vacuum line

p = atmospheric or intake pressure line

H = isothermal pressure curve, a true hyperbola

By following examples previously given in the metric system and by referring to the metric system appendix at the end of the book, these examples may be easily converted to metric measurements.

Fig. 3–11 shows a graphical method for determining pressures for various volumes when the initial pressure and the various volumes are known.

Assume:

p_1 = 10 psia, initial pressure

V_1 = 6 cubic feet, initial volume

V_2 = 1 cubic foot, final volume

First draw line $A-B$, representing V_1, the initial volume. Then measure off $C-B$ on this line representing V_2, the final volume, and erect line $C-D$, representing p_1, the initial pressure. Draw a line from B through point D and extend this line to form triangles $C-B-D$ and $A-B-E$. Draw line $E-F$ and line $B-F$. Extend line $C-D$ to G. Draw line from D to H. $A-H$ also represents the initial pressure p_1. Since triangles $C-B-D$ and $A-B-E$ are identical, we may set up the following equation:

$$\frac{C \text{ to } D}{A \text{ to } E} = \frac{p_1}{p_2} = \frac{V_2}{V_1} \quad \text{This is Mariotte's Law.}$$

Now, we can find the pressure if volume V_1 is compressed to half of its original volume, V_x, by erecting a line from I to J, and drawing a line from B to J. Where this line intersects the line $C-G$ at K

draw a line to line $I-J$. The line $I-L$ is then pressure p_x when volume V_1 is compressed to half its original size and we have,

$$\frac{p_x}{p_2} = \frac{V_2}{V_x}$$

Pressure p_y, when volume V_1 has been compressed to 3/4 of its original size, may then be determined by constructing triangle $M-B-N$ and drawing line $P-O$.

In like manner, pressure p_z may also be determined by constructing triangle $R-B-S$ and drawing line $T-U$.

The pressure line for isothermal compression is then a hyperbolic curve $H-O-L-U-G$.

Work Required for Compression.

Energy, as previously mentioned, is the force required to overcome resistance. Work, then, is the product of force necessary to overcome resistance and the distance traveled to perform this work. Resistance is the opposing force generated in performing this work, such as the compression of the gaseous medium plus the friction generated by all moving parts in the compressor.

In the U.S. system of measurements this work is given in units of inch-pounds, foot-pounds, or foot-tons. In the metric system the units are kilogram-meters.

Power is the product of force and distance traveled, divided by the time required to perform this work, or a given amount of work in a given time. This power, in the U.S. system, is given in units of inch-pounds per minute, foot-pounds per minute, or foot-pounds per second. In the metric system the units would be kilogram-meters per second (kgm/sec).

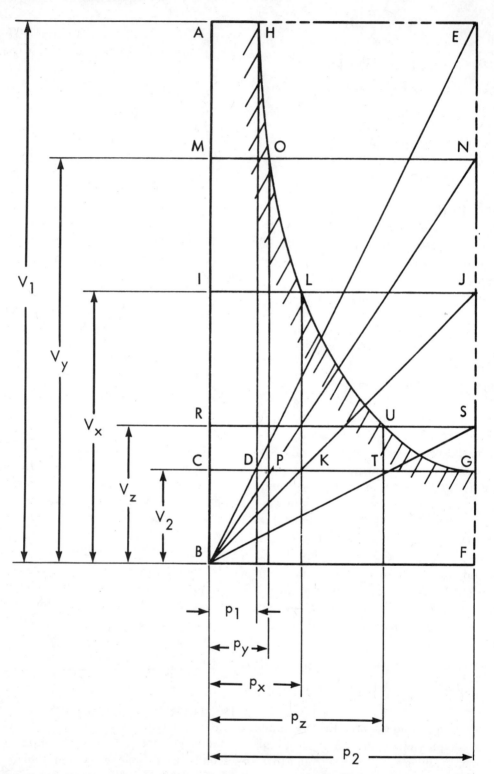

Fig. 3–11. Graphic layout of pressure for various volumes of constant temperature. The pressure line for iso-thermal compression is the hyperbolic curve *H-O-L-U-G*.

Horsepower, the most common unit of power for engineering work in the United States is figured in one of two ways:

1 HP = 33,000 foot-pounds per minute,

or

1 HP = 550 foot-pounds per second.

In the metric system the corresponding unit is a little less, or 75 kilogram-meters per second (which is 545 foot-pounds per second) or 32,550 foot-pounds per minute). This difference comes from the fact that it was found easier to use 75 than 76. For electrical work one horsepower is equivalent to 746 watts, or 0.746 kilowatt.

Indicated Horsepower. The mean effective pressure is used in calculating the actual power developed within the cylinder. To understand this procedure, let us refer to Fig. 3–12, which shows graphically the work performed during compression or expansion.

The construction of this isothermal compression curve was shown in Fig. 3–10.

Energy is transformed in the process of compressing a gaseous medium or expanding it. Fig. 3–12 illustrates the *work* performed during compression or expansion. Since work is the product of force and distance traveled, it consequently is the product of the mean effective pressure, p_m, times the volumetric displacement of the piston, V_d, which on the diagram is the distance traveled.

This is represented by the area of the rectangle $A-C-I-M-A$, which is equal to the area enclosed by the isothermal pressure curve $G-H$ and the straight sides $H-A-C-G$. Now, this is the actual work required for compression.

This work, the area under the isothermal curve $G-H-A-C-G$, may also be calculated by considering the area divided into rectangular strips of infinitesimal

widths and heights from the base line $A-B$ to the pressure line, the isothermal curve, $G-H$, each rectangle then added to represent the total area. For a clear illustration, the work area has been divided into 6 strips of equal widths. These 6 strips are enclosed by 7 pressure heights. Since the sides in each strip connecting p_1 to p_2, p_2 to p_3 etc approaches closely the hypotenuse in a triangle, the area (A) of the work produced would be approximately:

$$A = V_d \left(\frac{p_1 + 2p_2 + 2p_3 + 2p_4 + 2p_5 + 2p_6 + p_7}{12} \right)$$

(The height, or altitude of each small triangle is $\frac{V_d}{6}$, and you will recall that the area of a triangle is 1/2 the altitude times the base.)

As we found before, this is also the area of rectangle $A-C-I-M-A$, which is,

$$A = p_m V_d; \; p_m = \frac{A}{V_d}$$

We may therefore say,

$$p_m = \frac{p_1 + 2p_2 + 2p_3 + 2p_4 + 2p_5 + 2p_6 + p_7}{12}$$

This area under the curve $G-H$ could be calculated more exactly by integral calculus, but the approximate integration illustrated here is close enough for most practical applications.

Now, having determined the mean effective pressure, p_m, we are in a position to calculate the indicated horsepower, taking into consideration not only this pressure but the size and speed of the compressor. Keep in mind that 1 horsepower is 33,000 ft-lb per minute, or 75 mkg/sec in the metric system. The force

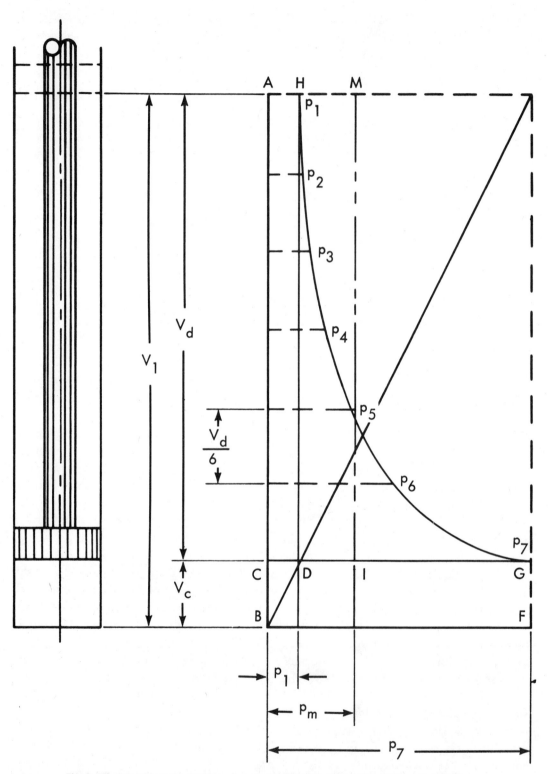

Fig. 3–12. Graphic representation of work performed during compression or expansion.

can readily be computed in pounds, and total distance traveled by the compression strokes in one minute can be computed in feet.

First consider the force. Since p_m is in pounds per square inch (or kg/cm²) and the area of the bottom of the piston can be determined by its diameter in square inches (or cm²), the "square inch" or "square centimeter" terms will cancel out in the calculation, leaving only "pounds" or "kilograms", which is the unit we want. First find the piston area:

$$A = \frac{\pi D^2}{4} = 0.785\ D^2,\ \text{where}$$

A = area of piston in square inches (or cm²)

D = diameter of piston in inches (or cm²)

The total mean effective pressure will then be:

$$F = 0.785\ D^2 \times p_m,\ \text{where:}$$

F = force in pounds

p_m = mean effective pressure in psi

The next thing to be found is the total distance traveled by the piston in 1 minute in the downward compression strokes, which is easily calculated in feet, (or meters), considering the length of the stroke and the speed in revolutions per minute, and bearing in mind that there is one compression stroke for each revolution.

$$S = \frac{L}{12} \times N,\ \text{or}\ L \times 0.001 \times N\ \text{in the met-}$$

ric system, where

S = total distance in feet or meters of compression strokes in 1 minute

L = length of stroke in inches (or cm),

so that $\frac{L}{12}$ = length of stroke in feet,

or L × 0.001 = length of stroke in meters

N = number of revolutions per minute = number of compression strokes

Now, combining the force and distance into a single equation will give power in terms of foot-pounds per minute (or mkg/sec), and this quantity divided by 33,000 will convert it into horsepower in the U.S. system, and divided by 75 for the metric system.

$$HP = \left(0.785\ D^2 \times p_m \times \frac{L}{12} \times N\right) \div 33,000$$

This equation can further be simplified to:

$$HP = 3.03 \times 10^{-5}$$

$$(0.0654 \times D^2 \times p_m \times L \times N)$$

By following examples previously given in the metric system and by referring to Appendix B at the end of the book, these examples may be easily converted to metric measurements.

Brake Horsepower. Since elimination of undesirable losses in transmission of power is inevitable, measurement of such losses are necessary to determine the efficiency of the compressor. An old, reliable method for resolution of this problem is the *prony brake*, or any other form of dynamometer. Many different designs of this method of measuring have been devised. Fig. 3–13 is a simple schematic illustration showing how the horsepower delivered to the shaft, usually called brake horsepower, may be determined as follows:

$$HP_b = \frac{2 \times \pi \times L \times N(W_g - W_i)}{33,000},\ \text{in the}$$

U.S. system,

where:

HP_b = brake horsepower

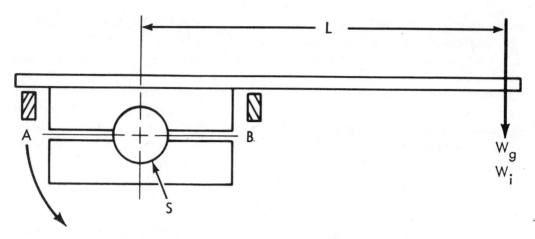

Fig. 3–13. Schematic illustration of Prony Brake. Parts are:
A and B, mechanical stops
S, shaft to which the Prony Brake is attached
L, lever arm
W_g, gross weight required to balance lever with shaft at rest
W_i, initial weight required to balance lever with shaft at rest

L   = lever arm, in feet or meters
N   = rpm of shaft
W_g = gross weight in pounds or kilograms required to balance lever with shaft at rest
W_i = initial weight in pounds or kilograms required to balance lever with shaft at rest

The metric equation is:

$$HP_b = \frac{2 \times \pi \times L \times N(W_g - W_i)}{75 \times 60}$$

Since there are so many types of this instrument, no attempt has been made to illustrate details of design such as materials, cooling, etc. The main components and means of operation are:

A = Mechanical stop a short distance from the lever arm to prevent mechanism from turning with the shaft when shaft is started.

B = Mechanical stop a short distance from the lever arm to prevent the mechanism from overrunning when the weight is applied.

S = Shaft to which the prony brake is applied. When there is clearance between lever arm and stops A and B, and the shaft is running, this indicates that the applied weight is correct.

Following are definitions of common expressions used in the examination of compressors:

1. **Volumetric Efficiency.** Ratio of the actual number of cubic feet or liters of free air at 14.7 psia (or 1.033 kg/cm²) and 60°F (or 15.6°C) compressed per unit of time, to the number of cubic feet or liters of piston displacement during that time. The smaller the clearance (volume of air left in the cylinder at the end of the stroke) in proportion to the displacement (total volume displaced), the better is the efficiency.

2. **Compression Ratio.** For a reciprocating compressor this is the volumetric piston displacement plus the volumetric clearance at the end of the stroke, divided by the volumetric

clearance. For this type of compressor it usually ranges between 3.5/1 to 8/1.

3. **Compressor Efficiency.** The ratio of theoretical power required to compress the amount of air actually delivered, to the actual power developed in the air cylinder as shown by an indicator diagram measures the compressor's efficiency. This depends on the method of cooling.

4. **Mechanical Efficiency.** The ratio of the air indicated horsepower divided by the brake horsepower.

5. **Slip Efficiency.** Ratio of air (actually measured) to the apparent volume accounted for by the indicator diagram. This is a constant for any compressor and is found by dividing leakage volume per minute by volumetric displacement per revolution.

6. **Overall Efficiency.** The product of efficiency of each element.

Variations in Compressors

There are two main classifications of compressors.

1. *Positive Displacement Compressors* of which there are several types as shown in this chapter. They are all distinguished by the fact that they compress the gaseous medium to a higher pressure by positively confining it in a gradually decreasing space. Compressors of this type are extensively used for industrial processes where the gas after compression is used as a medium for transmitting power.

2. *Dynamic Compressors.* These are high-speed machines which convert velocity to pressure in compressor volutes or other diverging passageways. Many of these machines are used for generating *mechanical power* by combustion and are thus extensively involved with thermodynamics. Since this book only treats thermodynamics to the extent that heat influences the behavior of fluid power and only deals with power transmission with gas or fluid as a medium for transmitting power, dynamic compressors will not be further described in this chapter.

Reciprocating Compressors. This is the most common of the positive displacement compressors and is also the most efficient compressor. It covers a greater range than any other method of compression, and can compress a gaseous medium from atmospheric pressure to as high as 6,000 psi or 422 kg/cm². Sizes range from a small fraction of a horsepower to 5,000 HP. It is very efficient at load applications.

Single-Acting, Single-Stage Compressors. These compressors come in many different arrangements. The simplest form of these is the single-acting, single-stage type shown schematically in Fig. 3–14. They are best suited for pres-

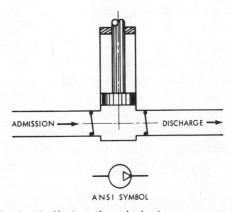

Fig. 3–14. Single-acting, single-stage compressor. Compression takes place every other stroke when forward and return strokes are considered two strokes.

Fluid Power: Pneumatics

sures up to 70 psi (or 5 kg/cm²) and sometimes up to 100 psi (or 7 kg/cm²). In this
type of compressor the gaseous medium is
compressed close to adiabatic compression, since heat generated during compression is not effectively dissipated. This
is the type of compressor most often used
in machine tools. A double-acting, single-
stage compressor is shown schematically
in Fig. 3–15.

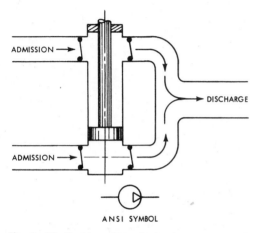

Fig. 3–15. Double-acting, single-stage compressor.
Compression takes place every stroke, both forward
and return.

Multi-Stage Compressors. Single-
acting, multi-stage compressors are also
used, particularly in machine tools. These
compressors are required for the higher
pressures above 100 psi (or 7 kg/cm²). A
two stage compressor is shown schematically in Fig. 3–16 and pressure curves for
a two stage compressor are shown in Fig.
3–17. These compressors come in sizes as
high as 500 CFM (or 236 liters per second)
and pressures up to 6,000 psi (or 422
kg/cm²).

If the intercooling is perfect, the pressure line has been lowered from A_1 to I_1 in
the displacement of the gaseous medium
V_{di}, and pressure P_{2i} is admitted to the

second stage of the compressor.

Assuming, then, that no cooling takes
place for the second-stage compression,
the pressure curve will be A_2, delivering
pressure P_{3a} to the receiver. The temperature of the gaseous medium will gradually be lowered to ambient conditions and
P_{3i} is then the available pressure at the
receiver.

There are a number of variations in cylinder arrangements:

1. In-line arrangement
2. Horizontal arrangement
3. Vertical arrangement
4. One horizontal and one vertical arrangement
5. V-arrangement
6. X-arrangement
7. Y-arrangement
8. Horizontally opposed arrangement

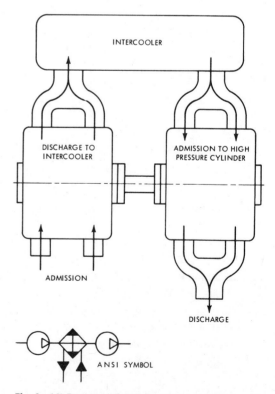

Fig. 3–16. Double-acting, two-stage compressor with
intercooler between stages.

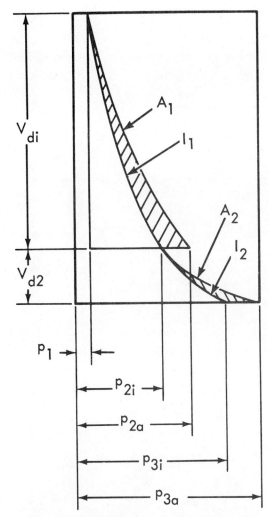

Fig. 3–17. Pressure curves for two-stage compression. If the intercooling is perfect, the pressure line has been lowered from A_1 to I_1 in the process of displacement of the gaseous medium V_{di}, and pressure P_{2i} is admitted to the second stage of the compressor.

lowest possible volume and maintaining low temperatures continually in the process of compression.

The closer the clearance, the more gaseous medium will be expelled at each stroke. Also, less high-pressure, high-temperature gaseous medium will remain in the cylinder to be expanded during the reversal of the stroke. Therefore, with a smaller amount of high-temperature gaseous medium expanded and remaining in the cylinder at reversal, the time cycle is shortened, sooner admitting a fresh supply of cool gas through the intake valves to the cylinder for compression in the next stroke.

Repeated compression and expansion of a gaseous medium without expelling it generates excessive heat. This heat carbonizes all parts in contact with the gaseous medium because the medium contains a certain amount of lubricating oil vapors.

Additional power required to compress unexpelled gas is not returnable by expansion because a large part of the energy generated as heat is dissipated by normal radiation and also by the circulating water used to cool the cylinder walls and cylinder heads. The cooling effect of water circulating through the jackets is most effective at the end of each stroke, when the temperature reaches the highest point.

Cylinders. The cylinder assembly consists of a combination of single and double-acting cylinders. Located on one throw is a double-acting first-stage cylinder, tandem and intermediate between a single-acting third-stage and a single-acting fourth-stage cylinder. With this design there are only two pressure stuffing boxes, and these stuffing boxes are not exposed to the high pressures.

This compressor has a piston displace-

Some of these types of compressors are shown in Fig. 3–18, 3–19, 3–20, 3–21, and 3–22.

Fig. 3–18 shows a compressor of the balanced, opposed type, designed for economical compression of a gaseous medium at high volumetric efficiency. High volumetric efficiency is achieved by reducing compression clearances to the

Fig. 3–18. Six-stage compressor of the balanced, opposed type, designed for economical compression at high volumetric efficiency. (Courtesy of Norwalk Co., Inc.)

ment of 995 CFM, or 470 liters per second, delivering capacity of 850 CFM, or 387 liters per second, at a speed of 300 rpm. Discharge pressure is 294 psig, or 20.7 kg/cm². and brake horsepower is 450.

Single-acting and double-acting single-stage compressors are illustrated in their simplest forms in Figs. 3–19 and 3–20.

Fig. 3–19 shows a cylinder for the six-stage compressor shown in Fig. 3–20. In this cylinder all valves *A* are located radially in the cylinder walls. The cylinder is cored out between the bore and its outside wall for a generous circulation of water to cool the structure and the gaseous medium as it is being compressed.

All connections between head water jackets and cylinder water jackets are direct, as shown at *B*, and these ports are located so as to provide perfect circulation. Such construction is preferred in good machine design because it elimi-

Fig. 3–19. Cylinder for the six-stage compressor shown in Fig. 3–18. Locations of valves are shown at *A*, and connections between head water jackets and cylinder water jackets are located as shown at *B*. (Courtesy of Norwalk Co., Inc.)

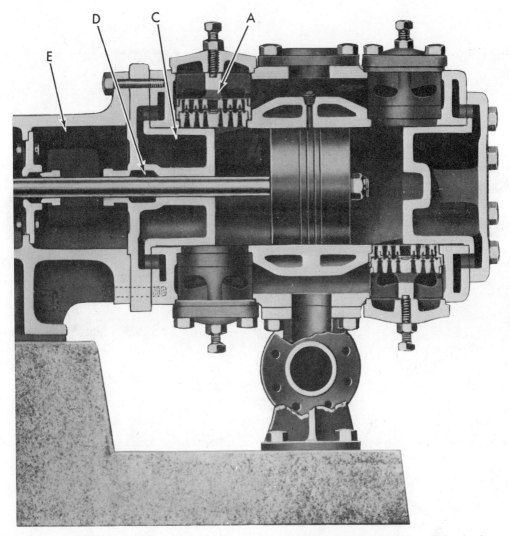

Fig. 3–20. Section through cylinder and heads for six-stage compressor. (Courtesy of Norwalk Co., Inc.)

nates the need to remove pipes and fittings when it becomes necessary to remove a cylinder.

Fig. 3–20 shows a section through cylinder and heads for a six-stage compressor. Valves A are large in area, of low lift, and are located radially. The cylinder heads, C, which are hollow for adequate water circulation, extend to the center of the valves A, a feature which reduces the compression clearance for a high volu-

metric efficiency, with the large valve area providing ample passage of the gaseous medium.

Stuffing box D is easily accessible through opening E in the adapter or neck of the main frame.

Fig. 3–21 is a photograph of a horizontal double-acting, single-stage, water-cooled compressor, and Fig. 3–22 is a sectional view of this type of compressor.

As shown in Fig. 3–22, this compressor

Fig. 3–21. Horizontal double-acting, single-stage, water-cooled compressor. (Courtesy of Gardner Denver Co.)

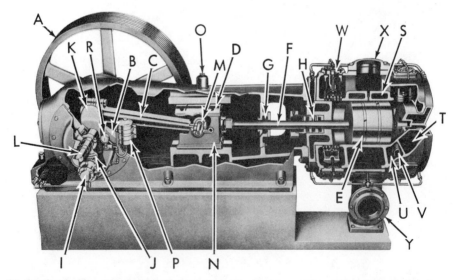

Fig. 3–22. Sectional view of horizontal double-acting, single-stage, water-cooled compressor shown in Fig. 3–21. (Courtesy of Gardner Denver Co.)

is driven through a balanced sheave *A*, and the power end is provided with correctly proportioned counterweights *B* for optimum balance. The rotary motion is converted to reciprocating motion through connecting rod *C* and a one-piece crosshead *D*, which slides on bronze shoes.

The piston *E* is connected to crosshead *D* with piston rod *F*. Metallic wiper rings at *G* keep oil in and at the same time keep dirt out of the power end.

A variety of piston packings at *H* may be used, depending on requirements. Metallic, Teflon, or carbon packings are a few of the packings commonly used. An oil pump *I*, driven through gears *J*, provide pressure lubrication to crankpin

bearings *K*, main bearings *L*, crosshead pin bearing *M*, and crosshead guides *N*. A wire mesh breather is shown at *O*. Oil strainer and filter are shown at *P*, and the oil pressure may be observed on gage *R*.

On the delivery end, cylinder *S*, head *T* and air passages are provided with water jackets to assure uniform cooling and low discharge temperature. Large unrestricted air passages reduce air friction at *U*. Valve cage rests in full circumference of valve, eliminating warpage, at *V*. Suction valve unloaders on all inlet valves give low power consumption during unloading periods, at *W*. Suction opening is shown at *X* and discharge opening at *Y*.

Fig. 3–23 is a V-type single-acting,

Fig. 3–23. V-type single-acting, two-stage, water-cooled compressor. (Courtesy of Gardner Denver Co.)

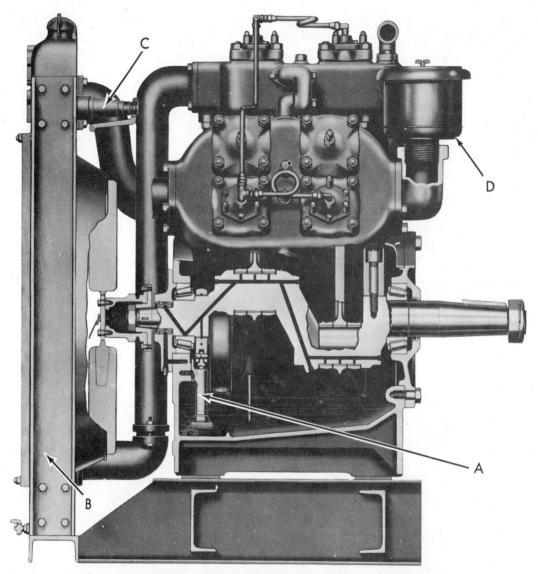

Fig. 3–24. Sectional view of V-type single-acting, two-stage, water-cooled compressor shown in Fig. 3–23. In this view the sheave has been removed to simplify the illustration. (Courtesy of Gardner Denver Co.)

two-stage, water-cooled compressor, and Fig. 3–24 is a sectional view of this type of compressor with the sheave removed. In this view, oil pump *A* assures positive pressure lubrication to important points as indicated in section by drilled holes. A combination radiator-intercooler is shown at *B*. *C* is a safety valve. An oil

bath suction air filter is shown at *D*.

Fig. 3–25 shows a sectional view of a V-type single-acting, two-stage, water-cooled compressor as seen from one end. Valves are located at *A*. Water-jacketed cylinders and heads *B* properly control operating temperature. The water circulating pump is shown at *C*.

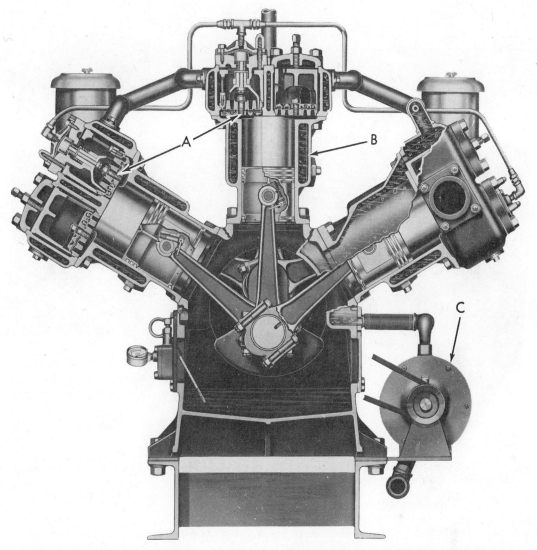

Fig. 3–25. Sectional view from end of V-type single-action, two-stage, water-cooled compressor. (Courtesy of Gardner Denver Co.)

Rotary Compressors

There are several designs of this type of compressor. Their distinguishing characteristic is that pressure is produced by the rotation of single or mating elements. Some of the most common designs are:

Sliding Vane Compressor. This is of a very simple construction and is characterized by low operating cost and low

starting torque. It has few, inexpensive moving parts, the operation is smooth, and vibration is very low. The output comes close to a continuous flow. Fig. 3–26 shows one type of a sliding vane compressor. In this case it is often used for creating a partial vacuum and therefore is classed as a pump. Since, however, it must compress the air being evacuated, it is actually a compressor.

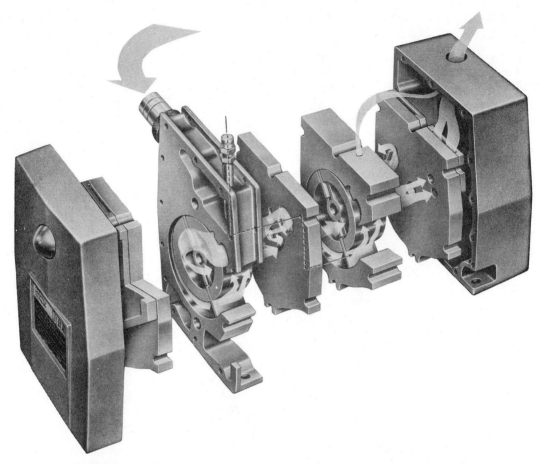

Fig. 3–26. Exploded view of sliding vane compressor, also known as a rotary vane vacuum pump, depending on how it is used. (Courtesy of Precision Scientific Co.)

This illustration clearly shows the compact and lightweight design and operation of this unit, used as an efficient, quiet vacuum pump, suitable for laboratory or industrial applications. Compressors, or "pumps," of this kind are designed to operate at an elevated temperature of 65°C (about 149°F) in order to reduce the amount of contaminating vapor liquified by the compression that occurs within the pump.

Standard equipment includes a gas ballast (vented exhaust). When opened, this balast admits a small amount of air to atmospheric pressure at the exhaust side of the pump, thus permitting the majority of condensable vapor to pass through the pump without condensing. The oil capacity of the pump is liberally proportioned to prevent rapid concentration of contaminants in the oil.

Oilback (back-up of oil into the gaseous medium) during such times as power failure has, in some cases, been of great concern. This problem has, however, been completely eliminated on this pump by designing the intake end-plate as a hollow trap with sufficient volume to accommodate the normal amount of oil which is above the exhaust valve.

If the pump is turned off under vacuum, the oil above the valve serving as a seal will merely drain into the stators and end trap. Oil will not back up beyond the intake. Normal back-streaming of oil vapors can easily be prevented by the use of proper, easily installed traps.

These pumps are single in operation and are designed in sizes from 300 to 1,500 liters per minute. The principles of operation are:

1. Gas enters a generously proportioned intake port, as indicated by the arrow. It is swept around by the rotating vanes, compressed, and then exhausted through large dual exhaust ports on both sides of the intake stage rotor.
2. Gas now flows through the hollow rotors, with minimum restriction, to the dual intake section of the exhaust stage.
3. Gas is exhausted through multiple exhaust ports.

Lobed Impeller Compressor. There are many types of these compressors. Most of them have two rotating impellers, revolving in opposite directions as shown schematically in Fig. 3–27. They are, however, also designed with multiple impellers, as shown in Fig. 3–28. For best and quietest operation the impellers should not touch each other, but should be kept apart with a small clearance. This is best accomplished with a gear-driven design. The clearance permits some of the air to escape back to the suction side, with some loss of volumetric pressure known as *slip*. Because the slip is constant, these compressors should be operated at the highest recommended speed to obtain maximum volumetric efficiency.

The rotors of the impeller compressor

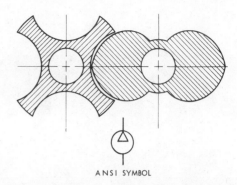

Fig. 3–27. Sketch of typical two-lobed compressor.

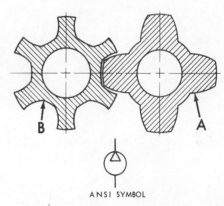

Fig. 3–28. Sketch of compressor with four-lobed main rotor meshing with six-fluted secondary rotor.

shown in Fig. 3–28 are components for the Helical Electra Screw compressor shown later in Fig. 3–32. These rotors are balanced and oil-sealed, work in synchronous mesh, and are designed for single-stage or two-stage compression. The main rotor A is four-lobed and the secondary rotor B is six-fluted. They are of a size to permit operation at electric motor speed.

Helical Compressors. Two helically generated elements revolve in opposite directions, entrapping air from the admission side, forcing the air out the discharge side at a higher pressure. Just the same as for lobed compressors, a small clear-

Fig. 3–29. Cyclo Blower helical compressor. (Courtesy of Gardner Denver Co.)

ance must be maintained between the moving parts for smooth, quiet operation, thus causing a certain amount of slip. These compressors have axial flow. Typical examples of this type of compressors are shown in Figures 3–29, 3–30, and 3–31.

Fig. 3–29 shows the Cyclo Blower helical compressor, capable of delivering 40 to 6,600 CFM up to 18 psig, or 19 to 3,257 liters per second up to 1.27 kg/cm² (or 40 cm Hg); dry vacuum to 16" Hg (or 40 cm Hg); wet vacuum to 24" Hg (or 60 cm Hg).

Some of the applications suitable for this type of compressor are:

1. Pneumatic Conveying
2. Waste Treatment (Aeration)
3. Air Drilling (Chip Removal)
4. Compressor and Engine Supercharging
5. Car Wash
6. Glass Manufacturing
7. Aircraft and Missile Ground Support
8. Packaging
9. Fuel Oil Atomization
10. Drying
11. Hospitals (Hyperbaric Chambers)
12. Tunnel Pressurization
13. Inflating

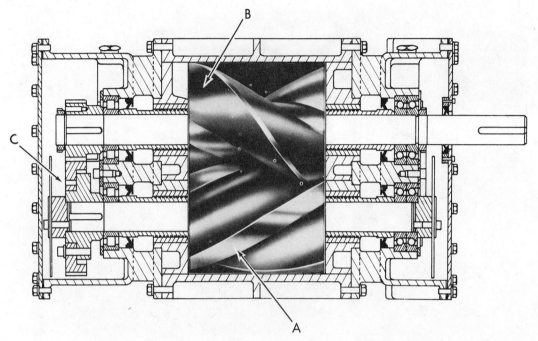

Fig. 3–30. Sectional view of helical compressor shown in Fig. 3–29. (Courtesy of Gardner Denver Co.)

Fig. 3–30 shows a sectional view of the same Cyclo Blower® helical compressor. The main operating parts are the two impellers. Due to their helical design, these impellers deliver axial flow. Since a very small clearance is maintained between the two impellers and also between the impellers and the housing, no lubrication is required for the parts in the compression chamber.

The drive of the four-flute gate rotor A is taken from two two-lobe rotors B through two timing gears C. The outboard location of rotor bearings and gears prevents contamination of the compression chamber and the gaseous medium being compressed.

The compression cycle of this screw-type, cycloidal rotor is balanced, and therefore a smooth, steady discharge is delivered, completely eliminating shock. This design may be applied to pressure or vacuum service.

Fig. 3–31 shows one model of an Electra Screw helical water-cooled compressor. These compressors are in either single or two-stage, delivering 150 to 1160 CFM at 40 to 150 psig, or 70 to 550 liters/sec at 2.81 to 10.5 kg/cm².

There are no valves in this compressor. The Electra-Screw air delivery is regulated by a compressor inlet valve which opens and closes in response to air demand, and is actuated by a piston, receiving air from the discharge line. The valve is pilot-operated from full open to full closed. There are three control systems:

1. **Constant Speed,** where air requirements are moderately heavy most of the time. This provides continuous compressor operation throughout full, reduced or zero capacity demand. A pilot automatically adjusts inlet valve position. A separate air

Fig. 3–31. Electra Screw helical water-cooled compressor. (Courtesy of Gardner Denver Co.)

receiver (tank), is not necessary in this case.

2. **Automatic Start and Stop**. For applications where air requirements are for short, intermittent periods. This provides intermittent compressor operation by using a pressure shut-down switch at the air receiver. An air receiver (Tank) is then necessary.

3. **Dual Control.** A combination of Constant Speed (1), and Start and Stop (2) for use where air requirements vary widely. A selector switch would then allow the operator to choose between control method 1 or 2.

Synchronous intermeshing of the rotor lobes and grooves produces a smooth, steady flow of the gaseous medium with nearly pulse-free delivery and vibrationless operation.

The compressor rotor chamber is flooded with a metered quantity of oil. The major portion of the oil is injected directly into the rotor chamber to absorb heat of compression and seal internal clearances; the balance is directed through internal passages to the bearings. Full flow oil filters with throwaway bag type elements protect the compressor against contaminants. Oil temperature is maintained by a water-cooled heat exchanger or by a fan-cooled radiator.

The compressed air is discharged through a check valve to an oil reservoir where more than 99% of entrained oil is removed by impingement and velocity change. This oil collects in the reservoir, while the air passes through a final separator which effectively removes the balance of the oil. A dry type inlet air filter, with reusable element, insures clean air to the compressor.

Fig. 3–32 is a schematic illustration showing the principle of a single-stage and two-stage Electra Screw compressor such as the one shown in Fig. 3–31.

Compression is accomplished by two multiple-lobe helical rotors turning in a

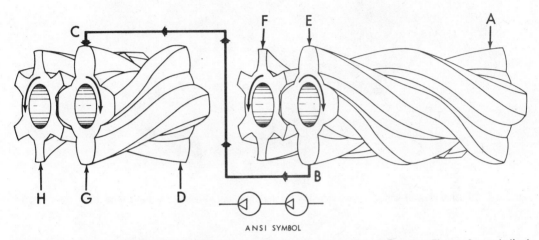

Fig. 3–32. Schematic illustration showing the principle of a single-stage and two-stage Electra Screw helical compressor. (Courtesy of Gardner Denver Co.)

Fig. 3–33. Helical, air-cooled Electra Screw compressor. (Courtesy of Gardner Denver Co.)

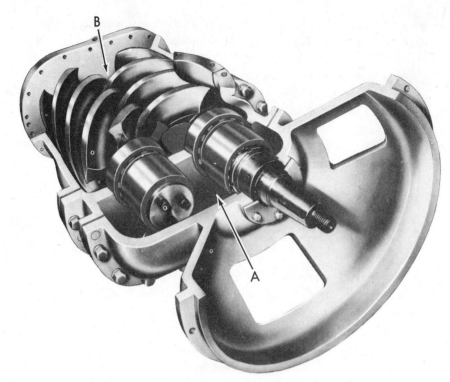

Fig. 3–34. Cutaway view of impellers and housing for a single-stage Rota Screw helical impeller. (Courtesy of Gardner Denver Co.)

synchronous mesh with close clearances between their meshing surfaces. As air enters the inlet port, it is drawn into an interlobe cavity. This space becomes progressively smaller as rotation continues. The gaseous medium moves axially as it is compressed until maximum compression is reached at the discharge port. Discharge airflow is thus continuous, smooth and shock-free.

In a two-stage compressor, as shown, the gaseous medium enters at port A of the first stage and is progressively compressed as it moves axially from port A to port B, between four-lobed drive impeller E and six-lobed driven impeller F. The gaseous medium is then channeled through interstage passages to port C of the second stage and moves axially to discharge port D between four-lobed impell-

er G and six-lobed impeller H, being progressively compressed to a higher pressure and is discharged at D. Impeller B is on the same shaft as impeller G and impeller F is on the same shaft as impeller H, all turning at the same speed.

Fig. 3–33 shows a helical Electra Screw compressor which is nearly identical to the compressor shown in Fig. 3–31 except that it employs air cooling by a fan and radiator system shown at the right.

Fig. 3–34 is a cutaway view of the impellers and housing for a single stage Rota Screw helical compressor. The gaseous medium enters the inlet port A and is progressively compressed in a single stage until it leaves at the discharge port B. It delivers from 185 to 1200 CFM at 100 psig, or 87 to 565 liters/sec at 7 kg/cm² gage.

Review Questions

1. What are the inherent characteristics of the behavior of the gaseous media?

2. Describe Pascal's Law.

3. Describe Boyle's Law.

4. Describe Charles' Law of compression and expansion of a gaseous medium.

5. Define adiabatic compression and expansion.

6. Define isothermal compression and expansion.

7. Give a good definition of gage pressure.

8. What is absolute pressure?

9. What is vacuum?

10. Name two technical terms generally used for pressure in vacuum technology and define their values.

11. When is the expression partial pressure generally used?

12. Define Dalton's Law.

13. Name some of the industrial processes depending on vacuum technology.

14. What is absolute temperature?

15. How was the relationship of absolute temperature established and what is the relationship of absolute temperature to absolute pressure and volume in compressing or expanding a gaseous medium?

16. What is known as the gas constant and how was it established for a gaseous medium?

17. What is one of the greatest energy wastes in compressing a gaseous medium if not controlled?

18. What is meant by clearance in a compressor?

19. What effect does compressor clearance have on volumetric delivery?

20. Why is clearance a necessary requirement for a compressor?

21. What is the theoretical shape of a true isothermal pressure curve?

22. What is Mariotte's Law?

23. Define energy, work and power required for compression. Define horsepower in the U.S. system. Define horsepower in the metric system.

24. What is indicated horsepower?

25. What is brake horsepower and how is it usually measured?

26. Define volumetric efficiency.

27. Define compression ratio for a reciprocating compressor.

28. Define compressor efficiency, mechanical efficiency, slip efficiency, and overall efficiency

29. What is the difference between a single-acting single-stage compressor and a double-acting single-stage compressor?

30. How may high volumetric efficiency be obtained in a multi-stage compressor?

SEE END OF BOOK FOR ANSWERS TO QUESTIONS

Pumps, Vacuum Pumps, and Storage Tanks

In everyday language the distinction between compressors and pumps is lost, and every device that moves fluid media is called a "pump". Then, to further confuse matters, industries have established the habit of calling many true compressors "vacuum pumps" when using them for the purpose of evacuating gaseous media from containers rather than filling the containers with gaseous media under higher pressure for storage and later use in performing useful work.

Some of the pumps decribed in this chapter are used for moving liquids, and you may well wonder why they are included in the study of pneumatics rather than a book on hydraulics. There is a reason for this, as you will see. In some cases these pumps depend on the behavior of gaseous media merely to cause a flow of liquid. In other cases compressed gaseous media are used to generate tremendously high pressure in a hydraulic system. In all cases these pumps use gaseous media to supply the necessary force to move the liquid, and their operation is based on pneumatic laws.

The first section of this chapter will deal with non-vacuum pumps, the second section will deal with vacuum pumps (actually compressors in many cases), and the third section will describe and discuss various types of tanks for storing gaseous media and liquefied cryogenic gases.

Pumps

Except for the special case of "vacuum pumps" to be described later, the pumps discussed in the first section of this chapter are definitely *not* true compressors such as those previously discussed in Chapter 3.

Pumps Depending on Atmospheric Pressure

These are some of the earliest pumps still in use, and may be classified in two main groups:

1. *The Suction Pump*
2. *The Pressure Pump*

They are used for transferring a liquid from one place to another, usually to a higher level, and they depend on atmospheric pressure for operation.

The Suction Pump. Since this type of pump is manufactured in many different designs, with valves, packings, pistons and cylinders in many variations, for simplicity of presentation it is shown schematically in Fig. 4–1.

This is a single-acting suction pump. Each upward stroke of the piston C lifts the water above the piston through discharge pipe G, at the same time creating a vacuum under the piston. This allows the atmospheric pressure to force water up to fill cylinder B under the piston. The return stroke only positions the piston for the next upward stroke.

Water at its highest density weighs 62.4 pounds per cubic foot (1 kg per cubic decimeter, which also is 1 liter in the metric system). We will assume, then, that we are required to move water of this density from sea level to a higher level. The question is: how high can we lift it?

In Chapters 1 and 2 we saw it was Torricelli who discovered that the standard pressure of atmosphere at sea level would support a column of mercury 29.921 inches, or 76 cm high. This is equivalent to 14.7 psia (1.033 kg/cm²) or a column of water 34 feet (or approximately 10 meters) high. This can be easily calculated as follows:

Multiplying 14.7 by 144 to convert pressure in square inches to pressure in square feet, and dividing by pounds per foot of height, will give the theoretical height in feet. That is:

$$\frac{14.7 \times 144}{62.4} = 34 \text{ ft (approx.)}$$

In the metric system this calculation is even easier. Remembering that 1 decimeter equals 10 centimeters, 1.033 kg/cm² = 1.033 × 100 = 103.3 kg/decimeter². The height calculation then becomes:

$$\frac{103.3}{10} = 10.33 \text{ meters}$$

Theoretically, this would mean that h_1 could be as high as 34 feet or 10.33 meters, but no higher. From practical experience we know that this is impossible because several factors are responsible for lowering this height. Some of these factors are:

1. Leakage through valves and packings
2. Friction offered through pipes and fittings

For an ideal condition, where the sealing surfaces are perfect, if pressure is applied to piston rod F to lower piston C in contact with bottom surface J of cylinder B, the air in the lower part of cylinder B would be compressed to a higher pressure, thus opening valves E allowing the air to escape to the upper part of the cylinder.

As the piston C progresses to the bottom, valve I would close. If then piston C is pulled up by piston rod F to contact upper end K of cylinder B, the pressure created in the upper part of cylinder B would close valves E. Since the lower part of cylinder B has no access to the atmosphere, a vacuum would be created here. The trapped air in pipe A would then

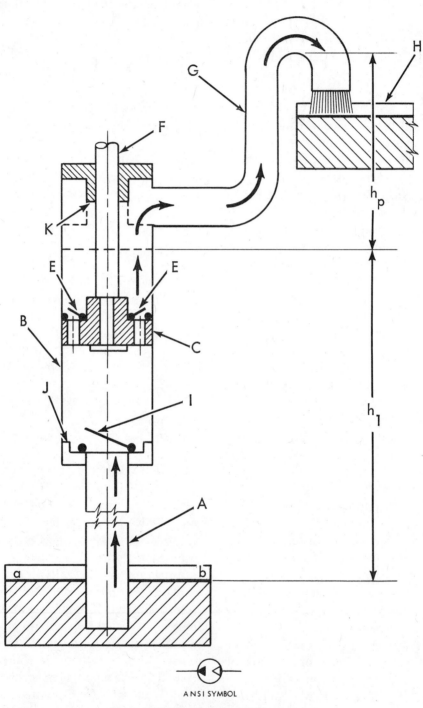

Fig. 4–1. The single-acting suction pump.

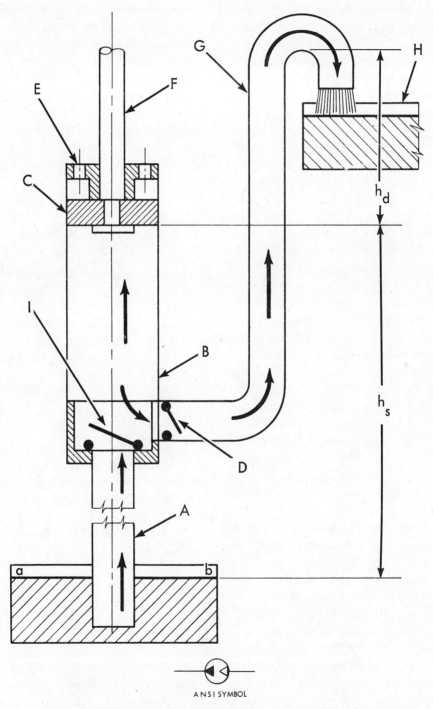

Fig. 4−2. Schematic illustration of single-acting pressure pump in its simplest form.

force valve I to open, allowing atmospheric pressure to force liquid upward to fill the lower part of the cylinder.

The atmospheric pressure on water surface *a-b* would then force water up in pipe A until equilibrium was obtained; that is, the entrapped air pressure would be equal to atmospheric pressure. Additional reciprocating motion of the piston C would finally bring the water up to a maximum height h_1 of 34 feet or about 10 meters.

The next stroke down would force the valves E open and close valve I as the top surface of the water remains at the top of h_1. The next upward stroke of piston C would open valve I and close valves E, raising the water up into pipe G. The water in the lower part of cylinder B would follow piston C, and additional strokes of piston C would raise the water level to the top of h_p, discharging into reservoir H.

As mentioned, it has been found from practical experience that it is impossible to pump the water to a theoretical height of 34 feet (about 10 meters), since so many variables which determine the efficiency of the pump must be considered. Furthermore, it is often found that the pump must be primed by pouring water into the cylinder to close leaks and get the cycle started.

The Pressure Pump. This type of single-acting pump is shown schematically in its simplest form in Fig. 4–2. No valves are required in the piston. If now the piston C is moved up to its top position, the air will escape through holes E. At the same time, a vacuum is created in the lower part of cylinder B, causing valve D to close and valve I to open. As with the suction pump, after successive strokes the water level would be raised to top of h_s. Now, the next downward stroke of the piston C would close valve I, and

valve D would open as the water is forced up the discharge pipe G.

Double-Acting Pressure Pump. This pump also depends on an atmospheric pressure for operation, as is shown in a simple, schematic drawing in Fig. 4–3. The efficiency of this type of pump is dependent on many variables in design, and also varies with difference in suction and discharge heads and volumetric delivery per unit of time. Disregarding these variables, the theoretical horsepower would be:

$$HP = \frac{Q \times (h_s + h_d)}{33,000} \text{ in the U.S. system,}$$

or $\dfrac{Q \times (h_s + h_d)}{75}$ in the metric system.

Q = pounds of water delivered per minute, or liters per second, since 1 liter of water weighs 1 kilogram

h_s = suction head in feet or meters

h_d = discharge head in feet or meters

The operation of this type of pump is easily understood by referring to Fig. 4–3. The suction pipe A is connected to the top and bottom of cylinder B. The discharge pipe G is also connected to the top and bottom of cylinder B. The two suction valves are C and E, and the discharge valves are D and F.

These pumps find a great variety of applications in industry.

Gaseous Medium Lift Pump

An interesting application of using a gaseous medium to perform useful work is illustrated schematically in Fig. 4–4. No moving parts here are required to be in contact with the liquid to be moved.

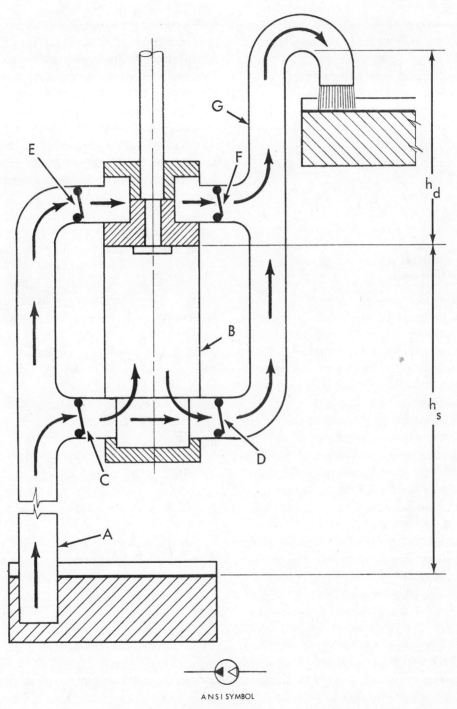

Fig. 4–3. Simple schematic drawing of double-acting pressure pump. This type of pump raises liquid in both forward and return strokes.

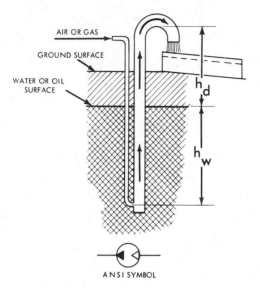

Fig. 4–4. Gaseous medium lift pump for raising liquid from great depths.

Air-Driven Hydraulic Pump

Whereas the gaseous-medium lift pump just described is only useful for lifting a liquid medium in large volumes to great heights, air driven pumps are used for developing pressures of tremendous magnitudes in liquid media, to perform work in locations inaccessible with other methods. No energy is expended in holding these high pressures for long periods of time. A miniature air-driven hydraulic pump is shown in cutaway view in Fig. 4–5, and the principle of its operation is schematically illustrated in Fig. 4–6.

Because pneumatic tools used in industry are designed for operating at 80 to 90 psi (or 5.6 to 6.3 kg/cm²) for highest efficiency, the theoretical pressure at the receiver is, as a rule, between 100 and 125 psi, (or between 7 and 8.8 kg/cm²). In some cases, however, the pressure may drop as low as 60 or 65 psi (4.2 to 4.6 kg/cm²). These pumps will operate at air pressures as low as 25 psi (or 1.76 kg/cm²) and are capable of producing hydraulic pressures up to 75,000 psi (or 5,273 kg/cm²). The double-acting pumps are so efficient in extracting energy from the compressed air that the exhaust air is approximately 90°F (50°C) colder than the incoming air. Thus, on a 70°F (21°C) day, the air will exhaust at −20°F (−29°C).

In Fig. 4–6, the pneumatic pressure is applied to a large area piston P_a to produce a high hydraulic pressure P_h on a small area hydraulic piston. The reciprocating motion of the pump is automatic by the action of a pilot-operated selector valve. This valve is unbalanced so the cycling system cannot stall in normal operation.

As the pressure system approaches the maximum, dictated by the setting of the air pressure regulator, the pump slows

This method is useful in raising water or oil from deep deposits, especially where grit or other contaminants mixed with the liquid would be harmful to the parts of a conventional pump.

Gas or air is lighter than water or oil. Therefore, when a gaseous medium is introduced close to the bottom of the submerged pipe, the unit weight of the liquid in the pipe becomes lighter than the liquid surrounding the pipe. Consequently, a large, steady flow is produced. Even though the efficiency of this type of pump is considered low, it is valuable in obtaining liquids from great depths – a result impossible to obtain with pumps operated by atmospheric pressure.

Increasing h_w will reduce the volume of air required, but will increase the pressure, because the pressure of the gaseous medium used must be more than the pressure of the liquid, due to depth h_w. Experience has proved that h_w should be from 1 to 4 times h_d. When oil is raised, a gaseous medium other than air is usually used.

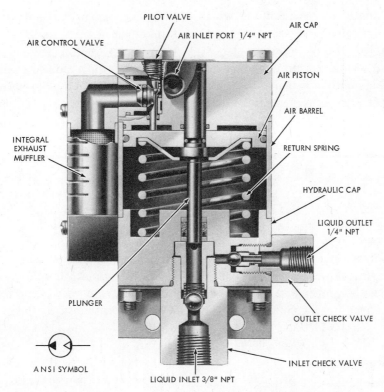

PILOT VALVE

AIR INLET PORT 1/4" NPT

AIR CAP

AIR CONTROL VALVE

AIR PISTON

AIR BARREL

INTEGRAL
EXHAUST
MUFFLER

RETURN SPRING

HYDRAULIC CAP

LIQUID OUTLET
1/4" NPT

PLUNGER

OUTLET CHECK VALVE

ANSI SYMBOL

INLET CHECK VALVE

LIQUID INLET 3/8" NPT

Fig. 4–5. Miniature air-driven hydraulic pump. (Courtesy of Haskel Engineering & Supply Co.)

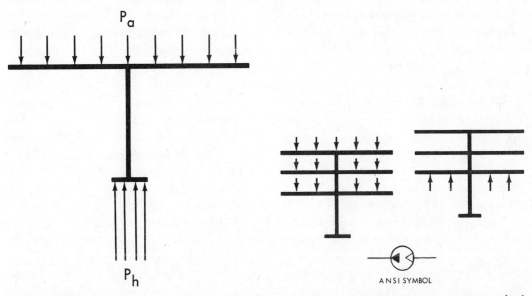

P_a

P_h

ANSI SYMBOL

Fig. 4–6. Schematic illustration of air-driven hydraulic pump, showing how low air pressure or pressurized gaseous medium may be used to generate hydraulic forces of tremendous magnitude. (Courtesy of Haskel Engineering & Supply Co.)

down and finally ceases pumping when the hydraulic force balances the pneumatic force. It will thus maintain the desired pressure while consuming no power. A single-head pump is shown at the left of this illustration. With a multiple head pump as shown at the right, the return stroke can be operated by one head thus consuming less air. The pneumatic drive section of this pump is prelubricated at the factory and may therefore be operated by dry nitrogen or natural gas.

Vacuum Pumps

In one of its simplest forms, a machine element may be moved from one location to another with a lever. The lever then becomes the medium for motion, and the motion stops only if the resistance is greater than the force applied. This is positive displacement.

We have an analogous case in moving a fluid medium from one location to another with a piston in a cylinder. The piston is then the medium for motion.

As explained briefly in the introduction of this book, a gaseous medium is stationary until there is a differential in pressures. Pascal's Law states that if a gaseous medium is confined in an enclosure the pressure is equal on all surfaces within the confinement. Now, if this enclosure is opened to a second enclosure there will be no movement of the gaseous medium unless a lower pressure exists or is created in the second enclosure, or unless the gaseous medium in the first enclosure is compressed to a higher pressure.

When releasing a gas (including the atmosphere) from an enclosed confinement, the medium causing this motion is a true compressor. Even in creating a vacuum this is true, because the gas being removed from the enclosure must be brought up to a higher pressure than the prevailing outside pressure to be assimilated. We cannot, therefore, correctly say that we have used a pump for doing this work, but rather a *compressor*. The gas itself becomes the principal medium for motion because by its distinguishing characteristics it will move only as compression and expansion take place.

Pump, therefore, is a misnomer for the machine or component used in creating a vacuum. It is well to have this fixed in our minds because it helps in understanding vacuum technology. The word "pump" will, however, be used in describing some of the methods of obtaining a vacuum only because this word is now well established in industry.

Since a compressor, or "pump", is used in most cases for obtaining a vacuum, especially in the majority of industrial cases, it may be easily understood that a perfect vacuum may never be obtained.

Some of the devices and methods for creating a vacuum are:
1. *Rotary Piston Pump*
2. *Rotary Vane Pumps* and *Blowers*
3. *Non-Mechanical Pumps.* These are vacuum pumps which operate on other than mechanical principles. This category includes ion pumps, differential ion pumps, diffusion

pumps, adsorption pumping, and cryogenic pumping. Uses of non-mechanical pumps are increasing for applications requiring very low degrees of vacuum unobtainable by ordinary machines. Some of these will be mentioned briefly in this chapter. The sophisticated systems on which their operations depend are based on electrical, atomic and chemical phenomena beyond the scope covered by this book, however. Therefore only enough can be included to awake the interest of the student who may wish to pursue the subject further.

Some of the different variations of positive displacement pumps used for creating a vacuum (which in reality are compressors) have been described in Chapter 3 under *Compressors*. The following facts should, however, be noted:

Rotary Piston Pumps. Almost all of these pumps have low capacities, and the single-stage designs are capable of reducing the pressure in the enclosure to be evacuated to about 10^{-2} torr. The two-stage design can reduce pressure to about

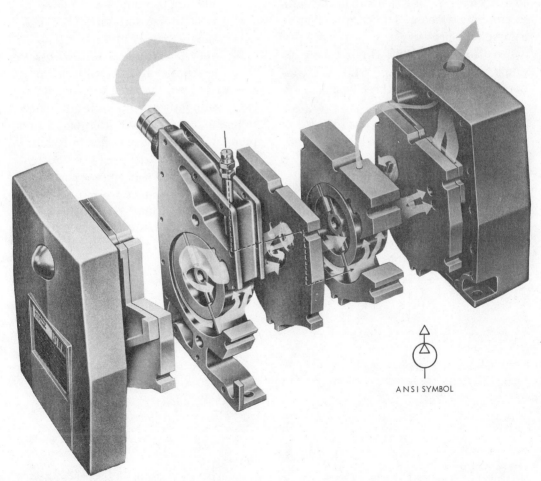

ANSI SYMBOL

Fig. 4–7. Rotary vane vacuum pump, sometimes also known as a sliding vane compressor, depending on how it is used. (Courtesy of Prescision Scientific Co.)

10^{-3} torr. These pumps run at low speeds, 300 to 1100 rpm, to keep vibration down. Sometimes they are built in duplex versions, with the eccentrics 180° apart, or triplex versions, with the eccentrics 120° apart in order to reduce vibrations.

Rotary Vane Pumps. A popular pump is the oil-sealed pump shown in Fig. 4–7. Here it is used as a vacuum pump. Fig. 4–8 is an efficiency chart for a rotary vane pump of this type, showing typical free-air displacement of 500 liters per minute (17.6 CFM). The guaranteed ultimate vacuum on McLeod gage is 0.1 micron of mercury (1×10^{-4} torr). Efficiency at 1 micron = 72%. Efficiency is the ratio of pumping speed at 1 micron to that at atmospheric pressure.

See also Fig. 4–9, showing rotary vane pump pumpdown curves. When a chamber is to be evacuated, three basic factors must be considered:

1. The ultimate vacuum desired
2. The time allowed to achieve that level of vacuum
3. The volume to be evacuated

The type of vacuum pump shown in Fig. 4–7 of this chapter is, in reality, the same shown as Fig. 3–26 of Chapter 3, where it was classed as a compressor. This type of compressor or vacuum pump, as we will now consider it, is made in sizes from 25 liters per minute to 1,500 liters per minute.

The four typical curves shown in Fig. 4–9 represent two-stage pumps with capacities of 300, 500, 1,000 and 1,500 liters per minute. These curves indicate the pumpdown times in minutes for each pump as a function of the ultimate vacuum, and are identified by the following letters:

A = 300 liters per minute
B = 500 liters per minute
C = 1,000 liters per minute
D = 1,500 liters per minute

Assume, now, that a 750-liter vessel is to be evacuated to 100 millitorr in 15 minutes. Since the time to evacuate one liter is 15/750 = 0.02 minute, the curves indicate that the 500 liter per minute pump will evacuate one liter to 100 millitorr in 0.02 minute.

The reason for using liters per minute rather than cubic feet per minute in this chart is that the metric system is the only

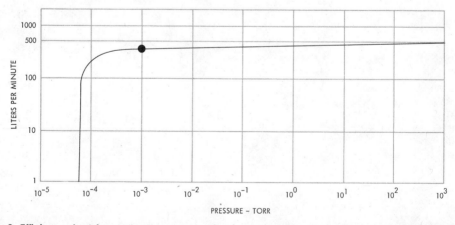

Fig. 4–8. Efficiency chart for a rotary vane pump, showing typical free air displacement of 500 liters per minute (17.6 CFM), with ultimate vacuum of 0.1 micron of mercury (1×10^{-4} torr). (Courtesy of Precision Scientific Co.)

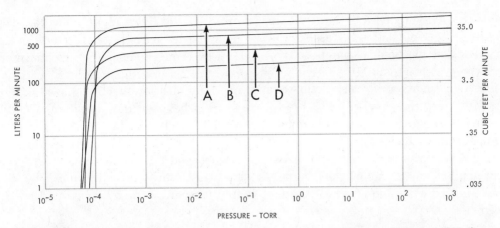

Fig. 4—9. Rotary vane pump pumpdown curves for four 2-stage pumps with capacities of: *A*, 300 liters per minute; *B*, 500 liters per minute; *C*, 1,000 liters per minute; and *D*, 1,500 liters per minute. (Courtesy of Precision Scientific Co.)

system used in some parts of the vacuum industry. The liter, unlike the gallon, is a true volumetric unit for both gaseous and liquid media. It contains exactly 1000 cubic centimeters or 1 cubic decimeter of any fluid medium regardless of weight or density.

You may have noticed that several different words are used for machines or devices for moving, blowing, compressing, or evacuating gaseous media. To clear up some possible confusion, the following distinctions are given:

1. *Compressor* is the proper name given to a machine or device whose principal aim is to raise the gaseous media (in reality a compressible fluid) to a higher pressure.

2. A *vacuum pump*, which also is really a compressor, is a machine or device for exhausting gaseous media from an enclosure.

3. A *blower* is a machine or device that compresses a gaseous medium to a relatively low pressure but in large volume compared to a true compressor. By attaching the inlet port of a blower to the container to be evacu-

ated, the blower removes a substantial amount of the gaseous medium, blowing it into the atmosphere or into another container. In the vacuum industry, blowers used in this manner are also called "vacuum pumps".

Roots Blowers. These blowers, originally made by Roots-Connersville Blower Corp., now Dresser Industries, Inc., are sometimes also used as vacuum pumps. As blowers they are used as superchargers, supplying large volumes of air under low pressure to gasoline engines. This improves the power output of the engines when operating at high altitudes where the oxygen per cubic unit of air has decreased.

The volumetric capacity of these blowers ranges between 100 and 12,000 CFM, or between 47 and 5,600 liters per second. Because their discharge pressure is low, these blowers when used as vacuum pumps cannot reduce the pressure lower than 1 to 500 microns. In many industrial applications this is entirely adequate.

When Roots blowers are used together with an oil-sealed mechanical pump, the

Fluid Power: Pneumatics

pressure may be reduced to 5×10^{-4} torr, and two stages of the blower assisted by an oil-sealed mechanical pump can reduce the pressure to 5×10^{-5} torr.

Fig. 4–10 shows a cutaway picture of a Roots blower. Figs. 4–11, 4–12, 4–13, and 4–14 show in detail and sequence the operation of this unit.

The blower consists essentially of two figure-eight shaped, hollow lobe impellers, indicated as *G* and *H* on all the fig-

ures. These lightweight impellers are mounted on parallel shafts running on anti-friction bearings. They rotate in opposite directions in a housing *F*, aircooled by a number of fins *E*, shown in Fig. 4–10. The clearance between the two lobes and between the lobes and the housing is very small. The space between the two lobes at all times during their operation is accurately maintained by two timing gears *A* and *B*, mounted on the

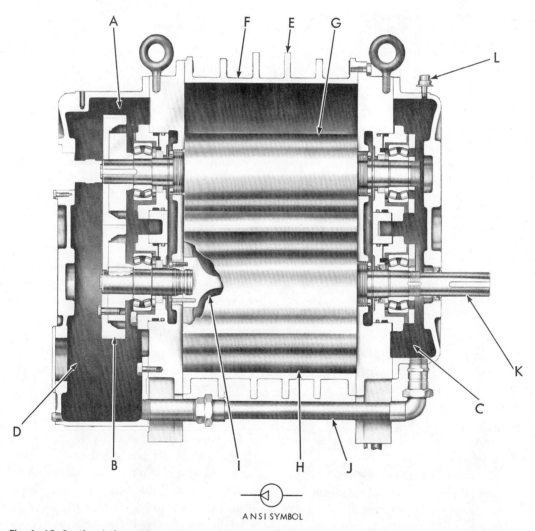

ANSI SYMBOL

Fig. 4–10. Sectional view of Roots blower, which can be used as a supercharger to improve performance of gasoline engines at high altitudes, can also be used as a vacuum pump for industrial uses. (Courtesy of Dresser Industries, Inc.)

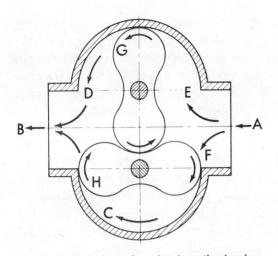

Fig. 4–11. First in series of schematic drawings showing operation of Roots blower. (Courtesy of Dresser Industries, Inc.)

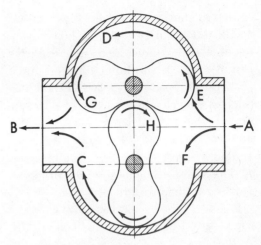

Fig. 4–13. Third in series of schematic drawings showing operation of Roots blower. (Courtesy of Dresser Industries, Inc.)

lobe shafts and driven by drive shaft *K*.

Lubrication is added at *L*, supplying oil to the two chambers *C* and *D*, which are interconnected by pipe *J* for lubricating all running parts. Oil seals keep the oil away from the air being moved.

As shown at *I*, the lobes are hollow for light weight. The position of the lobes in cutaway picture Fig. 4–10 corresponds to the position shown in Fig. 4–13.

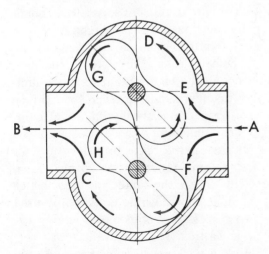

Fig. 4–12. Second in series of schematic drawings showing operation of Roots blower. (Courtesy of Dresser Industries, Inc.)

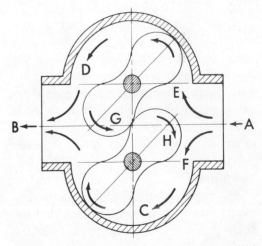

Fig. 4–14. Fourth in series of schematic drawings showing operation of Roots blower. (Courtesy of Dresser Industries, Inc.)

In schematic drawings Figs. 4–11, 4–12, 4–13, and 4–14, air is shown to enter at *A* and exhaust at *B*. Starting with Fig. 4–11, a definite volume of air is shown entrapped at *C* between the housing and lobe *H*. This chamber is now separated from the inlet port *A* and the exhaust port *B*. Lobe *G* has drawn some air through port *A* in the direction of arrow *E*. The air on the opposite side of lobe *G* is being pushed toward port *B*.

Fig. 4–12 shows how the air at *C* is now completely free to be expelled to port *B*. At the same time, lobe *G* is drawing air in from port *A*, as shown by arrow *E*.

Fig. 4–13 shows a definite volume of air entrapped at *D* between the housing and lobe *G*. Lobe *H* has drawn some air through port *A* in the direction of arrow *F*. The air on the opposite side of lobe *H* is being pushed out toward port *B*.

Fig. 4–14 shows how the air at *D* is now completely free to be expelled to port *B*. At the same time, lobe *H* is drawing air in from port *A*, as shown by arrow *F*.

Non-Mechanical Vacuum Pumps

Up to this point all the vacuum pumps described, like nearly all components used in pneumatic and hydraulic systems, operate by mechanical principles that are easily understood. The main difficulties are learning the nature and behavior of the fluid media, a little mathematics necessary to calculate what happens under given conditions, and some of the language used.

An example of the confusion caused by words rather than operations as they actually happen is seen in the case of the familiar household vacuum cleaner. Nowhere in its operation is any pressure even close to a perfect vacuum created.

Also, from one point of view, the so-called vacuum cleaner is really a blower.

As has been pointed out before, there must be a difference in pressure to cause any air movement. This is what happens with the vacuum cleaner. A blower driven by a motor is actually used for this purpose, forcing some of the air through the finely woven fabric of a bag. In doing this, a pressure slightly lower than atmospheric pressure is created at the inlet end in a hose or tube to which a nozzle is attached. This causes the air, along with any small solid particles, lint and dust, to move into the bag. Only nearly clean air will then escape through the fabric of the bag into the room where the vacuum cleaner is used. The small solid particles, lint, and dust will remain in the bag.

The operation of most pneumatic equipment for industrial uses is much more efficient and precise than the cleaner-blower just described, but the efficiency is still limited because of inherent mechanical factors. In order to extend the efficiency further, certain non-mechanical methods and equipment have been developed for critical applications such as creating ultra-high vacuums or separating chemically inert gases such as argon from gaseous mixtures such as air. Some of the phenomena that take place in the non-mechanical vacuum pumps may be difficult to understand. However, some things that happen in everyday life are also difficult to understand unless we have some training in the basic branches of engineering and physics that govern them.

Thinking of the simple vacuum cleaner example, this machine is generally used on a carpet. Most of us have found by experience that when we walk across certain types of carpets and then suddenly touch someone else or a metal object we experience a spark and an electric shock just an instant before actually touching the other person or the metal object. What actually takes place is that while we are walking across the carpet we are transforming mechanical energy to electrical energy. If the person we touched were insulated from the carpet he would act as

a capacitor, storing the electrical energy, and he, in turn, could send this electrical energy to someone else of opposite electrical polarity. But because he is not, in fact, insulated from the carpet, the electrical energy is soon "leaked away" or neutralized to the carpet. Another phenomenon

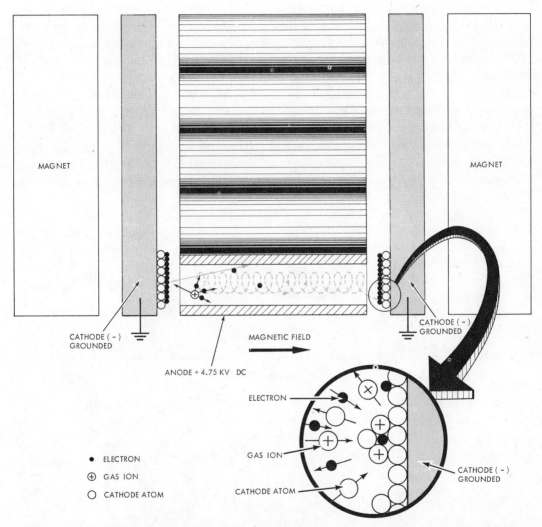

Fig. 4–15. Operation of a conventional ion pump is a very specialized kind of electrolysis. Gaseous atoms in a partial vacuum are stripped of their electrons by a direct current of high voltage (about 4,750 volts) across emitter and collector cathodes and hollow, cylindrical anodes. This causes the gas atoms to become positively charged ions which are attracted to the collector cathode. A magnetic field accelerates their motion so they strike the collector cathode with so much energy that the gas ions penetrate the cathode's metallic surface. They become embedded until "sputtered" metal atoms, also emitted from the emitter cathode, strike the collector cathode. This action dislodges some of the embedded gas ions, causing their re-emission, with some loss of efficiency and fluctuations in pressure. (Courtesy of Ultek Division of the Perkin-Elmer Corp.)

that happens in this ordinary experience is that some of the electrical energy may also be transformed to heat in the form of a spark.

Also, as you may have noticed, when certain types of vacuum cleaners are pushed over a carpet, the mechanical revolving devices transform mechanical energy to electrical energy and charge the carpet at that spot with electricity. Small particles of lint of opposite polarity may then be attracted to the carpet and will firmly cling to it. However, if you then touch the particle of lint or stop the cleaner the electrical charge is neutralized and the lint becomes loose. As soon as you start the cleaner again, the loose lint will be sucked up.

Phenomena such as these, which we see

in everyday life, have been applied scientifically in devices classed as non-mechanical vacuum pumps. The mechanical pumps previously studied on the preceding pages cannot, as a rule, reduce the pressure lower than 10^{-5} torr even with multiple stages of pumping. Principles of some non-mechanical vacuum pumps are illustrated in Figs. 4–15 and 4–16 in the form of diagrams. They operate on principles crudely similar to the example previously given. These pumps are capable of reducing the pressure (previously reduced to perhaps 10^{-5} torr by mechanical pumping) to 10^{-10} torr, which is ultra-high vacuum.

The first *ion pump*, developed in 1957, is now referred to as the *conventional ion pump*. Fig. 4–15 shows the principles of

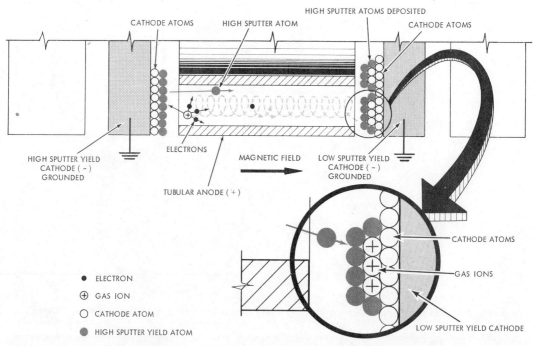

Fig. 4–16. Operation of a D-I (differential ion) pump is based on the same principles as those of the conventional ion pump. By selecting different metals for the cathodes, however, the positively charged gas ions which penetrate the surface of the receiver cathode are prevented from re-emission by a thin film of metal atoms that entrap and effectively "bury" the ions. This speeds the pumping action and eliminates pressure fluctuations. (Courtesy of Ultek Division of the Perkin-Elmer Corp.)

its operation. The ion pump was improved nine years later, in 1966, by using dissimilar metals in the cathodes on opposite sides of the the anode to prevent re-emission of gas *ions* (electrically charged atoms or groups of atoms) after they strike the receiver cathode, accelerated by a magnetic field in a partial vacuum. Pressure is lowered when the gaseous ions strike and penetrate several atomic layers below the metal surface of the cathode, where they become embedded or "buried". Fig. 4–16 shows the principles of improved *differential ion pump* (D-I pump). Notice in the enlarged portion of this diagram that positive gas ions are

"buried" beneath a thin film of *sputtered* metallic atoms forcibly ejected from the opposite cathode.

To achieve this result it is necessary to equip the ion pump with cathodes made of dissimilar materials, which explains the name *differential ion pump*. These cathodes are located on each side of the anode, which consists of a number of circular metal tubes.

In Fig. 4–16 the high sputter-yield cathode is shown at the left side of the diagram, and the low sputter-yield cathode is shown at the right. The atoms of the high sputter-yield cathode at the left of the tubular anode deposit at a higher

Fig. 4–17. The world's largest ion pump installed at Boeing's Space Laboratory, where it is used for space simulation. (Courtesy of Ultek Division of the Perkins-Elmer Corp.)

ANSI SYMBOL

Fig. 4–18. A small (1 liter per second) D-I appendage pump. This type of pump, specifically designed for use as a final pumping stage in connection with other sealed pumps, operates between 10^{-2} and 10^{-10} torr, but is normally operated at pressures below 10^{-5} torr. (Courtesy of Ultek Division of the Perkins-Elmer Corp.)

rate on areas of the low sputter-yield cathode on the right side at the periphery of the tubular anode, thus preventing re-emission. Loss of atoms from the partial vacuum further lowers the pressure beyond the capability of mechanical pumps.

See Fig. 4–17, showing the world's largest ion pump at Boeing, where it is used in a laboratory for space simulation. Fig. 4–18 shows a small D-I *appendage pump* used as a final pumping stage for high vacuums. This pump, designed for use on sealed vacuum devices, operates between 10^{-2} and 10^{-10} torr. When used in connection with another pump it is normally operated at pressures below 10^{-5}

torr. D-1 pumps consistently outperform conventional ion pumps at very low pressure and have a much longer operating life expectancy.

Other forms of non-mechanical pumps include *sorption roughing, titanium sublimation pumping, diffusion pumps, adsorption pumps, and cryogenic pumping.* The latter system lowers pressure beyond the range of mechanical pumping by means of adsorption or condensation of gaseous media at ultra low temperatures. The subject of non-mechanical vacuum pumps is too extensive for detail treatment in a book of this type and is involved in many fields of science and engineering.

Storage Tanks

Whereas most hydraulic systems generate a flow of oil or other liquid under pressure at the rate necessary for doing work, pneumatic systems in almost all cases compress air or gas and store it immediately in storage tanks or *receivers*.

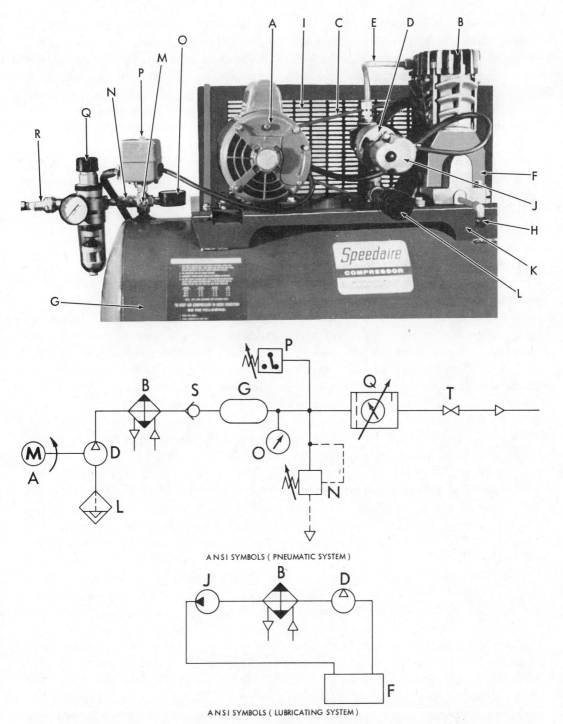

Fig. 4–19. Typical compressor-receiver hookup for supplying compressed air to operate pneumatic tools in an industrial plant. Circuit diagrams with ANSI symbols show operation of the main (pneumatic) system and the small (hydraulic) system to lubricate the air compressor, which is driven by a unidirectional electric motor. Systems where electric, pneumatic, and hydraulic equipment interface are not uncommon in industrial applications. (Photo Courtesy of C. A. Norgren Co.)

See Fig. 4–19. The compressed air or gas is then taken from the storage tank at the pressure needed for doing work, which is not necessarily the same pressure at which it is compressed to keep the tank pressurized.

As mentioned earlier, this ability to store the gaseous media under high pressure with no further expenditure of energy is one of the most important features of pneumatic power systems. In intermittent use, the compressed air or gas can be used for doing work at a rate that exceeds the compressor's capacity. The use of this storage tank or receiver also minimizes surges and lags in the pneumatic power and serves this purpose even when the compressed air or gas is used almost immediately after compression. The storage tank can be thought of as the second part of the combined compressor-storage pneumatic power unit. In selecting a good storage tank it is therefore important to carefully consider the requirements of the work.

Fig. 4–19 illustrates a typical compressor-receiver hookup used to supply clean, conditioned and pressure-regulated compressed air for operating pneumatic tools in an industrial plant. Systems of this kind are commonly used in applications where air-operated tools are in fairly continuous demand.

The hookup shown in the photo and accompanying circuit diagrams is driven by a unidirectional electric motor A, which operates air compressor D and also hydraulic pump J, used to circulate oil to lubricate the compressor. This motor also drives a fan to cool heat exchanger B. This heat exchanger has a double function: one, to cool compressed air as it is discharged from the compressor through pipe E to the receiver G. It also cools the lubricating oil as it is circulated from the

compressor by hydraulic pump J, to be returned to the lubricating oil sump F.

The electric motor A drives the shaft of the heat exchanger component B by means of a small sheave on the motor shaft and a large sheave on the heat exchanger, connected by a belt C. The shaft on the heat exchanger also has a small sheave connected to the larger sheave which is connected by a belt (not visible in the photo) to a larger sheave on compressor D. A drain pipe is shown in the photo at H, and I is a louver guard in the rear for protecting the drive.

The compressor is mounted on a sub-plate K, welded to the receiver G at four support feet. This sub-plate serves as a support for all the equipment on top of the receiver and also protects the compressor intake on the bottom side of the sub-plate. The air at the intake has ample access on all sides.

L is a filter-strainer located at the intake of the compressor. Compressed air is delivered for distribution from the receiver at M.

The pressure in the receiver is controlled by valve N. Gage O indicates the actual pressure in the receiver. P is a pressure switch which starts the motor if the pressure has fallen below the acceptable value and stops the motor when the maximum pressure is reached.

Q is a combination of filter, pressure regulator with pressure gage, and lubricator, for distribution of regulated and conditioned compressed air to supply line R. There is also a check valve S, not visible in the photo. The function of the check valve S is to prevent flow of compressed air from returning to the compressor. T is a shut-off valve which can be set to prevent flow of air in both directions for shutting the system when it is not in use.

The letters identifying the symbols are

the same as the identification letters on the photo. Some further facts should be noticed regarding these ANSI symbols.

The hydraulic pump *J* is a unidirectional, fixed-displacement type of pump for circulating the lubricating oil through the compressor. *L* is a filter-strainer with automatic drain, indicated by the small inner triangle at the bottom of the symbol. *N* is a pressure relief valve, with the arrow indicating that the pressure is adjustable. The dotted line shows that the excess pressure is relieved to the atmosphere. The arrow in pressure gage *P* shows that it is adjustable. *Q* is a simplified symbol for a filter, adjustable pressure regulator, pressure gage, and lubricator. The dotted line indicates the filter function, the arrow to the right indicates pressure regulation, the small circle with enclosed arrow indicates the pressure gage, and the small vertical line to the right indicates the lubricator. The check valve *S* is drawn in a direction indicating free flow toward the right (or downstream) and no flow toward the left (or upstream).

The single, curved arrow in the symbol for motor *A* indicates that it is of the unidirectional type, rotating in only one direction. The ANSI symbol for heat exchanger *B* illustrates how compactly descriptions can be made in circuit diagrams. The solid inside triangles indicate heat dissipation, and the open inside triangles indicate that the method for cooling is gaseous—in this case air cooling. Now compare the symbol for the air compressor *D* with the symbol for the hydraulic pump *J*. The small *open* triangle in *D* identifies it as pneumatic. The small *solid* triangle in pump *J* identifies it as hydraulic—the liquid in this case being lubricating oil.

Chapter 6 will show a complete pneumatic system with a main supply line and 3 branch lines operating typical pneumatic tools.

There are so many types of storage tanks for a great variety of gaseous media to be used under a variation of environmental conditions that proper selection is not always simple. However, design requirements to suit all cases are based on a few considerations, which may be enumerated as follows:

1. The material of the tank must be compatible with the gaseous medium stored and to the ambient environmental conditions.
2. It must have adequate strength and safety.
3. It must have capacity enough to meet emergency demands.
4. While retaining all requirements 1, 2, and 3, it should occupy the smallest space and have a pleasing appearance.

Three types of tanks in common use for storing gaseous media are:

1. Cylindrical tanks are used in a vertical or horizontal position. Most commonly these are used in a vertical position and placed in a horizontal position for transporation. See Fig. 4–20.
2. Flat-bottomed tanks, which are essentially cylindrical tanks with a flat bottom and a dome-shaped top. In the larger capacities these tanks are usually used in outside locations and are often constructed at the site of location. See Fig. 4–21. Some of the smaller sizes are used for transportation, storage and dispensing. See Figs. 4–22, 4–23, 4–24, and 4–25.
3. Spherical tanks, usually used for

ANSI SYMBOL

Fig. 4—20. Barge-mounted cryogenic storage tanks used to store and transport liquid oxygen or liquid hydrogen for the National Space Program. (Courtesy of Chicago Bridge & Iron Co.)

ANSI SYMBOL

Fig. 4—21. Group of four flat-bottom tanks for outdoor storage. Large tanks such as these are usually erected on the site. (Courtesy of Chicago Bridge & Iron Co.)

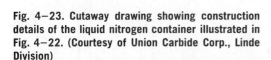

ANSI SYMBOL

Fig. 4–22. Small liquid nitrogen container. This is a portable container with unobstructed access. (Courtesy of Union Carbide Corp., Linde Division)

Fig. 4–23. Cutaway drawing showing construction details of the liquid nitrogen container illustrated in Fig. 4–22. (Courtesy of Union Carbide Corp., Linde Division)

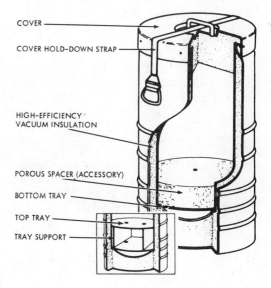

COVER

COVER HOLD-DOWN STRAP

HIGH-EFFICIENCY VACUUM INSULATION

POROUS SPACER (ACCESSORY)

BOTTOM TRAY

TOP TRAY

TRAY SUPPORT

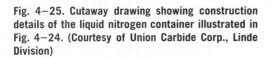

ANSI SYMBOL

Fig. 4–24. Another style of cryogenic container used for transportation, storage, and dispensing of liquid nitrogen. (Courtesy of Union Carbide Corp., Linde Division)

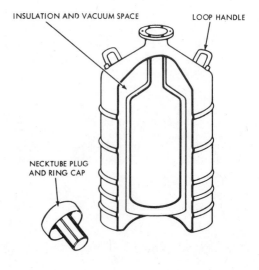

INSULATION AND VACUUM SPACE

LOOP HANDLE

NECKTUBE PLUG AND RING CAP

Fig. 4–25. Cutaway drawing showing construction details of the liquid nitrogen container illustrated in Fig. 4–24. (Courtesy of Union Carbide Corp., Linde Division)

ANSI SYMBOL

Fig. 4–26. Double-wall spherical tank designed to store liquified oxygen at cryogenic temperatures for NASA's Kennedy Space Center, Merrit Island, Florida. (Courtesy of Chicago Bridge & Iron Co.)

storage of large volumes of media. See Fig. 4–26, showing a tank for liquid oxygen.

Cryogenic Gaseous Media

Cryogenics is relatively a recent branch of fluid power which has made enormous progress, not only for industrial use, but in numerous other fields serving human needs. The word *cryogenics* was coined from the Greek *kryos*, meaning *icy cold*, and *genes*, meaning *to become* or *to produce*. It is the branch of physics concerned with phenomena that occur at very low temperatures, approaching absolute zero.

In recent years, cryogenic engineering has become a part of our industrial economy, primarily as a result of the expanded use of cryogenic liquefied gases. In industry, deep-freeze refrigerators are impor- tant for the treatment of steel. Advanced technology in the metal industries, chem- ical industries, military rockets and space exploration have greatly stimulated the use of cryogenic gaseous media. The liq-

TABLE 4-1. CRYOGENIC PROPERTIES OF LIQUEFIED GASES
(U.S. MEASUREMENT)

GAS	O_2 OXYGEN	N_2 NITROGEN	Ar ARGON	CH_4 METHANE	F_2 FLUORINE	H_2 HYDROGEN	He HELIUM	C_2H_4 ETHYLENE
DENSITY @ 68° F (LB/CU FT @ 1 ATM)	0.08311	0.07276	0.1037	0.04163	0.09877	0.005234	0.01039	0.07279
BOILING POINT (° F @ 1 ATM)	−297.4	−320.0	−302.4	−258.7	−306.5	−423.0	−452.0	−154.68
MELTING POINT (° F @ 1 ATM)	−361.1	−345.8	−308.7	−299.2	−363.3	−434.6	26 ATM −458.0	−272.47
VAPOR DENSITY @ N.B.P. (LB/CU FT)	0.296	0.288	0.368	0.1124	–	0.0830	0.999	0.130
LIQUID DENSITY @ N.B.P. (LB/CU FT)	71.19	50.46	86.77	26.47	69.2	4.37	7.803	35.49
HEAT OF VAPORIZATION @ N.B.P. (BTU/#)	91.6	85.7	70.0	220	73.7	194.4	10.3	207.6
HEAT OF VAPORIZATION @ N.B.P. (BTU/CU FT)	6521	4324	6074	6575	5100	849.5	80.37	7368
HEAT OF FUSION @ N.M.P. (BTU/#)	5.9	11.0	12.1	26.1	5.8	25.2	<1.8	51.3
CRITICAL TEMPERATURE (° F)	−181.1	−232.8	−188.5	−116.5	−200.2	−399.8	−450.2	49.82
CRITICAL PRESSURE (PSIA)	730.3	492.3	705.2	672.0	808.3	188.1	33.2	735

N.B.P. (NORMAL BOILING POINT) (Temperature at which boiling occurs when pressure is one atmosphere)
N.M.P. (NORMAL MELTING POINT) (Temperature at which melting occurs when pressure is one atmosphere)
HEAT OF VAPORIZATION (BTU/#) (Amount of heat added to change one pound of liquid to vapor at normal B.P.)
HEAT OF FUSION (BTU/#) (Amount of heat added to change one pound of solid to liquid at normal M.P.)
CRITICAL TEMPERATURE (The temperature above which the substance cannot exist in the liquid state)
CRITICAL PRESSURE (The pressure of the saturated vapor at the critical temperature)

Courtesy of Chicago Bridge & Iron Company

uefied cryogenic gas is the end product of fluid-power processing.

Tables 4–1 and 4–2 show the cryogenic properties of various liquefied gases in U.S. and metric systems.

Manufacturing of cryogenic gaseous media is actually a process of compression and ultra cold distillation. For instance, when air is first compressed to approximately 3,675 psi or 250 atmospheres and then cooled to about −310° F, or −190° C, it is liquefied. When slightly warmed, to

TABLE 4-2. CRYOGENIC PROPERTIES OF LIQUEFIED GASES
(METRIC MEASUREMENT)

GAS	O_2 OXYGEN	N_2 NITROGEN	Ar ARGON	CH_4 METHANE	F_2 FLUORINE	H_2 HYDROGEN	He HELIUM	C_2H_4 ETHYLENE
DENSITY @ 19.9° C (kg/m^3 @ 1 ATM)	1.331	1.166	1.661	0.667	1.582	0.0838	0.166	1.166
BOILING POINT (° C @ 1 ATM)	−183	−195.8	−185.8	−161.5	−188	−252.8	−268.8	−103.7
MELTING POINT (° C @ 1 ATM)	−218.4	−209.9	−189.2	−183.9	−219.6	−259.2	26 ATM −272.2	−169.2
VAPOR DENSITY @ N.B.P. (kg/m^3)	4.742	4.614	5.895	1.801	–	1.330	16.004	2.083
LIQUID DENSITY @ N.B.P. (kg/m^3)	1140	872	1390	424	1109	70	125	569
HEAT OF VAPORIZATION @ N.B.P. (CAL/kg)	50.9	47.6	38.9	122.2	40.9	108.0	5.7	115.3
HEAT OF VAPORIZATION @ N.B.P. (CAL/m^3)	58,222	38,607	54,232	58,705	45,535	7,585	718	65,785
HEAT OF FUSION @ N.M.P. (CAL/kg)	3,277	6.110	6.721	14.499	3.222	13.999	< 1.000	28.497
CRITICAL TEMPERATURE (° C)	−118.4	−147.1	−122.5	−82.5	−129	−239.9	−267.9	9.9
CRITICAL PRESSURE (kg/cm^2 ABSOLUTE)	50	34.6	49.6	47.2	56.8	13.2	2.3	51.7

N.B.P. (NORMAL BOILING POINT) (Temperature at which boiling occurs when pressure is one atmosphere)

N.M.P. (NORMAL MELTING POINT) (Temperature at which melting occurs when pressure is one atmosphere)

HEAT OF VAPORIZATION (CAL/ kg) (Amount of heat added to change one kilogram of liquid to vapor at normal B.P.)

HEAT OF FUSION (CAL/kg) (Amount of heat added to change one kilogram of solid to liquid at normal M.P.)

CRITICAL TEMPERATURE (The temperature above which the substance cannot exist in the liquid state)

CRITICAL PRESSURE (The pressure of the saturated vapor at the critical temperature)

Fig. 4–27. An operator pouring liquid air into a small container for further processing in a Norsk Hydro plant. (Courtesy of Norsk Hydro, Norway)

about −300° F, or −184° C, nitrogen is released as a pure gas, and oxygen leaves as a pure gas at about −297° F, or −182° C. This process is called *distillation* and may be easier understood when we say that alcohol can be distilled from another liquid of a higher boiling point. If we heat water containing alcohol to a temperature above the boiling point of alcohol but below the boiling point of water, the alcohol will escape as a vapor. If this vapor is permitted to escape to a cooler place it will condense and is therefore separated from the water as pure alcohol. Fig. 4–27 shows an operator pouring liquid air into a cryogenic container in a Norsk Hydro plant in Norway.

As has been mentioned before, the principal constituents of air are nitrogen and oxygen, two colorless, odorless gaseous media.

You may wonder why the man pouring the liquid air does not require gloves for protecting his hands. Let us consider some basic, important facts concerning thermodynamics.

Cold does not move to a warmer place. It is always heat that moves to a colder place. So, therefore, what you see is not the liquid air turning into a gaseous medium, but rather the air surrounding the man moving to a colder place and rapidly being cooled off to release some of the water vapor as saturated steam of a temperature somewhat lower than the ambient temperature.

Therefore the air surrounding the man's body is warmer than the air close to the liquid air, and the air moves away from the man towards the liquid air.

Steam produced by the boiling of water, on the other hand, would rapidly move to a colder place and could cause severe damage.

The process of liquefying oxygen and nitrogen is similar. We say that by distillation we have separated the oxygen or nitrogen from the air and can store each of these gaseous media as a liquid in a separate cryogenic tank. There are numerous useful applications of cryogenic gaseous media where no electrical power is available or where the sources of power have temporarily failed. When the liquid is raised to a higher temperature by letting it escape to the point of application it changes to a saturated gas and becomes a useful gaseous medium.

When, for example, liquid nitrogen is poured into a container there is no pressure in the container except the pressure from the weight of the liquid. Normal evaporation, however, in one actual case will build the pressure up to approximately 22 psig or 1.5 kg/cm² above atmospheric pressure in the space of 15 hours after filling the container. If, however, this pressure or a higher pressure is required immediately after filling, a special attachment may be applied which will speed up the rate of evaporation from liquid to a gaseous medium. This can be done by the method of convection, radiation or conduction.

The common cryogenic gaseous media are:

Liquid Oxygen, commonly expressed as LO_2 or LOX, normally exists in a gaseous, odorless form without color at 21% of dry air at sea level. Some of the major uses of oxygen are in the manufacture of steel, rocket engines, the chemical industry and environmental use. Steel manufacture is perhaps the largest consumer and accounts for 50% of all oxygen production. The chemical industry accounts for another 25% and the rocket industry consumes about 15% of the overall total. In the steel industry, oxygen is used to increase production capacity by two methods:

1. Oxygen *lances* (instruments) used in open hearth furnaces to feed pure oxygen into the melt and reduce heat time.
2. Basic oxygen steelmaking requires special vessels designed specifically to get the pure oxygen to the place of combustion. This basic oxygen process, developed in Europe, is being used for 20% of production in the United States. It is predicted that before 1985 this will increase to over 50 percent.

Oxygen furnaces for steelmaking will cause tremendous growth in the demand for oxygen. These furnaces use an average of 1,800 standard cubic feet (SCF) or 50,000 normal liters of oxygen per ton of steel produced. Open hearth furnaces generally use from 300 to 500 SCF, or

8,000 to 14,000 liters, while advanced designs use up to 1,500 SCF, or 42,500 liters. The oxygen is here changed from a liquefied to a gaseous medium.

In the chemical industry oxygen is finding increasing use in production of ammonia, methanol, acetylene and acrylonitrile. It is also used to oxidize select hydrocarbons to aldehydes, acids, and alcohols.

The use of oxygen in propellant systems of ballistic missiles and space vehicles is a much publicized fact. Up to 1,200 tons of liquid oxygen per day have been used in support of the missile and space programs. A much greater use is possible.

Liquid Nitrogen, expressed as LN_2, is the largest constitutent of the air, in its natural state being 78% at sea level in a gaseous, colorless, tasteless and odorless form. As the production of oxygen has greatly increased, so also the production of nitrogen. The fastest growing market potential for nitrogen is in the missile, food and chemical industries. Nitrogen has long been used in the production of fertilizer. It is also used in the manufacturing of ammonia for bright annealing of steel and for chilling processes in aluminum foundries.

Annealing is a process of relieving internal stresses in the steel by heating the steel to a certain temperature and then slowly and gradually lowering the temperature of the steel to ambient conditions. This also softens the material. If, however, the atmosphere surrounding the steel is not controlled, the oxygen in the atmosphere will give the steel a bluish oxide coating.

Bright annealing is accomplished by surrounding the steel with nitrogen while it is being annealed. The steel then keeps its bright color.

The chilling process for aluminum improves the structural quality of the aluminum. The chilling process has also been used in manufacturing plants. If a good quality alloy steel has been heat treated and high accuracy is important, the workpiece is kept at a low temperature for some time with the use of liquid nitrogen. This will improve the stability of the work piece as it is being ground to final dimensions.

Other fast growing uses of this gaseous medium are for purging, low-temperature refrigeration, oil-well fracturing, pressure medium in propellant feed systems, refrigerated food transportation and as a blanket in processes requiring an oxygen-free atmosphere.

As with other liquid gases at cryogenic temperatures, LN_2 cannot be stored in its liquid state indefinitely. For example, the small container previously shown in Figs. 4–18 and 4–19 has a maximum capacity of 46.6 liters. With this volume the static evaporation rate (that is, without removing or adding to the content) is 2.25 liters per day. Therefore, the maximum static holding time is 21 days.

The useful product capacity is dependent on the liquid nitrogen capacity and the holding time desired. For this reason the efficient use of the nitrogen requires an understanding of the differences and advantages of two types of storage.

The first of these, called *immersion storage*, is storage below the surface level of the liquid nitrogen. This allows the maximum LN_2 capacity and provides the longest possible holding time. As long as the product remains entirely below the surface of the liquid, the temperature remains at −310°F (−190°C).

The second type of storage, called *vapor-phase storage*, is the storage in the cold space above the liquid level. Since the temperature in this space varies from −310°F (−190°C) to −148°F (−100°C) depending on the distance above the liquid level, the desired temperature of the vapor can be maintained by a number of methods:

1. By the frequency of refilling with liquid gas.
2. By adjustment to maintain the distance between the vapor and the liquid level below it.
3. By use of conduction devices.

Heat is transient and always flows from a warmer to a colder place. This transient characteristic of heat lowers the temperature of the object. Air and any constituent of the air, such as nitrogen, is a poor heat conductor. Therefore, if a good heat conductor (a metallic object) is permitted to lead the heat from the part suspended in the gas to the liquid nitrogen which is colder, the temperature of the part may be kept the same as long as the liquid nitrogen lasts.

Vapor phase storage is particularly useful in cases where the desired refrigeration temperature is higher than the gas in its liquid state.

Argon (Ar) is a gaseous element occurring in volcanic gases and is about 1%, by volume, of air at sea level. This inert gas has also experienced a fast growth rate over the past several years. The main use of argon at present is in inert-gas, shielded-arc welding of stainless steel, aluminum and a few other metals. It is used in the production of incandescent light bulbs to retard filament evaporation, giving greater efficiency and longer life than ordinary vacuum bulbs. Future uses may be to provide inert atmospheres for work on nuclear and Space-Age metals. There is also a potential market in the use of argon to cut down impurities while pouring steel ingots or castings and in the production of stainless steel.

Hydrogen (H_2) is a colorless, odorless, flammable gas, the lightest of all elements, which combines chemically with oxygen to form water, H_2O. Liquid hydrogen is largely used in chemical rockets and in nuclear rockets. At present, its use in chemical rockets with such oxidizers as oxygen or fluorine is in the production stage. Hydrogen shows a high theoretical efficiency for chemical propulsion. Direct reduction of iron ore has spurred some market growth and there is a growing trend to use hydrogen atmosphere in metal heat treatments, cold treatments, and other metalurgical processes.

Helium (He) a light, chemically inert gas, is obtained by compression and fractionation of gases from certain wells and from several radioactive minerals. To date helium has largely been used in a gaseous form. Some is, however, now stored and transported as a liquid. Handling in liquid form is economically attractive and the industry is rapidly increasing its use of liquid helium transport, storage and transfer equipment. Commercially, helium is used in such processes as inert-gas, shielded-arc welding, inert atmosphere processing and cryogenic research in the area of electrical super-conductivity and other phenomena that occur at temperatures near absolute zero. The missile and space programs consume considerable quantities of helium. This gas is non-flammable.

Liquefied Natural Gas (LNG). Natural gas is one of the principal energy sources in the United States. It is a mixture of various gases and hydrocarbons including pentane, butane, propane, ethane, carbon dioxide, methane, nitrogen, and helium. Its major constituent is methane, which varies between 85% and 95% of the mixture. Methane (CH_4) is a marsh gas. It is odorless, colorless, flammable, and insoluble in water. It is found underground, a product of decayed vegetable matter, but can also be synthesized in several ways.

At atmospheric pressure the boiling point of methane is $-259°F$ (or $-157°C$) to $-290°F$ (or $-173°C$) because of the effect of its other constituents. Primary uses for LNG are for *peak shaving* (that is, extra gas produced during low demand periods, which is liquefied for peak demands) by transmission and utility distribution companies, and for base load gas supply systems. LNG is easily transported by truck, rail, barge, and ship. The ease of transportation is an attractive factor in broadening its use. Several projects have been completed to provide remote towns with base load gas by transporting LNG to a satellite storage vaporization point where the LNG will be vaporized, then distributed through a local pipe line network.

Through the use of a satellite system, gas companies can install a peak shaving liquefaction plant at one location and transport the LNG to another satellite location for peak shaving distribution. They can also purchase LNG from other distributors such as ocean terminals or other gas companies which have an excess of liquefaction capacity above their needs.

The use of natural gas to power engines for heavy equipment, such as trucks, is attractive because of low fuel cost, clean burning, and less engine maintenance.

Peak shaving is a means of balancing out pipeline supply demand requirements. Natural gas is liquefied during off-peak periods and stored for vaporization and use during peak periods.

Ethylene (C_2H_4) is a basic building block for the production of most of our plastics, which is a growing industry. Huge ethylene plants have been built on

Fluid Power: Pneumatics

the U.S.A. Gulf Coast and in foreign locations where natural gas liquids and naphtha are inexpensive and readily available.

Materials for Cryogenic Vessels. Selection of proper materials for the construction of cryogenic tanks is one of the most important considerations facing the designer. Of primary concern is how the material will perform at very low temperatures. Such properties as the value of tensile toughness generally known as *notch ductility*, specific heat, and coefficient of thermal conductivity at very low temperatures, must be known, as well as the usual strength and elastic properties of the material. Most metals increase in strength with a decrease in temperature. Some, however, such as carbon steels, suffer an almost complete loss of ductility at low temperatures, making them useless for construction of inner vessels. Copper, nickel, aluminum and most alloys of these metals exhibit no ductile-to-brittle transitions and therefore are suitable for cryogenic service. Stainless steel of the 18% chrome, 8% nickel classification also exhibits excellent ductility in extreme cold.

The liquid containers for field-erected cryogenic storage tanks at present are constructed of one of the family of aluminum-magnesium alloys such as the 0 temper of AA5083 or AA5086 (ASTM B-209 grade GM41A or grade GM40A, respectively) or A553 grade A or A353, 9% nickel steels for temperature service down to −320°F (−196° C) or of type 304 stainless steel, ASTM A-240 type 304. Generally, the outer casing of double-wall tanks is constructed of ordinary carbon steel, since it never comes in contact with cryogenic liquid or vapor.

Tank Design. After the material and environmental service conditions have been determined, the design procedure of a cryogenic tank does not differ materially from that of conventional tanks. Steps in the design are outlined as follows:

1. The geometric volume below maximum liquid level and required minimum vapor space must be determined. Enough vapor space is necessary to provide an adequate ebullition surface. If the incoming product is to be *flashed* (suddenly introduced) in the storage vessel, additional vapor space may be needed to minimize the number of off-on cycles of the vapor re-compression system. Usual values of vapor space volume range from 5% to 10% of the liquid storage volume. In the case of a flat bottom, dome-roof tank, these requirements usually are satisfied by volume beneath the curved top.

   For pressure vessels, this vapor space can vary depending on the capacity of the *vapor re-compression system* (space above the liquid, which is provided for the gaseous medium to re-compress). A minimum value to provide adequate ebullition surface is about 0.5%. To determine gross volume of the tank with the weight of the product known, the volume occupied should be computed with the liquid warmed to the *saturation temperature*, (where the liquid changes to gas) corresponding to a pressure of 20% above the maximum allowable working pressure, and 5% should be added to this to assure venting of vapor and not of liquid.

2. The inner tank must be designed for internal pressure arising from vapor-phase pressure and liquid weight. Where cryogenic tanks will operate over a range of pressures and temperatures with accompany-

98

ing variations in product density, maximum values must be taken. Maximum design loads occur with the tank at design pressure and with maximum liquid density. For tanks using the basic insulation system, the inner tank must be designed to resist external pressure from the insulating powder, insulating space gas pressure, and a small allowable internal vacuum. For vacuum-powder insulated tanks, the design pressure must include allowance for reduced external pressure. Special consideration must be given to concentrated loads in the region of support attachments and fittings, taking into account thermal displacements.

3. Outer tank design loads include wind, snow, dead load, internal pressure from insulating powder and insulating space gas pressure. The material is generally of a minimum nominal thickness necessary for construction. In the case of pressure storage, however, local loadings where outer tank supports are attached will require increased thickness, and structural systems are needed for inner tank suspension. For the *vacuum-powder insulation system*, in which an insulation of powder is used and the space between the inner and outer tank is also evacuated, the outer tank must be designed for loads described plus an external pressure of 15 psi (or 1.04 kg/cm²).

Foundations. Foundations for various types of cryogenic pressure tanks, such as spheres and pressure cylinders, do not differ materially from foundations for ordinary spheres and cylinders. Long established design rules for column-supported or skirt-supported tanks apply without change. One caution should, however, be observed, namely: most cryogenic liquids are lighter than water and the inner tanks are designed for these lighter liquids. Therefore, it is common practice to design foundations for the total weight of contained product and to hydrostatic test of 1.25 times the product weight. Some cryogenic liquids, such as oxygen, are heavier than water, and foundations must be designed for the maximum load which will occur when the tank is full of the liquid product.

Flat-bottom tanks set in locations where temperatures fall below 32°F (or O° C) foundations present an additional problem. The container is a heat-sink and, if no provision is made to supply heat to the surface underneath, a large quantity of soil eventually would reach temperatures below the freezing point of water. Moisture in the sub-soil would freeze and some heaving could occur. To prevent this freezing, a heat source is necessary just below the outer tank bottom to maintain temperature above 32°F. Electrical resistance heating cable or pipe coils with circulating liquid are effective means of supplying heat.

Certain minimum requirements have been established by ASME. Where they apply, design rules of the latest standards should be used.

Gas Storage. Spherical tanks are used for storage of natural or manufactured gas in municipal gas distribution systems. They are also used for digester gas storage at sewage disposal plants and by the petroleum and chemical industries for storing various types of gases. These tanks can also be used for compressed air storage and vacuum service. They range in sizes from 32 to 120 feet (or 10 to 37 meters) in diameter, and are designed for pressures from 32 psi to 273 psi (or 2.5 to 19 kg/cm².) Special designs have, however, been constructed for pressures up to 450 psi (or 32 kg/cm²) and shell plate thickness up to 2 inches (or 5 cm).

Construction. The cylindrical supports for these spherical tanks for storing a gaseous medium are usually designed to carry the dead weight of the shell plus a 100 mile (or 160 km) per hour wind load, but no contained liquid. The columns range from 6 inches to 24 inches (or 15 to 60 cm) in diameter. Rods with turnbuckles are usually installed to transmit the wind or other lateral loads to the foundations.

Foundations are designed so that the combined effect of dead weight and the lateral loading will not cause uplift, overturning or excessive toe pressure based on the allowable pressure for the soil conditions at the vessel site. The foundations are normally designed so that the maximum toe pressure from a combination of dead weight and wind load will not exceed 3,600 pounds per square foot (or 17.575 kg/m²).

Spherical vessels for gas storage are usually given an air test in accordance with paragraph UG–100 of the ASME code, since the supports are not normally designed for a liquid load. After applying a soap film to all seams that have not been 100% radiographed with low pressure in the tank, the air pressure is increased until the shell joints are stressed to 125% of the design stress. A magnetic particle inspection to detect invisible cracks is also made of all nozzles and manholes after shop or field welding, but before testing. The capacity of a gas storage pressure tank is the amount of free gas it will deliver in the operating pressure range, as expressed by the equation:

$$Q = V \frac{(p_1 - p_2)}{p}, \text{ where:}$$

$Q =$ Cubic feet (or liters) of gas, at atmospheric pressure, that the tank will deliver between the pressures p_1 and p_2

$V =$ Volume of tank, cubic feet or liters

$p_1 =$ Maximum operating pressure, psig or kg/cm², gage

$p_2 =$ Minimum operating pressure, psig or kg/cm², gage

$p =$ Atmospheric pressure, psia $= 14.7$ or 1.033 kg/cm²

Safety. A relief valve must be attached to all pressurized tanks, and so that the relief valve can be inspected with gas in the tank, a shut-off valve should be installed between the tank and the relief valve.

A spherical tank designed for a relatively low working pressure will not safely withstand atmospheric pressure with the tank evacuated. A spherical tank designed for an internal gas pressure of approximately 100 psi (or 7 kg/cm²) will safely resist the atmospheric pressure in an evacuated tank.

As previously stated, storage tanks, also called receivers for compressed air used in industrial plants, are usually of a simple, proven cylindrical shape.

Review Questions

1. What is the greatest theoretical height to which water may be pumped by a single-acting suction pump, in feet and in meters?

2. What are some of the main advantages of pumps driven by a gaseous medium?

3. What causes a gaseous medium to move in a vacuum pump?

4. Theoretically, what is a more appropriate name for a mechanical vacuum pump?

5. Approximately to what pressure can a single-stage and a double-stage rotary piston pump evacuate an enclosure?

6. What requirements are most important for a storage tank?

7. Describe the three most commonly used storage tanks.

8. Name three methods of maintaining the desired storage temperature in a liquid nitrogen container.

9. What is meant by *cryogenics*?

10. Describe the majority of uses for liquid oxygen.

11. Describe some of the reasons why liquid oxygen is very beneficial in the steelmaking industry.

12. What industries are the fastest growing market potentials for liquid nitrogen?

13. Which are the principal uses for argon?

14. What is the storage temperature of liquefied natural gas?

15. What is meant by *peak shaving* for liquefied natural gas?

16. Which gaseous medium is the chief building block for most of our plastics?

17. What is the usual vapor space required for a cryogenic tank in percent of liquid capacity?

18. What are the design considerations for the inner tank of cryogenic vessels?

19. What are the design considerations for the outer tank of a cryogenic vessel?

20. Describe considerations to observe in the preparation of foundations for cryogenic tanks.

21. What general type of tank is used for storage of natural and manufactured gases?

22. Describe considerations to observe in the preparation of foundations for storage tanks for natural and manufactured gases.

23. What inspection tests are given for possible leaks to tanks for natural and manufactured gas?

SEE END OF BOOK FOR ANSWERS TO QUESTIONS

| Chapter 5 | # Air-Operated Tools |

A great variety of air-operated tools are used in industry. In many cases air is the only safe source of power because there are often hazardous environments where other sources of power could cause explosions or fire. Air as a source of power also has several other advantages. The distinguishing characteristic of air is that it is highly compressible. There is therefore no shock load in applying this power source, because the pressure will be gradually built up to the degree necessary to cause motion. The speed of this build-up depends chiefly on the rate of flow.

If components of a pneumatic system have been designed to take the force of the load necessary for successful operation there is no danger of damage, since the forces applied can be closely controlled. A smooth increase in speed can therefore also be achieved without complicated accessories. Then if for any reason the tool or component operated by the gaseous medium should stall, perhaps encountering an unpredicted obstacle or opposition, no damage can be done to the source of power supply or to the driven tool or component.

If this power source is operating a linear or circular actuator, this actuator may in most cases be designed to entrap the escaping air so it will come to a sufficiently smooth stop with no bounce. The power is then built up gradually to a force of sufficient magnitude to hold the actuator securely in this position. As long as it remains in this position no further energy is expended.

The two main categories of air-driven tools are motors and actuators. Pneumatic motors may then be divided into four main types:

1. Rotary Vane Motors
2. Radial Piston Motors
3. Axial Piston Motors
4. Single Piston (Percussion) Motors

102

Whereas pneumatic actuators are used principally for moving an object or a machine element from one position to another and perhaps holding it in place under pressure until returning it to its original position, pneumatic motors are used to produce rotating or reciprocating motion, or a combination of these motions.

Pneumatic motors are by nature basically variable speed and variable torque motors, very similar to d-c electric motors whose speed will change with applied torque. The selection of a suitable pneumatic motor for a given application should be based on torque-speed, not horsepower.

Generally speaking, where high speeds are required a rotary blade type motor should be specified. Where relatively heavy loads are present a piston motor should be used.

Some of the principal applications for these air-operated motors are:

1. Grinders
2. Drills
3. Wood Borers
4. Saws
5. Hammers
6. Diggers
7. Hoists

Many applications could be added to this list, such as riveting machines, small presses, air screwdrivers, nutsetters, etc. The list is almost endless, and every individual case is really the result of ingeniously applying the basic laws for the behavior of the gaseous media as thoroughly explained in Chapters 2 and 3.

Pneumatic Motors

Since the introduction of the electric motor it has been recognized as the most logical method of drive in the majority of cases. There are, however, many cases where the use of an electric motor would be either impossible or inadvisable. For instance, there are cases where electric power is not available. In such cases compressed air could be delivered from a compressor driven by an internal combustion engine. In other cases, even where electric power is available, the use of electric motors would be inadvisable and dangerous because extension wires could be cut or damaged, causing short circuits and possible fires or explosions. In such cases the pneumatic motor may be the only choice. This type of motor can safely be used in explosive environments, in places of high ambient temperature, and even totally submerged.

The pneumatic motor, when operated within its limitations, often has many advantages over an electric motor or even a hydraulic motor. When either an electric motor or a hydraulic motor is stalled, energy is wasted, with probable damage to equipment and material being processed. When a pneumatic motor is stalled, on the contrary, no energy is wasted and no damage results.

In normal operation pneumatic motors are cooled by the expanding exhaust air. This feature, coupled with the very high

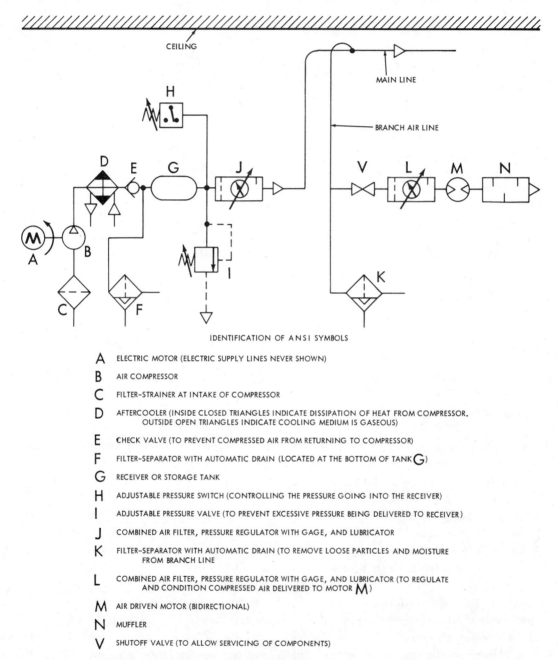

IDENTIFICATION OF ANSI SYMBOLS

A ELECTRIC MOTOR (ELECTRIC SUPPLY LINES NEVER SHOWN)

B AIR COMPRESSOR

C FILTER–STRAINER AT INTAKE OF COMPRESSOR

D AFTERCOOLER (INSIDE CLOSED TRIANGLES INDICATE DISSIPATION OF HEAT FROM COMPRESSOR.
   OUTSIDE OPEN TRIANGLES INDICATE COOLING MEDIUM IS GASEOUS)

E CHECK VALVE (TO PREVENT COMPRESSED AIR FROM RETURNING TO COMPRESSOR)

F FILTER–SEPARATOR WITH AUTOMATIC DRAIN (LOCATED AT THE BOTTOM OF TANK G)

G RECEIVER OR STORAGE TANK

H ADJUSTABLE PRESSURE SWITCH (CONTROLLING THE PRESSURE GOING INTO THE RECEIVER)

I ADJUSTABLE PRESSURE VALVE (TO PREVENT EXCESSIVE PRESSURE BEING DELIVERED TO RECEIVER)

J COMBINED AIR FILTER, PRESSURE REGULATOR WITH GAGE, AND LUBRICATOR

K FILTER–SEPARATOR WITH AUTOMATIC DRAIN (TO REMOVE LOOSE PARTICLES AND MOISTURE
   FROM BRANCH LINE

L COMBINED AIR FILTER, PRESSURE REGULATOR WITH GAGE, AND LUBRICATOR (TO REGULATE
   AND CONDITION COMPRESSED AIR DELIVERED TO MOTOR M)

M AIR DRIVEN MOTOR (BIDIRECTIONAL)

N MUFFLER

V SHUTOFF VALVE (TO ALLOW SERVICING OF COMPONENTS)

Fig. 5–1. Circuit diagram in ANSI symbols, showing motor-driven compressor, receiver tank, and air-operated motor as major components, conditioning and controlling the air.

speed that can be attained by some of them, make them ideally suited for such operations as small-hole drilling and tapping, for example.

Other features of pneumatic motors are their light weight and small size compared to electric motors of comparable horsepower rating. Compared to hydraulic motors, pneumatic motors in the majority of cases operate at lower pressures. Supply piping for them is therefore lighter and less expensive. They are cleaner than hydraulic motors, and when temporarily overloaded they will not damage material or workpieces being processed. All types of pneumatic motors are easily made reversible by using suitable valves —a distinct advantage over the type of electric motors in common use.

To operate a pneumatic motor efficiently, however, several conditions must be met:

1. The air pressure delivered to the pneumatic motor must be regulated to within 5 to 10 percent of the pressure the motor was designed for. This can be assured by using a hook-up similar to the one shown in Fig. 5-1. If the pressure delivered to the receiver tank is high enough, the pressure can then be regulated to the desired magnitude before it enters the motor or actuator. This pressure should be checked with no load and also under maximum load to make sure that the volume delivered is sufficient. Corrective steps may be required. For instance, long and small diameter supply lines with many sharp bends may cause a severe pressure drop. It has been estimated by one supplier of pneumatic motors that a drop in pressure of 11% would cause a drop in production efficiency of 13-1/2% and a drop

of 22% in pressure would cause a drop in production efficiency of 27%.

The compressor (or battery of compressors, depending on requirements) should be chosen to adequately meet the demand. Pressure loss is expensive and should be considered in the initial layout of the pneumatic system. This starts with the supply line from the compressor to all the branch lines at points of application. This is shown in Table 5-1 for the U.S. customary system and Table 5-2 for the metric system.

Sharp bends should also be avoided. Table 5-3 for the U.S. system and Table 5-4 for the metric system show how 90° and 45° bends reduce the pressure. These bends are compared to lengths of straight pipe of equivalent diameters as listed in Tables 5-1 and 5-2.

For example, in Table 5-1 we see that in the case of 100 psi initial pressure and 12.82 cfm there is a pressure loss of 7.8 psi per 100 ft length in a 3/4 inside diameter pipe. This is 0.078 psi for one foot of pipe. In Table 5-3 we see that for a 90° bend of a 3/4 inch inside diameter pipe there is a pressure loss equivalent to the loss in 2 ft of straight pipe, which would be $\frac{7.8 \times 2}{100} = 0.156$ psi. For a 45° bend the pressure loss should be $\frac{7.8 \times 0.92}{100} = 0.072$ psi.

Then, from Table 5-5, we see that for a 3/4 inch 2-way and 3-way valve the friction loss could be as high as the equivalent of 50 feet of straight pipe, or $\frac{7.8 \times 50}{100}$ $= 3.9$ psi.

For a 3/4 inch 4-way valve the friction loss could be the equivalent of 100 feet of straight pipe, or $\frac{7.8 \times 100}{100} = 7.8$ psi.

For a 3/4 inch cylinder the friction loss

Fluid Power: Pneumatics

TABLE 5-1. LOSS OF AIR PRESSURE IN PSI DUE TO FRICTION *
PRESSURE LOSS IS PER 100 FEET OF PIPE AND 100PSI INITIAL PRESSURE
(U.S. MEASUREMENT)

CFM FREE AIR	EQUIVALENT CFM COMPR. AIR	NOMINAL PIPE DIAMETER (INSIDE) IN INCHES					
		1/2	3/4	1	1 1/4	1 1/2	2
10	1.28	1.38	0.09	0.03	0.007		
20	2.56	1.42	.34	.10	.026	.012	
30	3.84	3.13	.74	.23	.056	.026	
40	5.13	5.55	1.28	.38	.096	.044	.013
50	6.41	8.65	2.00	0.60	0.146	0.067	0.020
60	7.69		2.84	.84	.210	.095	.027
70	8.97		3.85	1.12	.280	.130	.036
80	10.25		5.01	1.44	.360	.160	.046
90	11.53		6.40	1.85	0.450	0.200	0.058
100	12.82		7.80	2.21	.550	.250	.069
125	16.02		12.40	3.41	.850	.380	.107
150	19.22		18.10	4.91	1.200	.540	.150
175	22.43			6.80	1.640	0.730	0.200
200	25.63			8.79	2.120	.950	.260
250	32.04				3.300	1.480	.400
300	38.45				4.710	2.100	.570
350	44.86				6.450	2.860	0.770
400	51.26				8.300	3.700	.990
450	57.67					4.650	1.270
500	64.08					5.790	1.560
600	76.90					8.45	2.230
700	89.71						3.000
800	102.50						4.000
900	115.30						5.050
1,000	128.20						6.200

* FROM WILKERSON CORPORATION

TABLE 5-2. LOSS OF AIR PRESSURE IN Kg/cm^2 DUE TO FRICTION *
PRESSURE LOSS IS PER 30 METERS OF PIPE AND 7 Kg/cm^2 INITIAL PRESSURE
(METRIC MEASUREMENT)

LITERS FREE AIR PER MIN.	EQUIVALENT LITERS PER MIN. COMPR. AIR	NOMINAL PIPE DIAMETER (INSIDE) IN MILLIMETERS					
		12.7 mm	19.1 mm	25.4 mm	31.8 mm	38.1 mm	50.8 mm
300	37	0.027	0.006	0.002	0.0005		
600	75	.100	.024	.007	.0018	.0008	
850	110	.220	.053	.016	.0039	.0018	
1,150	150	.390	.090	.027	.0067	.0031	.0009
1,400	180	0.608	0.140	0.042	0.010	0.0047	0.0014
1,700	218		.200	.059	.015	.0067	.0019
2,000	255		.270	.079	.020	.0091	.0025
2,300	290		.350	.100	.025	.0110	.0032
2,550	330		0.450	0.130	0.032	0.0140	0.0041
3,000	364		.550	.155	.038	.0160	.0049
3,500	455		.870	.240	.060	.0270	.0075
4,250	540		1.270	.346	.065	.0380	.0105
5,000	640			0.480	0.115	0.0510	0.0140
5,700	730			.615	.150	.0670	.0180
7,000	900				.232	.1040	.0280
8,500	1,100				.332	.1480	.0400
10,000	1,300				0.455	0.2000	0.0540
11,000	1,500				.585	.2600	.0700
13,000	1,700					.3260	.0890
14,000	1,855					.4100	.1090
17,000	2,250					0.5950	0.1560
20,000	2,620						.2100
23,000	3,000						.2800
25,000	3,400						.3550
30,000	3,760						0.4350

*CONVERTED FROM TABLE 5-1

TABLE 5-3. FRICTION LOSS IN PIPE BENDS. FIGURES ARE EQUIVALENT FEET OF STRAIGHT PIPE,
SEE TABLE 5-1.
(U. S. MEASUREMENT)

ANGLE OF PIPE BEND	NOMINAL PIPE DIAMETER (INSIDE) IN INCHES					
	1/2	3/4	1	1 1/4	1 1/2	2
90° BEND	1.60	2.00	2.50	3.40	4.00	5.10
45° BEND	0.73	0.92	1.18	1.55	1.85	2.35

TABLE 5-4. FRICTION LOSS IN PIPE BENDS. FIGURES ARE EQUIVALENT METERS OF STRAIGHT PIPE
SEE TABLE 5-2.
(METRIC MEASUREMENT)

ANGLE OF PIPE BEND	NOMINAL PIPE DIAMETER (INSIDE) IN MILLIMETERS					
	12.7mm	19.1mm	25.4mm	31.8mm	38.1mm	50.8mm
90° BEND	0.48	0.60	0.75	1.02	1.20	1.53
45° BEND	0.22	0.28	0.35	0.47	0.56	0.71

TABLE 5-5. FRICTION LOSS IN COMPONENTS. FIGURES ARE EQUIVALENT FEET OF STRAIGHT PIPE,
SEE TABLE 5-1.*
(U. S. MEASUREMENT)

TYPE OF COMPONENT	NORMAL PIPE DIAMETER (INSIDE) IN INCHES					
	1/2	3/4	1	1 1/4	1 1/2	2
2 WAY OR 3 WAY VALVE	6 TO 30	10 TO 50	13 TO 65	15 TO 75	20 TO 100	25 TO 125
4- WAY VALVE	12 TO 60	20 TP 100	25 TO 125	30 TO 150	40 TO 200	50 TO 250
CYLINDER	6 TO 30	10 TO 50	13 TO 65	15 TO 75	20 TO 100	25 TO 125

* FROM WILKERSON CORP.

could be the equivalent of 50 feet of straight pipe, or $\frac{7.8 \times 50}{100} = 3.9$ psi.

Table 5-6 shows these friction losses in metric measurements.

For a typical pneumatic system we may then have 12.82 cubic feet per minute air at a pressure of 100 psi delivered from the receiver through a 2-inch pipe 200 feet long with two 90° bends. This main line would branch off to two 3/4-inch branch lines 10 feet long with two 90° and two 45° bends serving a spring-return cylinder operated by a 3-way valve and a double-

TABLE 5-6. FRICTION LOSS IN COMPONENTS. FIGURES ARE EQUIVALENT METERS OF STRAIGHT PIPE.
(SEE TABLE 5-2.)
(METRIC MEASUREMENT)

TYPE OF COMPONENT	NOMINAL PIPE DIAMETER (INSIDE) IN MILLIMETERS					
	12.7 mm	19.1 mm	25.4 mm	31.8mm	38.1mm	50.8mm
2- WAY OR 3-WAY VALVE	1.8 TO 9	3 TO 15	4 TO 20	4.5 TO 23	6 TO 30	7.6 TO 38
4-WAY VALVE	3.7 TO 18	6 TO 30	7.6 TO 38	9 TO 46	12 TO 60	15 TO 76
CYLINDER	1.8 TO 9	3 TO 15	4 TO 20	4.5 TO 23	6 TO 30	7.6 TO 38

* CONVERTED FROM TABLE 5-5.

acting cylinder operated by a 4-way valve. The pressure loss at the point of application could then be as high as:

2-inch pipe 200 feet long . . .	0.138 psi
Two 90° bends of 2-inch pipe	0.007 psi
Two 3/4-inch branch lines of 19 feet each	1.560 psi
Two 90° bends of 3/4-inch pipe	0.312 psi
One 3-way valve	3.900 psi
One spring-return cylinder .	3.900 psi
One 4-way valve	7.800 psi
One double-acting cylinder .	3.900 psi
Total pressure loss	21.517 psi

Restrictions (orifices) also control the flow of the gaseous medium to the point of application and are important in determining the speed of a pneumatic actuator. The flow of the gaseous medium has a definite relationship to the size of an orifice and the applied pressure, as seen in Table 5-7 and Table 5-8. The speed of an actuator may therefore be very accurately adjusted with an adjustable opening in the exhaust line. This could be a conically pointed screw entering a round hole.

2. Clean air is essential to maintain efficiency and eliminate downtime—a requirement in any automated system. This is accomplished by installing a filter-separator with automatic drain, as shown in the schematic diagram of Fig. 5–1.

3. Lubrication is absolutely necessary for efficient operation. This is easily obtained by installing a lubricator to inject an atomized stream of oil into the air before it enters the motor or actuator.

4. If noise is objectionable—as it usually is—this can be reduced considerably by adding a muffler, as also shown in Fig. 5–1.

Rotary Vane Motors

Air motors of the rotary vane type are relatively simple in design, widely used in many industrial applications, and are usually available in the smaller sizes ranging from 1/8 to 1-1/2 HP, maximum operating pressure of 100 psi (7 kg/cm²), and maximum operating temperature of 200°F (93°C). They are especially used where high speed is required but are less suitable than the slower piston-type air motors where high starting torque and extremely fast acceleration to full speed

Fluid Power: Pneumatics

TABLE 5-7. FLOW OF AIR THROUGH ORIFICE IN CFM*
(U.S. MEASUREMENT)

SUPPLY PRESSURE PSI	ORIFICE SIZE IN INCHES									
	1/32	1/16	3/32	1/8	5/32	3/16	7/32	1/4	9/32	5/16
65	1.15	4.49	10.10	17.90	27.90	40.30	55.20	71.80	89.90	111.70
70	1.21	4.77	10.80	19.10	29.70	42.80	58.80	76.40	95.70	118.80
75	1.30	5.06	11.40	20.20	31.50	45.40	62.30	81.00	105.50	126.00
80	1.37	5.35	12.10	21.10	33.30	48.00	65.80	85.60	107.40	133.10
85	1.44	5.64	12.70	22.50	35.10	50.60	69.40	90.30	113.20	140.30
90	1.52	5.92	13.40	23.70	36.90	53.20	72.90	94.80	119.00	147.50
95	1.59	6.21	14.00	24.80	38.70	55.70	76.50	99.40	124.90	154.60
100	1.66	6.50	14.70	26.00	40.50	58.30	80.00	104.60	130.70	161.80
125	2.03	7.94	17.90	31.70	49.50	71.40	97.78	127.10	159.80	197.50
150	2.40	9.28	21.20	37.50	58.40	84.40	115.40	150.40	189.00	233.30

*FROM WILKERSON CORPORATION

TABLE 5-8. FLOW OF AIR THROUGH ORIFICE IN LITERS PER SECOND*
(METRIC MEASUREMENT)

SUPPLY PRESSURE Kg/cm^2	ORIFICE SIZE IN MILLIMETERS									
	.79	1.59	2.38	3.18	3.97	4.76	5.56	6.35	7.14	7.94
4.57	0.54	2.12	4.72	8.45	13.30	19.10	26.00	33.80	42.35	52.60
4.92	.57	2.26	5.10	9.00	14.00	20.50	27.70	36.00	45.60	56.00
5.27	.61	2.39	5.38	9.52	14.85	21.40	29.35	38.20	49.60	59.50
5.62	.65	2.53	5.70	9.95	15.70	22.60	31.00	40.30	50.60	62.80
5.98	.68	2.66	6.00	10.60	16.55	23.85	32.70	42.60	53.40	66.30
6.33	0.72	2.79	6.33	11.30	17.40	25.30	34.35	44.60	56.20	69.50
6.68	.75	2.94	6.60	11.70	18.25	26.22	36.05	46.80	58.80	72.90
7.03	.78	3.06	6.94	12.35	19.10	27.50	37.70	49.30	61.50	76.25
8.79	.96	3.75	8.45	14.95	23.35	33.60	46.00	60.00	75.30	93.00
10.55	1.13	4.38	10.00	17.70	27.50	39.75	54.40	70.85	89.00	110.00

*CONVERTED FROM TABLE 5-7.

Fig. 5–2. Air-operated rotary vane motor. (Courtesy of Gardner-Denver Co.)

ANSI SYMBOL

are desired. A typical rotary vane motor is shown in Fig. 5–2, and Fig. 5–3 is a cutaway drawing showing its inner construction. Rotary vane motor free speed of 10,000 to 150,000 rpm is not uncommon.

In Fig. 5–3 note that rotor *A* is mounted eccentrically in relation to cylinder bore *B*. Two of the vanes are shown at *C*.

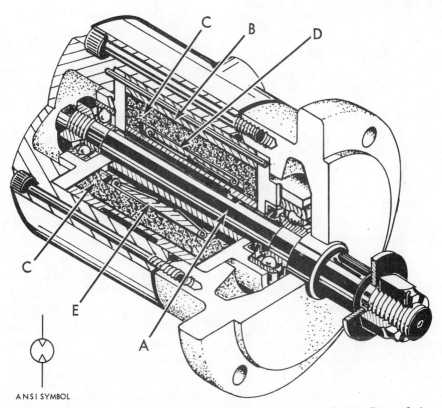

ANSI SYMBOL

Fig. 5–3. Sectional view of rotary vane motor shown in Fig. 5–2. (Courtesy of Gardner-Denver Co.)

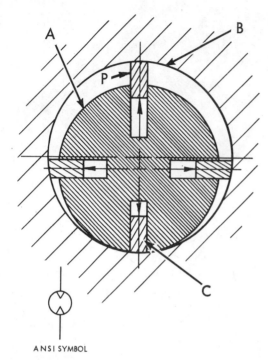

A N S I SYMBOL

Fig. 5–4. Schematic drawing showing operation of a 4-vane rotary motor. Note that rotor *A* is mounted eccentrically in relation to cylinder bore *B*.

The spring shown at *D* is fully compressed with no exposed area of the vane between the outside of the rotor and the cylinder bore. At *E*, the spring is shown with the maximum area of the vane exposed.

The operation of a four-vane air motor is illustrated schematically in Fig. 5–4. Rotor *A* is mounted eccentrically in relation to cylinder bore *B*. The vanes slide radially in the rotor as it turns. Spring pressure, pneumatic pressure, or a combination of both types of pressure is applied to the inside edges of the vanes to keep them in constant contact with the cylinder bore. Adequate lubrication must be supplied by a lubricator in the air line. This lubricator (not shown here) provides a fine oil mist to incoming air.

The effective torque developed at the shaft is a product of the applied pressure *p*, the area of the vanes exposed between the outside diameter of the rotor and the cylinder bore, and the moment arm of the vanes. Therefore the torque is increased by one of the following means or by all three:

1. Increasing the applied air pressure.
2. Increasing the exposed vane area.
3. Increasing the moment arm by increasing the diameter of the bore in which the vanes rotate.

The number of vanes in this type of motor is not generally critical unless uniform torque at a low speed is necessary. Starting torque may be increased by increasing the number of vanes.

The chart shown in Fig. 5–5 compares designs of three rotary vane motors designated as A, B, and C. The torque and horsepower curves show how these characteristics are affected by speed and by pressure applied at the vanes. The intersection of torque curves with horsepower curves indicate the torques and speeds for maximum horsepower at various applied pressures. From this chart it is apparent that maximum horsepower in no case is obtained at maximum speed. In fact, torque and horsepower drop to zero at high speed.

Piston Motors

Piston type motors are manufactured in two main categories: the radial piston motor and the axial piston motor. The inherent characteristics of both types are essentially the same. Both develop high torque, which makes them especially desirable for applications with high starting loads. Another desirable feature of these motors is that they are of a well balanced construction, usually having five pistons. This design provides for even torque at all speeds and gives very smooth delivery of

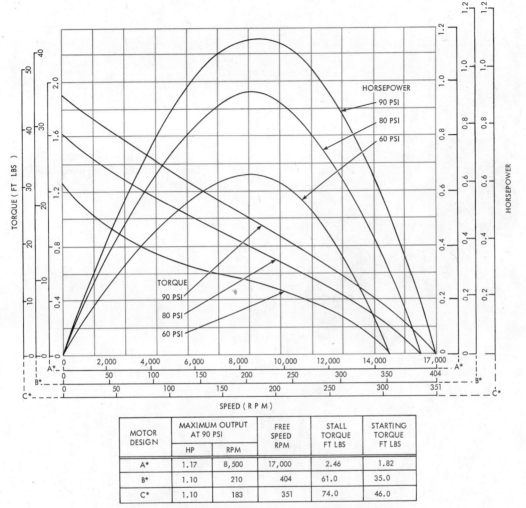

MOTOR DESIGN	MAXIMUM OUTPUT AT 90 PSI		FREE SPEED RPM	STALL TORQUE FT LBS	STARTING TORQUE FT LBS
	HP	RPM			
A*	1.17	8,500	17,000	2.46	1.82
B*	1.10	210	404	61.0	35.0
C*	1.10	183	351	74.0	46.0

* To evaluate the three different designs of motors A, B, and C, notice that the three horizontal speed lines, the vertical torque lines and the corresponding vertical horsepower lines are shown as A, B and C respectively.

Fig. 5–5. Graph showing performance of three different motors of the rotary vane type. These motors are identified as A, B, and C.

full power for each revolution of the motor in either direction of rotation. At least two pistons are always on the power stroke.

Radial Piston Motors. Compared to a vane-type motor, the radial piston motor has a much slower operating speed. This is because it has a heavier construction due to its reciprocating parts. The free speed is usually kept at 3,000 rpm or under, with the upper range about 5,000 rpm, and the maximum horsepower is usually developed at 1,000 rpm or a little more. The smooth, overlapping power flow and accurate balancing of radial piston motors make them vibrationless at all operating speeds. This desirable feature is especially noticeable at the lower

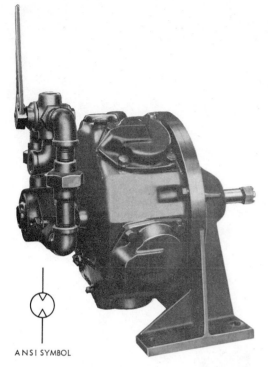

ANSI SYMBOL

Fig. 5-6 Air-operated radial piston motor. (Courtesy of Gardner-Denver Co.)

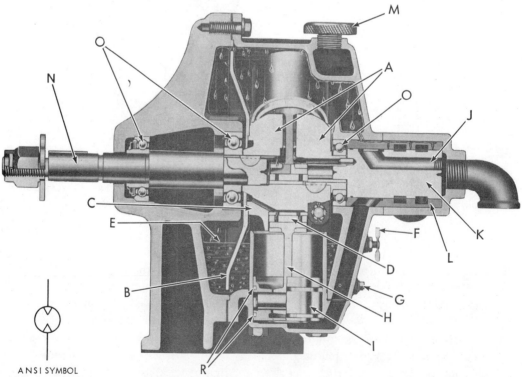

ANSI SYMBOL

Fig. 5-7. Sectional view of air-operated radial piston motor illustrated in Fig. 5-6. (Courtesy of Gardner-Denver Co.)

speeds where they develop maximum horsepower. A typical radial piston motor is shown in Fig. 5–6, and Fig. 5–7 is a sectional view of this motor showing its inner construction.

Lubrication of this motor is accomplished by the splash and oil slinger design, and this method of lubrication is quite adequate for intermittent duty and frequent reversal. However, if the motor is to be run continuously for long periods, an in-line lubricator is necessary. In-line lubrication is always a desirable protection to ensure trouble-free operation of any pneumatic tool. For continuous operation, these radial piston motors may be

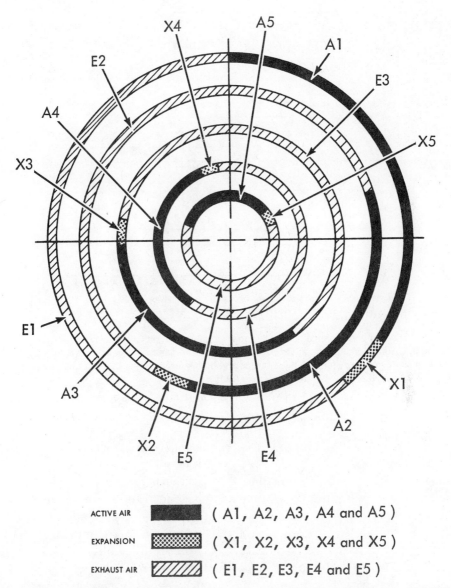

ACTIVE AIR (A1, A2, A3, A4 and A5)

EXPANSION (X1, X2, X3, X4 and X5)

EXHAUST AIR (E1, E2, E3, E4 and E5)

Fig. 5–8. Schematic drawing showing how the power strokes of a 5-cylinder piston motor overlap. The duration of active air on each piston is designated as A1, A2, A3, A4, and A5. Expansion is indicated as X1, X2, X3, X4, and X5. Exhaust is indicated by E1, E2, E3, E4, and E5. (Courtesy of Gardner-Denver Co.)

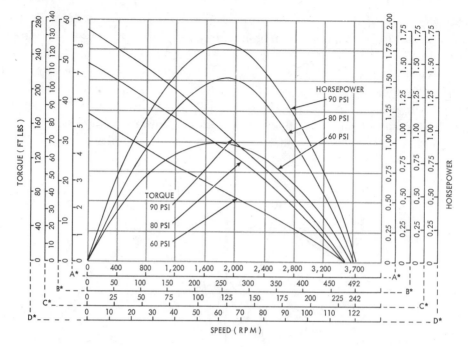

MOTOR DESIGN	MAXIMUM OUTPUT AT 90 PSI		FREE SPEED RPM	STALL TORQUE FT LBS	STARTING TORQUE FT LBS
	HP	RPM			
A*	1.8	1,850	3,700	8.6	4.0
B*	1.6	246	492	65.0	30.0
C*	1.6	121	242	133.0	61.0
D*	1.6	61	122	262.0	122.0

* To evaluate the four different motor designs A, B, C and D, notice that the
horizontal speed lines, the vertical torque lines and the corresponding
vertical horsepower lines are shown as A, B, C and D respectively.

Fig. 5–9. Graph showing performance of four different motors of the radial piston type. These motors are designated as A, B, C, and D. Intersections of torque curves with horsepower curves for the four motors indicate speeds and pressures required for maximum torque and horsepower. Notice that torque and horsepower drop to zero at high speeds. (Courtesy of Gardner-Denver CO.)

used up to a maximum of 225°F (107°C) and 100 psi (7 kg/cm²).

As shown at *A* in Fig. 5–7, the crankshaft is balanced to eliminate vibration. The slinger ring shown at *B* picks up oil from the reservoir and distributes the oil by centrifugal force to the inside surface of the housing, where it gradually drips off for lubrication of the moving parts. Centrifugal force is again used for distributing oil to all five connecting rod bearings. This is shown at *C*. A small hole drilled at an angle throws the oil in the direction of the arrow to the five segment-type crank pin bearings shown at *D*. The oil level is shown at *E* and may be checked at *F*. The drain plug is located at *G* and the filler plug at *M*. *H* shows the connecting rod and I shows one of the pistons. *R* shows two piston sealing rings.

The air enters at *J* and is distributed consecutively to the five pistons as the

ANSI SYMBOL

Fig. 5–10. Air-operated 5-cylinder axial piston motor. Because these motors are usually designed with five pistons, the overlapping feature of the power impulses is the same as for the radial five-cylinder piston motors as illustrated in the schematic drawing of Fig. 5–8. (Courtesy of Gardner-Denver Co.)

distributing valve K rotates in a bushing L, which is removable for replacement as it wears. The drive shaft N rotates on three ball bearings at O.

Fig. 5–8 is a schematic illustration showing how the power strokes overlap. The duration of active air on each piston is designated by A1, A2, A3, A4, and A5. Expansion is indicated by X1, X2, X3, X4, and X5, and the exhuast is indicated by E1, E2, E3, E4, and E5. Motors of this type have relatively little exhaust noise and, if objectionable, this can be reduced by the addition of a muffler.

The chart shown in Fig. 5–9 compares designs of four radial piston motors designated as A, B, C, and D. The torque and horsepower curves show how these characteristics are affected by speed and by various applied pressures. From this chart

it is apparent that maximum horsepower in no case is obtained at maximum speed. High torque is an inherent characteristic of piston-type air motors, and because they are mainly used in applications where starting torque and stall torque are important considerations. These are shown at the bottom of the chart, based on maximum output of each of the four motors operated at 90 psi pressure.

Axial Piston Motors. Air motors of the axial piston type, like motors of the radial piston type, are usually designed with five pistons and therefore the overlapping feature of the power impulses are the same as for the radial five-piston motors previously shown in Fig. 5–8. The axial piston motors are available only in small sizes, usually less than 3 HP. See Fig. 5–10.

117

Fluid Power: Pneumatics

Like other piston motors they are characterized by fast starting torque, reaching their full operating speed almost instantly. Their mechanical design is quite different from that of the radial piston motors, however. Their small pistons reciprocate axially (parallel to the drive shaft) in sequence. Their piston rods are attached to a wobble plate. The wobble plate, at an angle to the axis of rotation, then causes a rotary motion to a gear train which turns the drive shaft.

Factors that determine the power of these motors are:

1. Inlet line pressure.
2. Number of pistons.
3. Area of pistons.
4. Length of piston stroke.
5. Speed (rpm).

Fig. 5–11 is a cutaway drawing showing the inner construction of the axial piston motor shown in Fig. 5–10. The sectional views in Figs. 5–12, 5–13, and 5–14 show the complete flow of air pressure

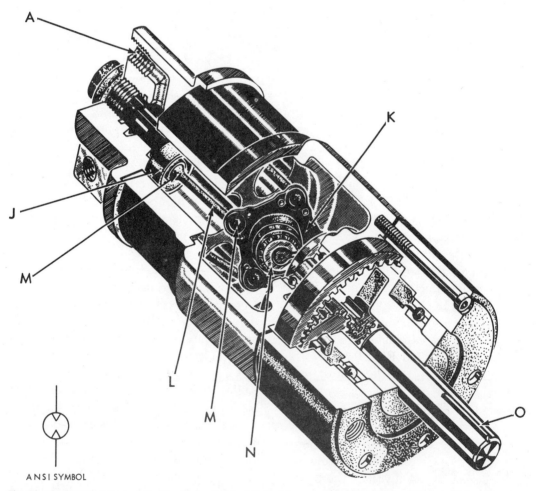

ANSI SYMBOL

Fig. 5–11. Sectional view of the 5-cylinder axial piston motor shown in Fig. 5–10. (Courtesy of Gardner-Denver Co.)

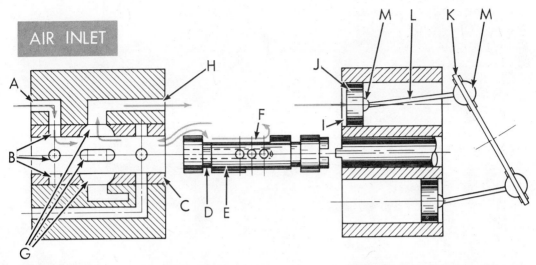

Fig. 5–12. Following air inlet pressure through motors shown in Fig. 5–10 and Fig. 5–11. (Courtesy of Garner-Denver Co.)

and exhaust in the sequence for one of the five pistons, which all operate in consecutive order. These sectional drawings are all exploded views, whose sections on both sides of the centerline are not necessarily exactly opposite in the actual motor. The drawings are simplified.

Air Inlet. The air enters the motor at port A (see Fig. 5–12) flowing in the direction of arrows through small holes B in the distributor bushing C into annular groove D in the distributor E. The groove D opens to a slot F in the distributor E, thus permitting the air to flow through an elongated slot G in the bushing C and through hole H to cylinder I, putting pressure on piston J.

There are five pistons, so there are five slots G in the bushing C and five holes H, one for each piston. The air pressure then forces the piston J forward. The pistons are connected to the wobble plate K with connecting rods L. There are five connecting rods, one for each piston. The connecting rods are fastened to the piston and the wobble plate with ball bearings M so they

may be free to assume a non-axial position. The wobble plate is mounted on ball bearings N on the drive shaft O, as shown in Fig. 5–11. Bevel gears (not visible) are mounted on the cylinder housing and the wobble plate. These gears keep the wobble plate in its proper central position as it imparts rotary motion to the drive and the distributor E. The distributor is connected by a key X and a slot Y, Fig. 5–13.

Primary Exhaust. As shown in Fig. 5–13, when the piston reaches the *nearly-in* position the distributor exhaust holes P will align with a slot Q in the distributor bushing. This permits the air that was used to drive the piston to exhaust to the atmosphere through a hole R in the center of the distributor E. This primary exhaust starts just before the piston J reaches the end of its travel.

Secondary Exhaust. In Fig. 5–14 the piston J is shown at the end of its inward stroke ready to return, Even if all the pressurized air used to drive the piston in had been exhausted at this point,

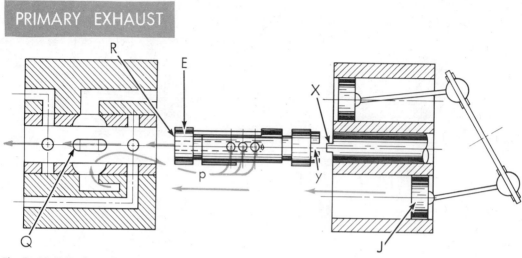

Fig. 5–13. Following primary exhaust of pressurized air used for driving piston in as illustrated in Fig. 5–12. (Courtesy of Gardner-Denver Co.)

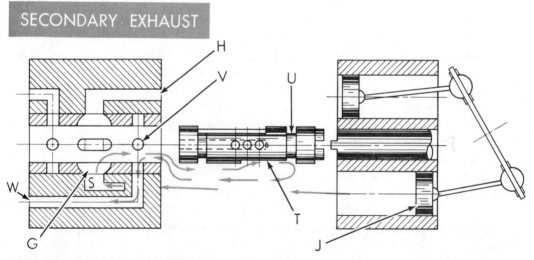

Fig. 5–14. Following secondary exhaust. This is the air subject to recompression if not properly exhausted. (Courtesy of Gardner-Denver Co.)

the air present in the cylinder would have a tendency to be compressed as the piston J returns. However, to provide free exhaust to the atmosphere a passageway S is provided (entrance indicated by arrow) in the motor head, where the air is forced out through slot G in the distributor bushing into a slot T in the distributor and into an annular groove U in the distributor.

From this point the exhaust escapes through the small holes V to hole W, which would be the air inlet port for reverse rotation of the motor. Therefore, when the motor is used for one direction of rotation only, the exhaust port must not be plugged because this would result in a great reduction of power caused by considerable back pressure. For reversible motor rotation a 4-way valve will provide the necessary escape for the secondary exhaust air, eliminating back pressure.

The direction of rotation and speed of air motors may be controlled by a variety of valves operated by hand, foot, solenoid, or other electrical or electromechanical means. However operated, the valve should have a full-flow air passage to utilize the full power of the motor. Speed is controlled by the volume and pressure of air admitted into the motor. The speed of any air motor may be regulated from minimum to maximum rpm without damaging the motor. Valves may be operated remotely, either for a single motor or multiple combinations of motors

Air-Driven Actuators

The oldest type of air-driven actuator is probably a piston sliding in a cylinder, similar to actuators used for hydraulic systems. For pneumatic operation this type of actuator requires a seal or packing at the piston to keep the leakage at this point down to a minimum. This, of course requires good lubrication. The lubrication necessary for good sealing also reduces friction. Corrosion may be a serious problem for pneumatic actuators and should always be considered when selecting material for these actuators.

Double-Acting Diaphragm Cylinders

Fig. 5–15 is a cutaway view of an air-operated, double-acting diaphragm cylinder. This type of actuator is virtually frictionless and may be designed in many configurations and sizes for different applications. Power loss due to friction is almost negligible, consisting only of the small amount of friction at the piston rod and the minute amount of power re-

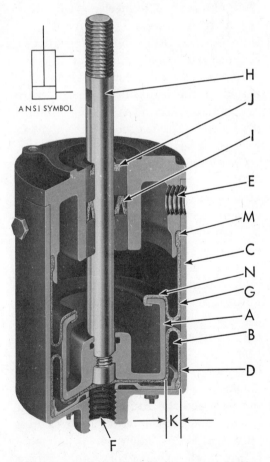

Fig. 5–15. Sectional view of air-operated double-acting diaphragm cylinder. (Courtesy of Bellofram Corporation)

121

quired to flex the tough, resilient diaphragm material.

The stroke is long in proportion to the rolling diaphragm height. For instance, a 4-inch (or 10 cm) diameter and 4-inch (or 10 cm) high diaphragm will provide a stroke of about 7 inches (or 18 cm). Similarly, a 6-inch (or 15 cm) diameter and 6 inch (or 15 cm) high diaphragm will provide a total stroke of 10-3/16 inches (or 26 cm). The manufacturers claim a working temperature range from −85°F (or −65°C) to 550°F (or 288°C), and in some cases a range of −120°F (or −85°C) to 700°F (or 370°C) is possible.

There are carefully designed diaphragm materials to meet a great variation in applied pressure, ranging from as little as about 2 torr to 500 psi (35 kg/cm²). Because the major portion of the diaphragm carrying the working load is supported by the piston area, the pressure may in some cases be as high as 1,200 psi (85 kg/cm²). Service life is also high, in some cases up to 100 million cycles.

Operation of the cylinder shown in Fig. 5–15 is very simple. Assume that line air pressure is supplied to port F. Diaphragm D will then roll off piston A onto cylinder wall C. Diaphragm G will roll off cylinder wall C onto piston A.

According to Pascal's Law, air in a confined space is distributed equally in all directions. Therefore the pressure in space B keeps the piston in a central position within the cylinder without need for bearings to guide it. The only friction, therefore, is the force required to flex the diaphragms plus the small amount of friction between the resilient rod seal and bushing and piston rod H as it moves up.

To reverse this action, port E previously used as the exhaust port would receive line air pressure and become the inlet port. Port F, previously the inlet port,

would then be the exhaust port. This reversal is easily done with a four-way valve operated either manually or automatically depending on the application.

With proper valving and controls this type of linear actuator can be made to reciprocate at selected rates of cycling, but in the majority of applications such as positioning, applying pressure, holding and retracting, the time interval between forward and reverse strokes is fairly long and subject to variations. In such cases the actuation is often manually controlled.

As shown in Fig. 5–12, this is a double-acting cylinder where pneumatic pressure moves the piston in both directions, forward and reverse. Therefore the piston rod H requires a seal as shown at I to prevent pressure from escaping and also a seal as shown at J to keep dust and contamination out. Several designs are available. Some have a spring return, and no air leak whatsoever is possible.

The convolutions, which are in the radial space K between cylinder C and piston A is relatively very small, depending on the diameter of piston and thickness and type of material used for the diaphragm. Standard convolutions range from 1/16″ (or 1.5 mm) to 1/4″ (6 mm). The sidewall thickness of material ranges from 0.015″ (0.4 mm) to 0.035″ (0.9 mm). The diaphragms are usually fastened securely in place by providing a bead along the edge as shown at L and M. In other cases the air pressure will hold the diaphragm in position as shown at N.

Because the space K is very small, the tension on the side wall of the material is also very small. This tension is easily calculated by assuming the following:

S = stress on material, in pounds per inch of circumference

p = applied pressure, psi

K = width of space in inches

Since the stress S is calculated for 1″ of side wall material, the pressure sould be calculated for an area of $1 \times K$, so that:

$$S = \frac{p \times K \times 1}{2}$$

In the metric system the formula would be the same, with the following values:

S = stress on material in kg per centimeter of circumference

p = applied pressure, kg/cm²

K = width of space in centimeters

Whereas the diaphragm cylinder shown in Fig 5–15 can be designed for no air leak whatsoever, the oldest type of cylinder most commonly used as a linear actuator requires seals, and is shown in Fig. 5–16. Several seals are necessary for efficient operation. A mist of lubrication is also necessary in most cases unless the materials used are self-lubricating. Oil mist would then be supplied by a lubricator in the pressure line.

The cylinder may be operated by a 4-way two-position valve as shown by the ANSI symbol. In the position shown, the piston *C* has moved to the right by pressure supplied to port *A*. Full speed as determined by the volumetric delivery of air occurs until the pilot *D* contacts seal *E*. Until that occurs, full flow of exhaust air has escaped through port *B*. As soon as pilot *D* contacts seal *E* the air behind the piston can only escape through the small hole *F*. Each end has a small hole *H*

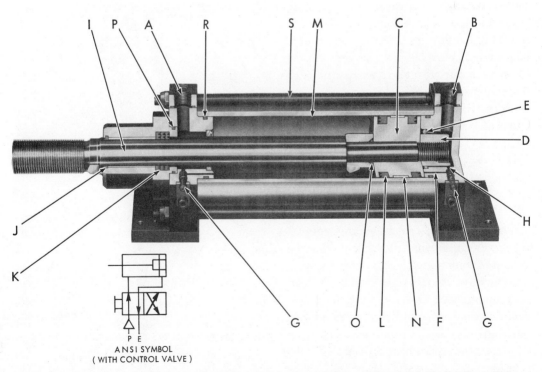

Fig. 5–16. Sectional view of typical pneumatic double-acting cylinder cushioned in both directions. The accompanying diagram, using ANSI symbols, shows this cylinder operated by a 4-way, 2-position valve, manually operated, with spring return. (Courtesy of Bellows-Valvair Co.)

whose opening is minutely adjustable with a micro adjustment screw G. The last part of the piston travel can thus be slowed down to the speed desired.

As soon as the 4-way valve is shifted, the piston is reversed by full flow on the exposed area of pilot D, and full speed again occurs until slowed down at the end of the stroke as before. As the piston C has moved to the right, the piston rod I has been prevented from letting contaminants enter the cylinder by wiper ring J. The three packing rings K, as they are expanded against the housing bore and the outside of the piston rod I, prevent the air entering at port A from escaping. Similar seals L are shown at each end of the piston C. They also expand against the cylinder bore M and the piston groove diameter to prevent the air from escaping to the opposite end of the piston. N is a Teflon wear ring. Several O-rings O, P, and R make this an air-tight assembly. S is a tie rod, and is one of 4 tie rods used to hold the end caps tightly pressed against the ends of the cylinder to withstand high internal pressure.

Space will not permit showing all the different varieties of linear actuators available. The basic principle of operation has, however, been shown clearly in these illustrations.

Percussion Motors

Linear actuators such as the double-acting cylinder just described can be made to reciprocate the piston rod in regular forward and reverse strokes. However, more specialized tools called *percussion motors* have built-in mechanisms and control valves to provide fast reciprocation, or fast reciprocation coupled with rotation, automatically. Many of these are air-driven. Some familiar applications are riveting guns, small air-driven

riveting machines, impact hammers, impact wrenches, paving breakers, and sinker drills, to mention just a few. Space allows the inclusion of just two examples of tools in this category.

Air-Operated Paving Breaker. This rugged tool, which nearly everyone has seen in operation at one time or another, is shown in Fig. 5–17, and Fig. 5–18 is a cross-sectional illustration of this paving breaker, showing its internal construction.

In both Fig. 5–17 and Fig. 5–18 the air inlet is shown at A. Under normal operation the operator grips both ends of handle G holding the tool M in contact with

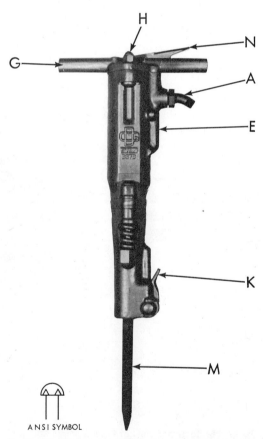

Fig. 5–17. Air-operated paving breaker. (Courtesy of Gardner-Denver Co.)

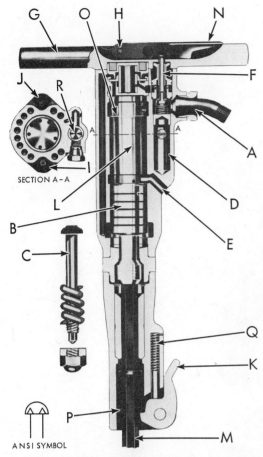

Fig. 5–18. Sectional view of paving breaker illustrated in Fig. 5–17, showing inner construction. (Courtesy of Gardner-Denver Co.)

opens the throttle valve *F*, directing the air through throttle valve *F* to the face contact valve *O*. As the pressure builds up, the piston *L* is forced down, driving the piston hammer *B* down against the tool *M*. At the end of the stroke the compressed air used for driving piston *L* down escapes to the atmosphere through exhaust port *E*, shown in both Fig. 5–17 and Fig. 5–18. As the tool *M* under normal operation is held in contact with the pavement by the operator, the piston is immediately ready for the next downward stroke.

The lubrication reservoir is shown at *D* in the main section of Fig. 5–18 and also in section *A–A* at *R* of the same illustration. The face contact valve *O* is easily accessible for service by removing two side bolts *C*, one on each side of the operating handle *G*, shown at *H* on the main section of Fig. 5–18 and also at *I* and *J* in section *A–A*.

Air-Operated Rotary Hammers, or "Sinker Drills". Rotary hammers, called by several other names, operate by a combination of fast reciprocating motion and rotary motion, imparting these simultaneously to a spindle. By chucking specially designed drill bits to the end of this spindle and attaching the inlet port to an air line, an operator can drill holes through reinforced concrete, chopping through the reinforcing rods. A variety of other interchangeable bits is also available for use with this tool, including bullpoint drills for demolition drilling, concrete slotting tools, scaling chisels, and clay spades for digging holes in dirt and clay.

Fig. 5–19 shows an air-operated rotary hammer or sinker drill, and Fig. 5–20 is a sectional view of the same tool.

Refering to Fig. 5–19, the air enters at inlet port *G* through a throttle valve *H* by

the pavement. The lever *K*, under pressure of spring *Q*, clamps the tool *M* against a renewable liner *P* when the tool is not in use. This prevents the tool from slipping out. Before applying air pressure, the operator releases clamp lever *K* (shown in both Fig. 5–17 and Fig. 5–18), with his foot or arm. The lever *K* is then held in the released position with the same spring *Q*.

To start operation the operator depresses lever *N*. (This lever is shown in the released position in Fig. 5–17 and in the depressed position in Fig. 5–18). This

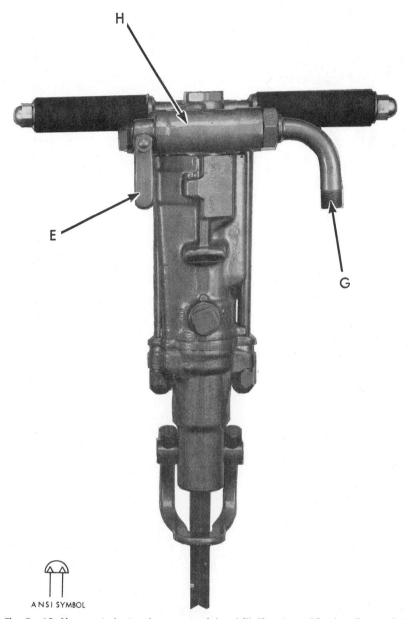

Fig. 5–19. Air-operated rotary hammer or sinker drill. (Courtesy of Gardner-Denver Co.)

depressing the conveniently located throttle valve lever E. This directs the air to an automatic valve located at A (in Fig. 5–20), pressurizing the piston B.

As the piston moves up and down, a reciprocating, spirally directed motion is also imparted by a combination of rifle nut, rifle bars, ratchet rings, and spring-controlled pawl located at D (in Fig. 5–20). The control valve F diverts full line pressure through a hole I in the tool J to the bottom of the hole being drilled.

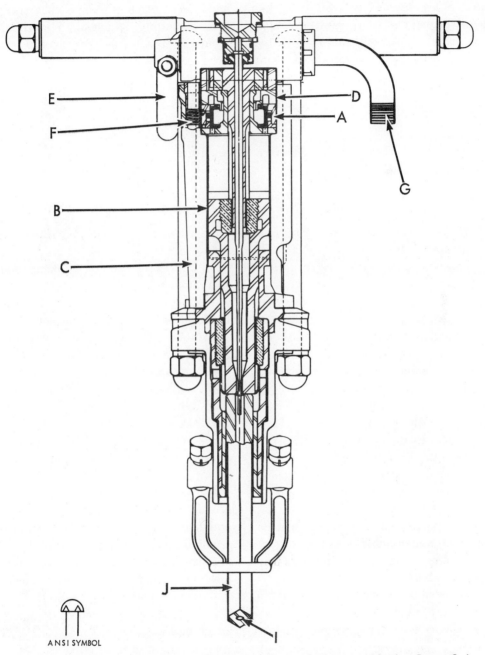

ANSI SYMBOL

Fig. 5–20. Sectional view of the sinker drill shown in Fig. 5–19. (Courtesy of Gardner-Denver Co.)

Air-Operated Rotary Actuators. Pneumatic actuators have been designed and built to deliver rotary power over angles of less than 1 full revolution, then reverse direction. These are either single-vane or double-vane actuators with two ports. In principle they appear very simple but in practice they can cause a great deal of trouble because of sealing difficulties, resulting in serious escape of the gaseous medium. Any required rotary motion is much better done with straight-line actuators connected to mechanical linkages or other devices, as will be described in Chapter 8.

Review Questions

1. Describe some of the advantages of air-operated tools.

2. Describe the four main types of pneumatic motors.

3. Give some of the main reasons why a pneumatic motor may be preferable to an electric motor even when electric power is available.

4. What is the principal function of a pneumatic actuator?

5. How should the pressure be checked for a pneumatic system?

6. If the pressure is too low what corrective steps may be taken?

7. What is most important to consider for efficient operation of a pneumatic motor?

8. How may clean air entering a pneumatic motor or actuator be assured?

9. How are pneumatic components usually lubricated?

10. How may noise be reduced for a pneumatic component?

11. Describe how the torque may be changed in an air operated rotary vane motor.

12. How is the starting torque increased in a rotary vane motor?

13. Describe some of the desirable characteristics of piston type motors

14. How is the performance of air-operated piston type motors affected by the operating speed?

15. What is an air-operated actuator?

16. What is a diaphragm cylinder?

17. Describe how the speed may be slowed down and accurately adjusted at the end of the stroke of a pneumatic actuator.

18. Which is considered the best way to produce rotary reciprocating motion with pneumatic power where accuracy and economic operation are important?

19. Why must the pressure leaving the receiver be higher than the pressure required at the point of application?

20. How may the speed be adjusted in an actuator?

SEE END OF BOOK FOR ANSWERS TO QUESTIONS

Accessory Equipment to Control Flow, Vibration, and Noise

Chapter

6

Up to this point in our study of pneumatics we have gradually advanced from the basic laws governing the behavior of the gaseous media. We have then been concerned with methods of generating the necessary pressure of adequate volume in the gaseous media, examining a variety of components for performing this work. We have also studied methods for storing this energy for future use, possibly transporting it to remote locations, or as is the case in most manufacturing plants, storing the energy at a high enough pressure and capacity to prevent fluctuation in pressure and volume delivery as the gaseous medium is directed to the point of application.

We have learned that energy cannot be destroyed. Gaseous media can, however, be stored without any loss in energy if proper inspections have been made in the process of manufacturing the storage components. The end purpose of fluid power for industrial use has been to convert the manufactured and stored up energy to mechanical power for performing useful work. We have studied several

components capable of performing such work. These components were described as motors and actuators. As is the case in many phases of our daily life, we have a source of supply and a point of application, and to take good advantage of our source of supply we must have good means of directing the source of supply to the point of application. All along the way there must be dependable components for directing, starting, regulating, measuring and keeping the supply clean from contaminating agents. This entire system contributes to dependable operation at the point of application.

In pneumatic applications the compressed gas is the source of supply. We have, however, learned that a gaseous medium must be confined in an enclosure to do useful work in industry. For this purpose we connect the source of supply to the point of application with a conduit: a pipe, a tube, or a hose. A tube or pipe is rigid and does not expand measureably as the pressure is applied. A hose is made of flexible material and expands as pressure is applied, using up some of the energy in expanding the hose. In some cases where accuracy is important, this may be harmful. In most cases now the conduits for pneumatics are similar to hydraulic conduits.

Some of the components studied in this chapter are valves for admitting, directing, and exhausting the fluid medium. Noise and vibrations are very harmful to all parts of the equipment as well as machinery, instruments, etc., and personnel in close proximity to the equipment, so we will study means for correcting these problems.

The conduits, valves, and components just mentioned are only a few of the many pieces of accessory equipment used in pneumatic circuits. They are needed for successful operation because of the peculiarities of gaseous media we have studied in earlier chapters. Keep in mind that a system operated by compressed air, for instance, must use *conditioned* air, not merely air at a certain pressure. The gaseous medium, the compressed air, must be closely controlled as to cleanliness, temperature and humidity, as well as flow rate and pressure.

How Accessory Equipment is Used

A typical illustration of how accessory equipment is used in conjunction with compressors, storage tanks and pneumatic tools is shown in the circuit diagram, Fig. 6–1. This diagram shows a single compressor and receiver connected to the points of application by a main line. This line should have a smooth inside surface void of pockets and should also be of sufficient diameter. Bends in the pipe should be as few as possible, and if the bends are necessary they should be of a large radius. The same is true with the three branch lines serving the various tools.

As you will notice, the main line running close to the ceiling is slanted downward in direction of the end. This is done so that if any contaminants or moisture are present most of these undesirable agents can be expelled at the dropline at the end of the circuit. You will also see that all branch lines are taken from the top side of the main line and they should have a large radius as the line is directed downward to the point of application. All

these precautions are taken to ensure a supply of clean gaseous medium to the point of application with as small a pressure drop as possible. Small diameters and sharp bends in supply lines are serious causes for pressure drop. Cleanliness of the compressed air is an important requirement whether the air is used for cleaning or ejecting a part being processed or for operating any pneumatic component. To ensure this requirement we must start at the very beginning, the intake of the compressor. Starting with A in the lower corner of the diagram, then, A is a filter-strainer at the intake of compressor B, which is operated by electric motor C, whose symbol has an arrow showing it is unidirectional. (The diagram does not show the electrical hookup of this motor, which has no relevance to the pneumatic system.)

In the process of compression the temperature of the air may be raised to over 400°F (or 204°C) and the air could then hold much more water as a vapor than it

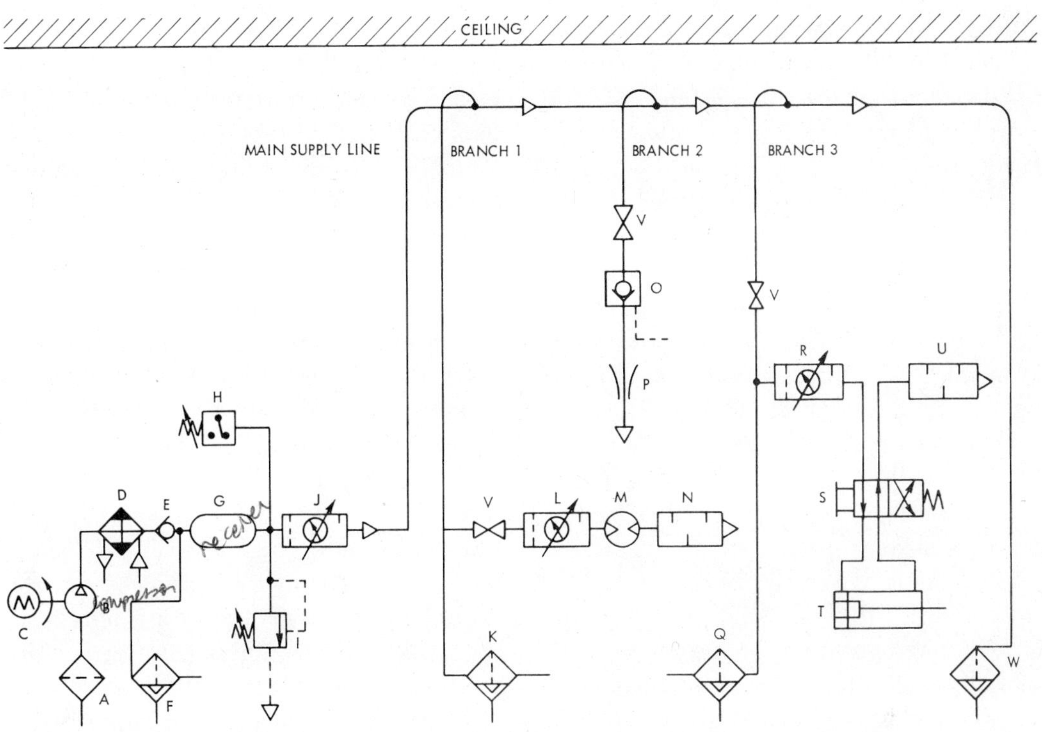

Fig. 6–1. Circuit diagram for compressed air system with main line near ceiling and 3 branch lines delivering air to different air-operated tools.

could at room temperature. The hot air leaving compressor B goes immediately to an aftercooler D, which dissipates the excess heat. Dissipation of heat is indicated by the inside solid triangles of symbol D, and the outside open triangles indicate that the method of cooling is a gaseous medium.

The cooled air then passes through check valve E, which prevents this compressed air from returning to the compressor.

F is a filter-separator with automatic drain. This should be located at the bottom of the receiver or storage tank G. The function of this filter-separator is to remove water condensation, oil mist, and other contaminants from the compressor and aftercooler. G is the receiver, also called a storage tank.

H is an adjustable pressure switch which starts the motor M if the pressure in the receiver through use of the gaseous medium has dropped below the required level. I is an adjustable pressure relief valve to guarantee that the pressure in the receiver does not exceed a predetermined amount.

J is a combination of components consisting of a filter, pressure regulator with pressure gage, and lubricator that adds a minute quantity of oil as a fine mist. Air passing this unit is at proper line pressure, cooled, purged of condensation, grit and other contaminants, and conditioned with a metered amount of lubricant in the form of a fine mist.

The main supply line is usually run close to the ceiling where the temperature may be several degrees above the temperature at floor level where most of the tools are used. As the air is conducted close to the floor level for use, it is cooled off. The cooler air cannot hold as much water vapor as the warm air at ceiling level and therefore some of this vapor condenses. If this water were not removed it could be carried into air-operated tools. Therefore it is removed by K, a filter-separator with an automatic drain at the bottom of branch line 1. V indicates a simple shutoff valve placed in three locations, so that components in all three branch lines may be serviced.

L is another unit containing a filter, pressure regulator with gage, and lubricator. This unit assures sufficient lubrication, double filtering, and provides for individual regulation of pressure and therefore speed and operating characteristics of pneumatic motor M, which the symbol shows is reversible. Exhaust air from this motor goes through muffler N, which reduces the noise to a less objectionable level at the expense of creating a certain amount of back pressure.

Branch line 2 is used to operate an air nozzle which might be used for automatic ejection of small stampings from a mechanical punch press. O is an air-operated pilot valve for operating the nozzle P. Full supply line pressure is used in this case.

Q, shown at the bottom of branch line 3, is another filter-separator used in the same manner as K in branch line 1, to remove water that has condensed due to lowered temperature. The symbol indicates that this unit is manually drained.

At this point the student may wonder about the insistence on draining condensation from the system. The problem is always present. On a hot summer day a small tank containing 10 cubic feet of air compressed to 100 psi could have 2 quarts of water. For comparison in the metric system, we may say that a receiver with a capacity of 280 liters at 7 kg/cm² could have 2 or more liters of water at the bottom of the tank. If passed on to the points of application this water could cause extensive damage.

Now, returning to branch line 3, R is another unit similar to L in branch line 1, and it is used for the same purpose. It regulates the pressure which, in turn, controls the force applied by the double-acting pneumatic cylinder I, which is shown cushioned on the return stroke as well as on the forward stroke. This adjustable speed control for both ends of the stroke was shown and described in Chapter 5. A similar method of speed control could be applied for the entire length of the stroke by inserting such a device directly at the ports of the cylinder.

S is a manually operated spring return, 4-way 2-position valve for operating the piston in pneumatic cylinder T. Exhaust air goes back through the 2-position valve S and passes through muffler U to reduce the noise.

Finally, filter-separator W, with automatic drain, removes any remaining condensation, scales, oil, and contaminants from the main supply line.

As was mentioned before, the branch lines take off from the top of the main supply line, then go down vertically to the filter-separators. This is done so most of the compressor scales and other contaminants can be blasted to the end of the line to filter-separator W, where they are removed. The liquids are drained automatically. Solid contaminants must be removed by disassembling the unit.

The operation of these filters, lubricators, pressure regulators, and pressure measuring instruments, which do not really direct the flow of the gaseous medium to the point of application but rather condition, regulate and measure it for efficient, dependable service, will be described more thoroughly in the following chapter.

We have now followed the flow of the gaseous medium from the source of supply (the compressor) to the points of application in Branch 1, Branch 2, and Branch 3, in Fig. 6–1. Flow control valves open, stop, limit, or direct the flow of gaseous medium. These valves, illustrated in Figs. 6–2 to 6–11 inclusive, will be de-

scribed more fully in paragraphs that follow.

As the pressure of the gaseous medium is generated in the compressor and then flows along its confined path, some undesirable effects are created. We are aware of these effects as we see, feel, and hear some of the results created by a moving air stream. If uncontrolled, this useful form of energy could be harmful but can be greatly subdued, as described under *Acoustic Filters* at the end of this chapter.

The Actual Hardware

At this point we should examine some of the hardware used to direct and control the flow of gaseous media to utilize the stored-up energy originated in the compressor. The main types of hardware described in this chapter are flow control valves and acoustic filters, which are designed to reduce noise and vibration. These units complement each other in achieving efficient, smooth, and reasonably quiet operation.

Flow Control Valves

Some of the most important considerations in selection of these valves are:

1. Dependability in performing required functions such as timing and pressure drop, and unquestionable safety for use in the environment where they are installed.
2. The design must permit the required flow with the least possible resistance and must be such that it can stop the flow completely with the simplest parts. If controlled regulation is required, the adjustments should be simple and dependable.

3. If the above requirements are adequately met, it is then important to decide if the valve should be mechanically, pneumatically, or electrically operated. These decisions may be influenced by hazardous environments, availability of mechanical or electrical power, and cost.

Because the stored-up energy in a gaseous medium originates in the compressor it seems logical to begin at this point. Two simple valves are usually required for satisfactory performance: the suction valve located at the intake of the compressor, and the discharge valve located at the delivery end. These two valves are quite similar in design except that the suction valve may have an unloader device to lower the power consumption, which will be explained in the description of the valve.

Compressor valves serve three main purposes:

1. They are designed to admit or expel an adequate volume of the gaseous medium.
2. They are designed to prevent the

Fluid Power: Pneumatics

gaseous medium from escaping back to a lower pressure.

3. They are designed so that a large percentage of solid contamination in the air will be prevented from following the gaseous medium as it is compressed and delivered from the compressor.

These three requirements have a simple solution in the so-called *face valve* subassembly of compressor valves. This *face valve* is usually designed for a pres-

sure differential of 1 to 5 psi, or 0.07 to 0.35 kg/cm². It is the face of the valve, the flat side, that does the sealing, as we shall see.

Fig. 6–2 shows a suction unloading compressor valve. The valve mechanism is fastened to a flange *A* in the compressor housing with screws *B*. A seal is shown at *C*. The valve assembly is seated firmly in the counterbore of the compressor housing at *D*. This design of compressor valve is easily removable for service.

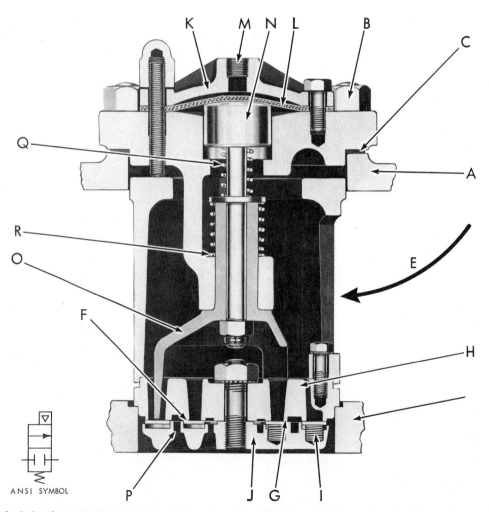

Fig. 6–2. Suction unloader compressor valve actuated by coil springs. (Courtesy of Gardner-Denver Company)

134

Filtered air enters the compressor and proceeds in the direction of arrow E into the valve. In the cutaway view of Fig. 6–2 the valve is shown in the closed position, with the inside face of the valve disc F firmly contacting surface G of part H of the assembly. A number of springs I keep the valve disc F in contact with part H. Part H and part J are provided with a number of small holes, rounded and elongated. This is so that loose particles entering with the air at E will be prevented from entering the compression chamber.

An unloader device is shown under cap K. By this arrangement pressure entering at M, generated by the end of the compressor piston (not shown) can be distrib-

uted over a large area of diaphragm L, pushing piston N downward, forcing plunger O to push disc F away from surface G, at the same time compressing springs I.

This assures full volume flow entering between surface F and G, out through holes P. It also lowers the power consumption because the pressure being generated holds the valve entirely open, permitting free passage of air. The light spring Q assures that piston N is seated against diaphragm L. Spring R keeps plunger O away from valve disc F so springs I can close gap when there is no intake of air.

Fig. 6–3 shows another design of suction unloading compressor valve. It is

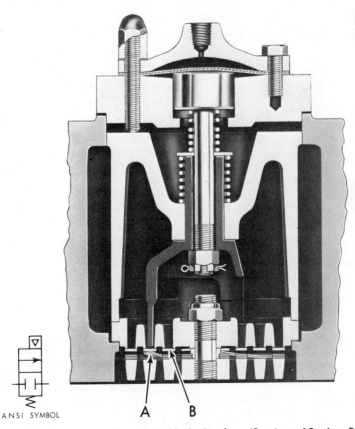

ANSI SYMBOL   A   B

Fig. 6–3. Suction unloader compressor valve actuated by leaf springs. (Courtesy of Gardner-Denver Company)

similar to Fig. 6–2 in all respects except that leaf springs as shown at *A* are used for seating the valve disc *B* instead of coil springs as shown at *I* in Fig. 6–2.

Fig. 6–4 is a photo of the valve subassembly as shown in Figs. 6–2 and 6–3 without the unloader arrangement. Fig. 6–5 is a sectional view of Fig. 6–4. This shows a leaf-spring design at *A*. Fig. 6–6 shows this type of valve as an exploded illustration.

The essential parts of the assembly shown in the exploded view of Fig. 6–6 are assembled by tightening nut *A* on screw *B*. Pin *C* prevents the working parts, spring discs *D* and *E*, from moving circumferentially, so the elongated holes for passage of the gaseous medium will be held in their correct position. An advantage of this type of valve is that the moving parts, discs *D*, *E* and *H*, are light-weight to reduce inertial forces. Since the

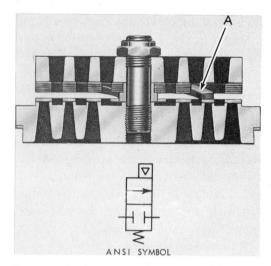

Fig. 6–5. Sectional view of discharge compressor valve (Courtesy of Gardner-Denver Company)

diameters are large, they also move a very short distance axially, usually less than 1/4 inch (6 mm). The spring pressure furnished by leaves in the discs shown at *F* is light, but must be strong enough to prevent chatter. The air passes through side openings in housing *G* through the elongated holes in parts *I*, *E*, *H*, and *J*. A sealing ring is shown at *K*.

Whereas compressor valves, which are 2-way valves, most often are designed for passage of large volumes of a gaseous medium, preventing a large percentage of contaminants from entering beyond the valve, the standard design of a 2-way valve for a pneumatic system is simply to admit or stop flow of the gaseous medium. The exclusion of undesirable contaminants are taken care of with filters or strainers.

The most common valves are 2-way, 3-way, and 4-way valves. Many varieties of these valves are available. Only a few will be shown to present the simplicity of their construction. Rotary valves are also available but, because they are much

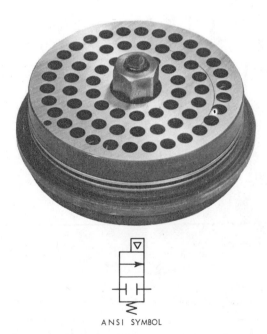

Fig. 6–4. Discharge compressor valve. (Courtesy of Gardner-Denver Company)

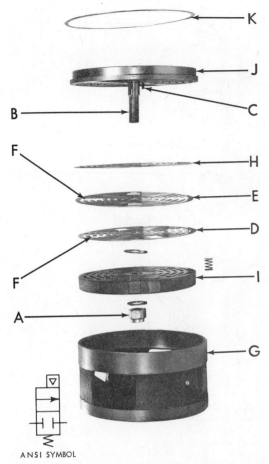

ANSI SYMBOL

Fig. 6–6. Exploded view of discharge compressor valve, showing leaf spring design. (Courtesy of Gardner-Denver Company)

adjusted as a flow control valve in both directions, as indicated by the ANSI symbol in the top diagram. Or it may be adjusted for controlled flow in one direction and free flow in the opposite direction, as indicated by the ANSI symbol in the middle diagram. Or it may be adjusted as a spring-loaded check valve as indicated by the ANSI symbol in the bottom diagram. Other simple designs are possible, but not shown, by substituting spring loading with an electrical solenoid or with air pressure.

The air is admitted at A and directed to the point of application at E when the valve is open. Ball B when seated against the conical surface C stops flow from A to E. This can only happen if screw D is retracted so that spring F can seat the ball against surface C. The air pressure will then also help to keep the ball seated against the conical surface.

The flow in the opposite direction from E to A would then be free if screw G is withdrawn from the ball, because the pressure would compress the light spring F. A ball and conical surface are ideal contact surfaces for a valve because the contact surface is small and slight inaccuracies in machining are easy to control.

When used as a volume-control valve, screw D would be adjusted to permit the desired volume of flow between ball B and conical surface C. The spring F would hold the ball against screw D. If desired, this adjustment could be locked by tightening screw G firmly against the ball. The flow would then be the same in both directions. The air will flow freely around the entire circumference of the ball, which stays centered in the conical hole because the unit pressure is the same on all surfaces in the same enclosure. Seals are provided at H to prevent air from leaking out between threaded parts.

more difficult to seal, they cannot be recommended for pneumatic systems and will not be discussed here. In nearly all cases the linear valve design is much more favorable.

Air is much more difficult to seal than a liquid. Therefore, if the sealing takes effect by contacting two metallic surfaces, these surfaces must be clean and accurately machined. This is shown in a simple illustration, Fig. 6–7. Many variations of this basic design are possible.

As illustrated, this type of valve may be

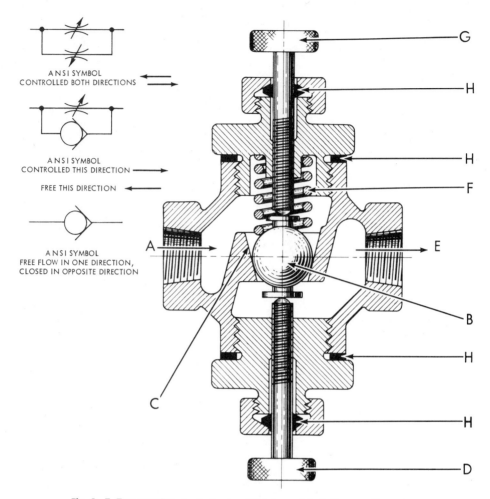

ANSI SYMBOL
CONTROLLED BOTH DIRECTIONS

ANSI SYMBOL
CONTROLLED THIS DIRECTION

FREE THIS DIRECTION

ANSI SYMBOL
FREE FLOW IN ONE DIRECTION,
CLOSED IN OPPOSITE DIRECTION

Fig. 6−7. Two-way flow control valve. (Courtesy of C. A. Norgren Company)

Fig. 6–8 shows an adjustable control valve. Here the flow is shown free in one direction. It may, however, be adjusted from zero flow to free flow in the opposite direction, or the flow may be stopped completely in both directions.

The pressure of the gaseous medium on the large area of valve part B forces this part up against spring F, providing a large opening between part B and the valve body at G, permitting free flow to escape through port E.

In the opposite direction the gaseous medium enters at E and flows in the direction of the arrow through holes not shown. The spring pressure already holds the valve part B firmly against the valve body at G. The gaseous medium puts additional pressure on valve part B and flow can only occur between restricted adjustment of the conical point of screw C and valve part B. H is an O-ring seal.

Simple 3-way valves are illustrated in Figs. 6–9 and 6–10. They may be de-

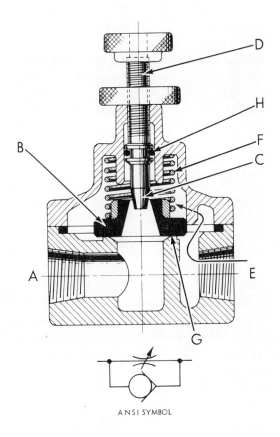

ANSI SYMBOL

Fig. 6–8. Adjustable two-way flow control valve (Courtesy of C. A. Norgren Company)

signed to be operated by hand, by air pressure, or by an electrical solenoid. The valves in Figs. 6–9 and 6–10 are operated by air pressure. In both illustrations the pressure enters at P and is directed to the point of application from port A. The gaseous medium is always exhausted at E.

A normally closed valve is shown in Fig. 6–9 with the proper ANSI symbol of the valve connected to a spring-returned piston and cylinder. When pilot pressure is applied at port B, piston F, sealed with O-ring I, forces disc G in contact with the valve body. At the same time, disc H is separated from the valve body, permitting the gaseous medium to flow to the point of application in direction of arrow D. As soon as pilot pressure is released,

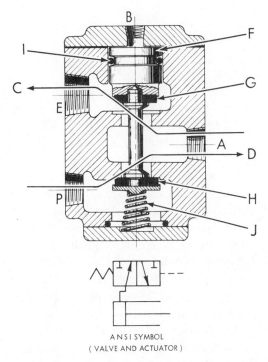

ANSI SYMBOL
(VALVE AND ACTUATOR)

Fig. 6–9. Three-way normally closed air-operated valve. (Courtesy of C. A. Norgren Company)

Fluid Power: Pneumatics

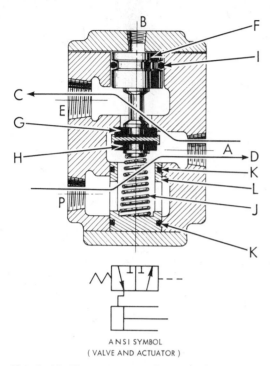

ANSI SYMBOL
(VALVE AND ACTUATOR)

Fig. 6–10. Three-way normally open air-operated valve. (Courtesy of C. A. Norgren Company)

nately in two directions a 4-way 2-position valve is required. There are many design variations available on the market. A simple, proven design used by the author in machine design is shown in Fig. 6–11. This valve as shown is operated mechanically in both directions. This could be actuated by a cam. Some models are available that are spring-centered and operated either by pilot air pressure or by solenoid, in either direction. There may also be models that are spring-operated in one direction and mechanically or pilot-air operated in the other direction.

Notice that the pressure enters at the center of the valve at P. The lands G and H of spool D never cross the pressure port. In the position shown, the pressure enters at port P and flows through the recessed portion of spool D out through port B to the point of application. Port A is an exhaust through the recessed portion of spool D to exhaust port E. The holes E may be connected so if a muffler is desired in the system one muffler is sufficient for both ends.

If the valve spool is shifted over to the left, pressure flows from port P through the recessed portion of spool D and through port A to the point of application. Port B is an exhaust through the recessed portion of spool D to exhaust port E.

Sleeve C is made up of 5 sections with O-rings in a tight squeeze, sealing off at lands G and H of spool D. The lands of the spool have very little clearance between the inside of sleeve C. For symmetrical distribution of pressure, sleeve C has a circular groove at all ports and an even number of holes through the sleeve diametrically opposed. In this design spool D, O-ring, and sleeve C are easily accessible for removal and service. The ANSI symbol of the valve with a double-acting cylinder is shown.

spring J will return the sealing disc H to contact the valve body, sealing off the pressure from the point of application in direction of arrow C through exhaust port E.

A normally open valve is illustrated in Fig. 6–10. The operation is similar, but in this case the spring J holds the valve disc G in contact with the valve body, preventing the gaseous medium from exhausting from port A through port E. At the same time, disc H is separated from the end of sleeve L, permitting the gaseous medium to flow in direction of arrow D through holes in sleeve L through port A to the point of application. O-rings provide good seals at K.

Where pressure is desired to flow alter-

140

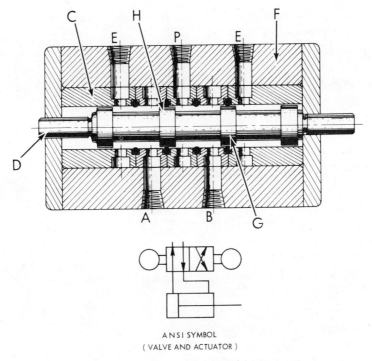

ANSI SYMBOL
(VALVE AND ACTUATOR)

Fig. 6–11. Four-way valve, mechanically operated.

Acoustic Filters

There is a definite relationship between noise and vibration. Since both of these, above a certain level, are harmful to man's nervous system and also to structural components in machinery, much research has been done to reduce them in the performance of fluid power for industrial use. The close relationship between acoustic pulsation and identifiable noise is, however, a subtle distinction not evident to the average person. A low frequency pulsation such as produced by a low-speed pump—usually less than 15 *hertz* (cycles per second)—is felt as a shock or tremor rather than distinctly heard. When the frequency is between 15 and 30 hertz, as with an atmospheric intake line of a compressor, the tremor is accompanied by noises and rumbles. Often it is very difficult to differentiate between perception by hearing and perception by feeling.

At about 30 hertz pulsations pass into audible range, which extends to an upper limit of human perception of about 15,000 to 20,000 hertz. Even though this is usually the upper limit of frequency heard by humans it has been established by tests that frequencies above this range can be sensed by the body and can result in fatigue, irritability and acute nervousness.

When a piano is tuned to concert pitch—slightly higher than international pitch—the middle *A* string vibrates 440 cycles per second. It should be noted, however that this may be a pleasing sound or a disagreeable sound, depending on the force applied. This value is the *amplitude*, not hertz, and is measured in *decibels.* The threshold of sound in terms of amplitude is considered to be 0 (zero) decibel. The rustle of leaves is about 25 decibels. Household noises of an average residence would probably register about 60 decibels during the busy part of the day. A passing subway train would register about 120 decibels. This level of noise is very obnoxious, and 130 decibels is generally considered to be the threshold of pain.

The study of acoustics can only be considered in general terms in this book. It is a highly specialized field and many technical treatises are available.

A great variety of noise-attenuating devices are on the market under a number of different trade names. It is always wise to contact a reputable specialist in the field because there are so many variables which determine the selection of a component best suited for each individual case.

Pulsation dampeners and mufflers are for pulsations from 1 to 20,000 hertz and overlap in their range of applications. Some operate on the phase-shift principle, analogous to the cancelling out or stabilizing of 3-phase alternating electric current. Others are of the baffle type, like the ordinary automobile muffler, causing considerable back pressure. Others are of the absorptive and dissipating type, where the gaseous medium passes over perforated surfaces, preferably of small holes closely spaced, opening to chambers stuffed with sound absorptive material. The absorptive mufflers offer much less resistance and therefore the pressure loss is small.

For a quick evaluation of acoustic components, refer to Figs. 6-12, 6-13, and 6-14. The recommended allowable vibration levels are illustrated in Fig. 6-14. Vibration in piping and heavy machinery

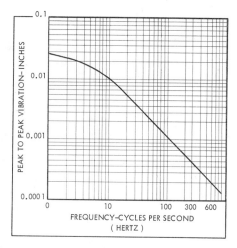

Fig. 6-12. Illustration showing recommended allowable vibration levels. (Courtesy of American Air Filter Company, Inc., Pulsco Division)

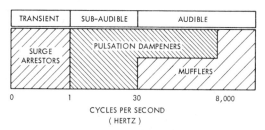

Fig. 6-13. Graphical illustration of pulsation frequencies. (Courtesy of American Air Filter Company, Inc., Pulsco Division)

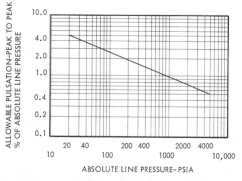

Fig. 6-14. Illustration showing recommended allowable pulsation levels in percentage of absolute line pressure. (Courtesy of American Air Filter Company, Inc., Pulsco Division)

becomes more hazardous as frequency and amplitude increase. A thousandth of an inch (0.0254 mm) movement at 100 hertz may, for instance, be as critical as a hundredth of an inch (0.254 mm) movement at 10 hertz. Adequate analysis of vibration and properly designed pulsation dampeners will achieve desired safe vibration levels.

Pulsation seriously affects piping and machinery vibrations. High pressure systems are particularly critical. As the absolute operating pressure of the system is increased, the allowable pulse level (expressed as a percentage of the operating pressure) should be reduced. Conversely, higher pulse levels may be tolerated at lower operating pressures.

Fig. 6–15 shows a separator pulse trap based on the reactive phase-shift principle. This method is an acoustic arrangement designed so that all pressure pulsations entering the pulse trap at frequencies above its design frequency

are cut off or substantially reduced. The unit illustrated is a combination pulsation dampener and mist extractor. The manufacturer claims that this component will virtually eliminate valve failure in compressor systems due to liquid carry-over, line dirt and foreign matter during start-up.

The separator pulse trap relies on *infrasonic* (low frequency) effect of pressure pulsations to clear the gaseous medium of mist. *Infrasonic* is on the opposite end of the spectrum from *ultrasonic*. This pulse trap is used on the suction side of a reciprocating compressor to prevent liquid carry-over and on the discharge side to capture compressor cylinder lubricating oil. In both cases it also serves as an effective pulsation dampener.

When used on the suction side of the compressor, flange *A* is attached to a corresponding flange on the compressor. When used on the discharge side, flange *A* is fastened to a corresponding flange on

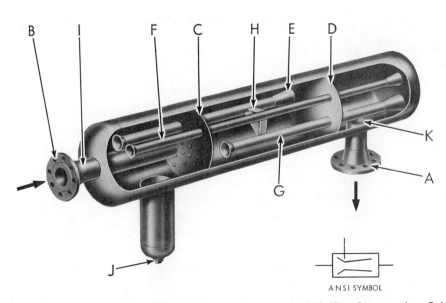

A NSI SYMBOL

Fig. 6–15. Cutaway view of separator pulse trap. (Courtesy of American Air Filter Company, Inc., Pulsco Division)

Fluid Power: Pneumatics

the discharge side of the compressor. If the air intake is from a pipe through an outside wall, this pipe may be fastened to flange B. A pulsation dampener is a complicated instrument based on extensive research. When used on a reciprocating or axial flow compressor, the peak frequencies are approximately 3,000 hertz. The design of the pulsation dampener must then be based on this frequency. Before a satisfactory design is perfected the baffle plates C and D may have to be shifted lengthwise. The small holes in baffle plate C may also have to be varied in size or relocated. The main parts are the two baffle plates C and D and three tubes E, F and G, flared at both ends and located with triangle H. The inlet tube is at I, the exhaust tube at K, and the drain at J.

When air enters through tube I, some will go through small holes in baffle plate C and some will rebound and enter the flared ends of the two tubes E and F. These two tubes are of different lengths, so some of the air will travel to the end of the unit through tube F and bounce off the inside of the rounded end of the unit and travel out through tube K. Some air will travel through tube E. Since this is a shorter tube, the air bounces off baffle plate D and enters the flared end of tube G through which it will travel to the inside of the rounded end of the unit and then exhaust at tube K.

In this process we may say that the frequency of the air has been attenuated or reduced by lowering the peaks of the frequency. This is accomplished by splitting the main stream of air at the entrance into two branches, throwing these two streams 180° out of phase with each other. Contaminating agents in the air such as scale and oil may then be drained through the lower end of drain J.

Review Questions

1. How does a hose differ from a rigid tube in delivering pressure to a working component?
2. What are some of the important requirements for pneumatic supply lines?
3. Mention some of the requirements to consider for supply lines to keep the pressure drop to a minimum.
4. How high may the temperature rise in a compressor if no precautionary measures are taken to lower this temperature?
5. What is the function of a separator/pulse-trap?
6. What precautionary measures should be taken to prevent damage to tools when a supply line is lowered from ceiling level to floor level?
7. What is the function of a pressure switch for a compressor?
8. Why may a relief valve be required at the receiver?
9. Why is a branch line taken from the top side of a horizontal supply line?
10. Where are the valves located in a compressor and why are these valves required?

11. What is the purpose of an unloader device for a compressor valve?

12. What is the advantage of a leaf-spring compressor valve?

13. How can chatter be reduced in a compressor valve?

14. Mention three main methods of operating flow control valves.

15. When is a two-way valve required?

16. When is a three-way valve required?

17. When is a four-way valve required?

18. Describe the difference between amplitude of noise and frequency level of noise. How is amplitude of noise designated?

19. Describe the basic principle of a phase shift acoustic filter.

SEE END OF BOOK FOR ANSWERS TO QUESTIONS

Accessory Equipment to Clean, Condition, and Measure the Gaseous Media

In Chapter 6 we traced the sequence of operations in a small, fairly typical pneumatic system in which one compressor, driven by an electric motor, delivered compressed air to a receiver tank and from there to the main supply line with three branch lines, each powering a different type of air-operated tool. The emphasis was on the instruments to direct and control the flow of air, with only passing mention of other accessory equipment such as filters, drains, lubricators, regulators, and gages. In this chapter we will examine some of these instruments and see how they operate.

Instruments to Clean and Condition Gaseous Media

Clean air is important not only to prevent damage to instruments, valves, and other components, but also to assure efficient operation of the tools. For example, by installing filters such as those shown in Figs. 7–1, 7–2, and 7–3, we have lowered the cost of operation by reduced interruption of service and more efficient performance of the tools. There is, however, a slight additional operating cost involved that we should be aware of: installation of these instruments in the main supply line and the branch lines causes a certain amount of pressure drop. Therefore we should remember that the cost of this necessary equipment is not

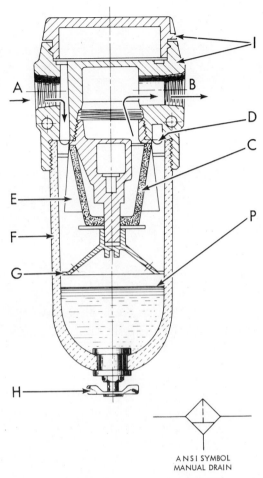

ANSI SYMBOL
MANUAL DRAIN

Fig. 7—1. Air filter with manual drain. (Courtesy of C. A. Norgren Company)

In service, the air enters at *A* and leaves at *B*. Since the only outlet to *B* is through an air filter element *C*, the air must first travel downward. In order to divert the air to a circular flow pattern, a louver deflector is installed as shown at *D*. To better understand the action of this deflector, refer to the enlarged view of it in Fig. 7–2. This deflector has a conical skirt *E*, shown in both Fig. 7–1 and Fig. 7–2. We can readily see that as the air flows down it is given a circular flow as it hits the louvers. Then, in addition to the centrifugal force produced by the circular travel, the skirt *E* of the deflector also helps to keep the air flow close to the inside wall of the transparent bowl *F*.

Any liquid present in the air will then follow the wall of the transparent bowl *F* through notches at the periphery of baffle

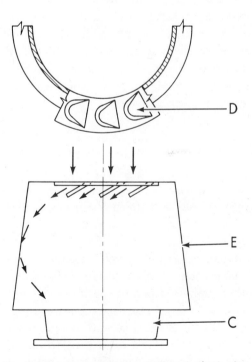

Fig. 7—2. Louver deflector (enlarged view) also shown at *D* in Fig. 7—1.

just the initial cost but also the continuous cost of pressure drop, as shown in Figs. 7–4 and 7–5.

Air Filters

Fig. 7–1 shows a sectional view of an air filter. When this instrument is used in an automated production line it is advisable to have another identical unit on hand, and a shutoff valve must be installed ahead of this component so the filter can be removed and replaced with the least interruption to production.

G. Solid particles not left above the louvers in deflector *D* will then settle on baffle *G.*

Since the only outlet for the air when the drain cock *H* is closed is through port *B*, the flow of the air will be inward to the central portion of filter element *C.* Turbulence of the air flow may have a tendency to pick up liquid deposited at the lower part of bowl *F* and carry it back through the filter element *C.* Therefore, the baffle *G* has an additional purpose, namely to create a *quiet zone* in the lower part of the instrument, preventing the liquid from being recirculated in the air flow.

When all the heavy contaminants have been deposited, and as the air flows through the filter element *C*, the remaining light contaminants are deposited on the filter element.

Filter elements are usually made to filter out particles in ranges from 5 to 50 microns. (1 micron = 0.001 mm or 0.000039″.) Filter bowl *F* is transparent so the level *P* of accumulated liquid is visible from the outside. The liquid can then be removed by opening drain cock *H.* Solid contaminants may be removed by unscrewing cap *I.*

Fig. 7–3 shows the same filter designed for automatic drain of liquid as it accumulates. *J* is a cylindrical, fine-mesh screen which protects the working parts of the automatic drain from solid contaminants.

As liquid fills up in the bowl, float *K* rises, causing piston-type automatic drain assembly *L* to open and release the liquid under pressure. This is a good, practical application of the Pascal Law, stating that a gaseous medium of fluid in a closed system exerts pressure equally in all directions. Because of this fact, float *K* is always held in a central position. The combined top surfaces *M* are, however, larger than surface *N*, which is reduced

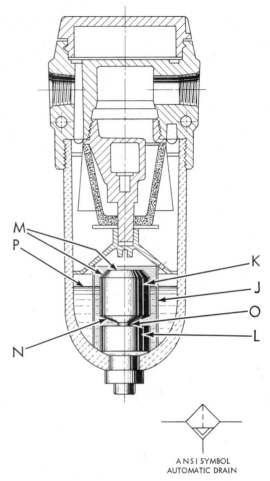

ANSI SYMBOL
AUTOMATIC DRAIN

Fig. 7–3. Air filter with automatic drain. (Courtesy of C. A. Norgren Company)

by the sealing cylindrical part *O.* Therefore float *K* is kept down by the additional downward force. As soon as enough liquid collects at the bottom of the bowl, the float *K* rises, and a small diameter piston on the lower end of float *K* then permits the accumulated liquid to escape as it is rapidly forced out by the air pressure being applied to the large area *P* of the liquid. Immediately following this, the top area of float *K*, which is still larger than the bottom area and therefore has a greater total force acting on it, causes the float downward and the small piston at the bottom of the float again seals the filter, preventing escape of the air.

Float *K* in this automatic drain system is a good example of bouyancy or equilibrium of pressure. The float is hollow and therefore much lighter than the liquid it would displace if it were fully submerged. As the liquid rises its pressure on the float becomes greater than the downward pressure from the air, causing the float to rise again and permit the accumulated liquid to be expelled.

The graphs shown in Figs. 7-4 and 7-5 analyze the recommended air flow

for 1/2-inch standard pipe size air line and a 50-micron filter element. Where curve *A* intersects the pressure curves, the maximum recommended flow may be found.

Drip Leg Automatic Drain

Fig. 7-6 shows a drip leg automatic drain. This type of instrument is installed at the end of a line to rid the line of liquid and contaminants accumulated along the way. This instrument has a safety vent valve *E* which opens if excessive pressure is reached. *B* is a screen which traps solid contaminants such as scales, rust particles, and so forth. These contaminants must be removed manually by unscrewing cap *I*. You will notice that the component shown in Fig. 7-6 is similar to the

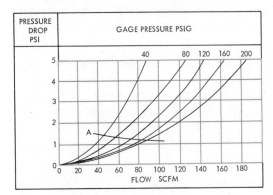

Fig. 7-4. Filter flow characteristics. (Courtesy of C. A. Norgren Company)

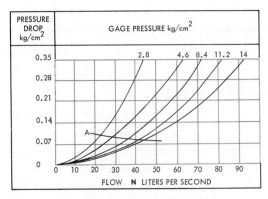

Fig. 7-5. Filter flow characteristics (metric).

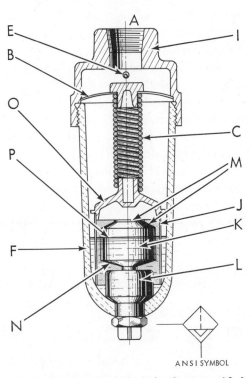

Fig. 7-6. Drip-leg automatic drain. (Courtesy of C. A. Norgren Company)

ones shown in Figs. 7–1 and 7–3, but has no filter element. Spring *C* holds the working parts in assembled position with baffle *O*, which catches some of the remaining contaminants.

The moisture-laden air enters at *A* and, after depositing the solid contaminants on screen *B*, travels on to deposit the moisture at the bottom of bowl *F*. Cylindrical screen *J* prevents small solid contaminants that may have been carried through screen *B* from entering the working parts of the unit.

As the moisture builds up to a certain level *P*, the float *K* rises in the same manner as previously shown in Fig. 7–3, causing piston-type automatic drain assembly *L* to open and release the accumulated liquid under pressure.

Here, as in Fig. 7–3, the float K is hollow, so the liquid it displaces when submerged to level *P* of the liquid is heavier than the weight of the float, and the float will therefore rise and permit the accumulated liquid to escape.

Refer again to the ANSI symbol shown in Fig. 7–3 and in Fig. 7–6. The filter shown in Fig. 7–3 has an inlet port *A* and an outlet port *B*, so the ANSI symbol has three exterior lines, one for *A*, one for *B*, and one for the drain. In Fig. 7–6 there is only inlet port *A* and the drain, so there are only two exterior lines in the symbol.

In review, you may recall from Chapter 2 that the relationship of volume and weight of air varies with variations in both temperature and pressure. To express the rate of air flow through a filter or other component it is necessary, therefore, to specify a standard condition which takes both variables into consideration. The expression *scfm* or *SCFM* is often used dealing with flow of a gaseous medium, and these letters stand for *standard cubic feet per minute*, which under standard conditions (before being compressed) is at a density of 0.075 lb per cubic foot at 68° F and a barometric pressure of 29.92 inches of mercury with a relative humidity of 36 percent. When the air has been compressed to 90 psi, for instance, the weight of air compressed from standard density would be about 0.5 lb per cubic foot.

In the metric system the flow of a gaseous medium is most often given as *N liters per second*. The letter *N* in this case stands for *normal*, which in most Western European languages is the word for *standard*. Because of the vast difference in the units used in the customary U. S. system and the metric system, the numerical values in *scfm* and *N liters per minute* are far apart, as you can see by comparing Figs. 7–4 and 7–5.

Instruments to Regulate and Condition Gaseous Media

Adjustable Pressure Regulators

As has been mentioned before, correct pressure is a necessary requirement for efficient operation of pneumatic tools. We started to provide for this requirement by using pipes of adequate size with large bends where bends are necessary. We did, however, find (as was shown in Fig. 7–4 and Fig. 7–5) that some *in line* instruments as shown in Fig. 7–1 and Fig. 7–3 will cause additional pressure drop. For this reason the pressure delivered to the point of application must be above requirements and the pressure must be regulated to exact requirements with a sensitive instrument called a pressure regulator.

There are many varieties of these instruments. Fig. 7–7 shows the basic principles of operation. This instrument has a spring *C*, which by correct adjustment determines the delivered pressure. The

inlet port is shown at *A* and the outlet port at *B*. It is difficult to seal commercial threaded parts for air, so an O-ring is provided in a pocket on valve guide plug *D*, sealing against a conical surface in valve body *E*.

The working parts are the diaphragm *F*, made of tough, flexible material and clamped with screws (not shown) between bonnet *G* and valve body *E*. Pressure relieving valve seat *H* clamps the diaphragm *F* to the spring seat *I* at the center of the diaphragm. Spring *C* may be adjusted with screw *J*, *K* is a replaceable threaded insert. The pressure regulating valve *L*, with O-ring, slides in valve guide plug *D*. A sealing ring is shown at *M*. Pressure regulating valve seat is shown at *N*. A floating pin *O*, with free sliding fit in regulating valve *L* and upper end free to float in valve body *E*, connects the diaphragm *F* with the regulating valve *L*. *P* is a light valve spring which holds the valve *L* with sealing ring *M* against valve seat *N*.

This is the position of the valve when the screw *J* is withdrawn, leaving spring *C* at its free length, with no pressure exerted by spring *C*. The pressure (primary) entering port *A* will also hold the valve firmly against the seat with no flow of air possible to outlet port *B*. The spring *C* normally supplied for this instrument is for pressures adjustable from 0 to 125 psi (0 to 8.79 kg/cm^2). Springs are also available for 0 to 50 psi (0 to 3.51 kg/cm^2) or 0 to 250 psi (0 to 17.58 kg/cm^2).

Assume now that a pressure of 90 psi (6.33 kg/cm^2) is desired at the outlet port *B*. Screw *J* is adjusted until 90 psi (6.33 kg/cm^2) registers on a pressure gage fastened to the outlet side.

To illustrate the operation clearly, assume that the pressure entering port *A* were shut off at this adjustment. Valve

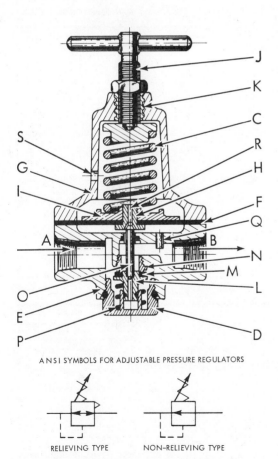

ANSI SYMBOLS FOR ADJUSTABLE PRESSURE REGULATORS

RELIEVING TYPE   NON-RELIEVING TYPE

Fig. 7–7. Adjustable pressure regulator. (Courtesy of C. A. Norgren Company)

Fluid Power: Pneumatics

seat H would then be forced down in contact with valve body E by spring C compressing the light valve spring P. This would leave the same opening between sealing ring M and valve seat N as is now shown on the drawing between valve seat H and valve body E. As soon as the pressure is turned on the air will flow through this opening and through small pipe Q, forcing diaphragm F up until the pressure under the diaphragm equalizes the pressure that the spring C was adjusted to.

The instrument shown is a pressure-relieving type valve. Assume then that a sudden shock load is applied to the component being operated by the regulated (secondary) pressure. The pressure cannot rise above the regulated pressure since the air then would escape through the small hole R in valve seal H and to the atmosphere through the vent hole S. The pressure has been relieved.

Figs. 7–8, 7–10 and 7–12 for the U.S. system, and Figs. 7–9, 7–11 and 7–13 for the metric system give the maximum recommended flow for pressure regulators of 1/4″, 3/8″ and 1/2″ pipe size. The tables show variations in regulated or secondary pressure leaving port B when the primary pressure entering port A is 100 psi (7.03 kg/cm²), as shown in Fig. 7–7. The maximum recommended flow may be found where curve A intersects the secondary pressure curves.

High Precision Pressure Regulator

Whereas in the majority of pneumatic industrial applications it is sufficient to have pressure regulating valves keeping the delivered pressure reasonably steady and high enough to perform the work desired, and pressure relief valves to guarantee safety in the system, there are often cases where ultimate precision control of

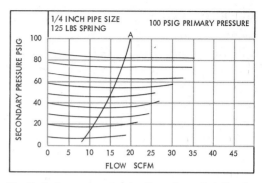

Fig. 7–8. Pressure regulator flow characteristics for 1/4″ pipe size. (Courtesy of C. A. Norgreen Company)

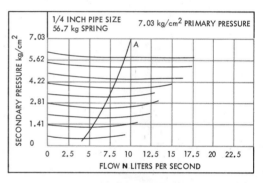

Fig. 7–9. Pressure regulator flow characteristics, Fig. 7–8 converted to the metric system.

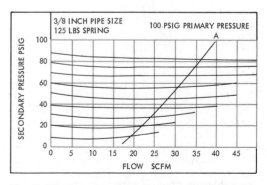

Fig. 7–10. Pressure regulator flow characteristics for 3/8″ pipe size. (Courtesy of C. A. Norgreen Company)

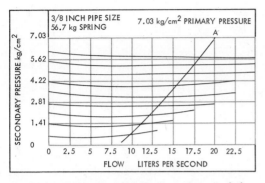

Fig. 7–11. Pressure regulator flow characteristics, Fig. 7–10 converted to the metric system.

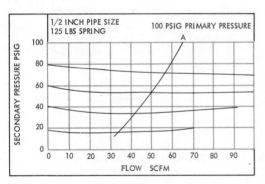

Fig. 7–12. Pressure regulator flow characteristics for 1/2″ pipe size. (Courtesy of C. A. Norgren Company)

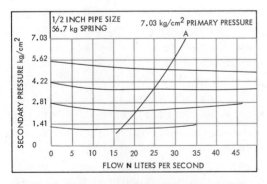

Fig. 7–13. Pressure regulator flow characteristics, Fig. 7–12 converted to the metric system.

Fig. 7–14 High precision pressure regulator. (Courtesy of Bellofram Corporation)

pressure is necessary to successfully perform a required task.

Fig. 7–14 shows a high precision pressure regulator that was originally developed for sensitive aircraft altimeters, and Fig. 7–15 is a cutaway drawing showing its construction details and operation.

As illustrated in Fig. 7–15, this is actually a pressure controller using a servo-balanced system in which the main valve is operated by the servo valve.

The downstream regulated pressure is conducted up into the chamber surrounding the measuring capsule, which is made of a high quality stainless steel alloy. A

153

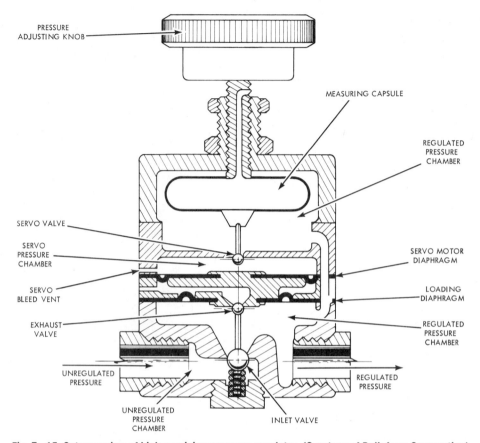

Fig. 7–15. Cutaway view of high precision pressure regulator. (Courtesy of Bellofram Corporation)

small amount of air flows through the servo valve into the servo pressure chamber and out through the servo bleed vent to the atmosphere. The bleed rate is less than 0.08 SCFM, or 0.038 liter per second.

A minute motion of the measuring capsule will move the servo valve with respect to its seat, causing a substantial change in the control pressure in the servo pressure chamber. This change in pressure then reacts directly on the servo diaphragm, which causes an appropriate movement of either the inlet valve or the exhaust valve, thus correcting any minute errors in the downstream pressure.

The regulated pressure applies an upward force to the underside of the loading diaphragm. If the regulated pressure build-up exceeds .01 psi (or 0.7 gm/cm²) above the adjusted pressure, exhaust air escapes through the exhaust valve and out through a series of exhaust vents contained in the spacer ring between the servo diaphragm and the loading diaphragm permitting a substantial reverse flow.

The primary reason for the high accuracy is the fact that the relative motion between the servo valve and its seat, required to effect substantial changes in the main valve position, is extremely small, usually less than 0.0001" (or 0.0025 mm). The high gain of this servomechanism permits desired downstream pressure to be maintained with exceptional accuracy. Standard instruments have a controlled pressure range of 2 to 25 psi, 2 to 60 psi and 2 to 120 psi, using standard filtered shop air. In the metric system this would be: 0.14 to 1.76 kg/cm², 0.14 to 4.22 kg/cm² and 0.14 to 8.44 kg/cm².

Lubricators

In Chapter 2 we found that if we could create a differential in pressure we could cause flow in a fluid. In this case, as long as an unbalanced air pressure existed the water would keep on flowing, and the air was the medium for causing flow. When a balanced condition was reached, the flow would stop. There are many practical examples of this in instruments and components used in fluid power circuits.

Fig. 7–16 shows a practical example of an instrument for supplying oil to a pneumatic system using air as the medium for atomizing the lubricant and moving it as a fine mist to the points of application. We have mentioned before how important it is to lubricate moving parts in a pneumatic system. This is not just to keep metallic surfaces separated with a minute film of lubricant when in motion, but also to keep parts from corroding, especially when there may be moisture in the air.

The air enters this instrument at port *A* and leaves at port *B*, conditioned with a fine mist of lubricant. However, as is the case with most commercial instruments, the simplicity of operation is obscured by the complexity of the mechanical design. A transparent bowl *D* is filled with lubricant to level *E*. The lubricant is forced from bowl *D* by the air entering at port *A* in the following steps:

1. Part of the air entering at *A* is directed through a venturi *F* into the chamber *G* above the oil reservoir. A

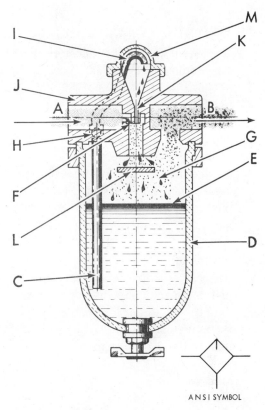

Fig. 7–16. Operation of a micro-fog lubricator. (Courtesy of C. A. Norgren Company)

venturi tube is usually a short tube narrowed down to a small opening at the center portion. This will cause the fluid flowing through the narrowed portion of the tube to flow at a much higher velocity than at the end portions. This causes a differential in pressure, which is the reason for a higher pressure on surface *E*, forcing the oil up through tube *C* opening check valve *H*, then through a hole in body *J* through pipe *I* dripping into the center portion *K* of the venturi. Check valve *H* prevents the oil from flowing back to the reservoir. Baffle plate *L* keeps the air stream entering chamber *G* from causing turbulence in the oil. The action of the air and oil at the venturi creates a finely divided oil fog in the upper part of the chamber *G*. All oil particles larger than 2 microns fall out, returning to the oil reservoir. The smaller particles remain airborne and represent about 5% of the oil which passed through tube *I*. This oil mist will be carried through port B to the point of application. The work of the Italian physicist G. B. Venturi (1746–1822) led to the invention of the venturi tube.

2. The remaining part of the air entering port *A* is diverted around an adjustable vane by-pass (not visible) directly to the outlet port *B* and is the main medium for carrying the oil mist to the point of application. *M* is a transparent dome for observing the oil flow.

The principle of operation of the instrument illustrated in Fig. 7–16 may be easier understood as illustrated by the operation of a simple spray gun shown in Fig. 7–17.

Here the main air stream enters at port *A* and is carried directly across to outlet port *B*. The opening around tube *C* at port *B* may be adjustable.

The remaining part of the air stream enters small tube *D* and is carried through the venturi *E* to surface *F* of the liquid, where the intensified pressure causes the liquid to be drawn up through tube *C* and expelled at a higher pressure and atomized as it is mixed with the pressurized air stream flowing through port *B*.

Performance characteristics of the lubricator shown in Fig. 7–16 are shown in Fig. 7–18 in customary U.S. units and in Fig. 7–19 in metric units. Curve *A* shows minimum flow at various pressures when the adjustable portion of the ventu-

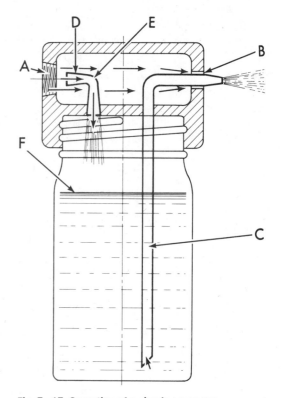

Fig. 7–17. Operation of a simple spray gun.

ri by-pass *K* in Fig. 7–16 is closed. Curve *B* shows maximum flow at various pressures when the adjustable portion of the venturi by-pass K in Fig. 7–16 is fully open.

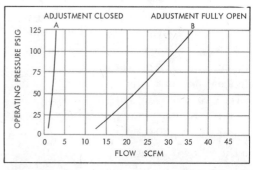

Fig. 7–18. Performance characteristics of micro-fog lubricator shown in Fig. 7–16. (Courtesy of C. A. Norgren Company)

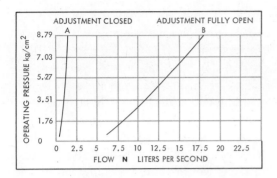

Fig. 7−19. Performance characteristics of micro-fog lubricator. Fig. 7−18 converted to the metric system

Instruments for Measuring Pressure

The simplest instrument for measuring pressure, the barometer, was described in Chapter 3. Other instruments using no liquid have been developed for measuring variations in low or atmospheric pressures, but they are not as accurate as the liquid barometer. One of these is the *aneroid* barometer, named from a Greek expression meaning literally "without water". The aneroid barometer consists of a hollow, elastic, air-tight container whose outside is exposed to the atmosphere and inside has been evacuated to partial vacuum. The container is connected to a magnifying device that indicates any variation in atmospheric pressure. It is a small, portable instrument of limited accuracy.

Bourdon Gages

Many of the pressure gages used in pneumatic circuits are *bourdon gages*, named after their nineteenth century French inventor Eugène Bourdon. These are sufficiently accurate for nearly all industrial applications provided they are calibrated against known pressures

and their design provides for recalibration after use. The pressure is transmitted to the open end of a curved elastic tube which is closed at the opposite end. The tendency of the tube under pressure on the inside is to straighten out. This motion is transmitted to a pointer to indicate the pressure on an accurately calibrated dial. Some of the more common materials for bourdon tubes are copper alloy, alloy steel, stainless steel, and monel.

Figs. 7−20, 7−21, and 7−22 show the operating principles of these instruments. They are made in pressure ranges from zero to 10,000 psig (or 703 kg/cm²), with full-scale accuracy as high as 0.05 percent available in the highest quality gages such as those illustrated.

The highest quality bourdon gages with balanced pointers are used principally for testing shop gages which are based on the same principles but are not so accurate because high accuracy in most cases is not necessary for the ordinary industrial use. These gages are compact and can give a mechanical output, but are subject to certain types of errors, as are also the similar bellows type gages. One limitation is that they are poor for low pressures and in applications where there are strong fluctuations resulting in mechanical vibrations. The percentage of error due to mechanical friction is small. The gages do, however, have scale errors, *hysteresis* errors, or sluggish response to sudden minor pressure fluctuations, and temperature errors higher than those of liquid gages. Another inherent fault of these

gages is that after long use the calibration of the dial may change due to metal fatigue and wear of moving parts.

Bourdon gages are made in several designs for various ranges of pressures, including pressures higher than those measured within the practical range of liquid gages. They are used extensively in fluid power systems for industrial use, for gaseous as well as liquid media. One important thing to observe, however, is that the material used in these instruments must

Fig. 7—20. High accuracy bourdon test gage, face side. (Courtesy of Marsh Instrument Company)

always be compatible with the medium being measured.

The gage shown in Fig. 7–20 is a high-accuracy test gage for calibrating and checking laboratory and production instruments. The measuring range of this particular instrument is from 0 to 10,000 psi (0 to 703 kg/cm²). These gages are usually manufactured in ranges from 0 to 15 psi as the lowest range (0 to 800 mm Hg) and 0 to 10,000 psi as the normal high range (0 to 50,000 mm Hg) with several lower ranges in between. The operating principle is, however, similar except that in the ranges up to 1,500 psi (105 kg/cm²) a circular bourdon tube is used, whereas above 2,000 psi (140 kg/cm²) a helical bourdon tube is used.

The graduations C are accurately spaced in exact equal increments. One increment on the gage shown is 10 psi. This accuracy is possible because the pointer A is balanced as shown at B to reduce the effects of gravity when the

Fig. 7–21. Working mechanism of bourdon gage for pressures up to 1,500 psi. (Courtesy of Marsh Instrument Company)

gage is used with the face in a vertical plane, which is the normal operating position. The pointer may be adjusted to zero reading with the screw shown at *D*. Level *L–L*, the zero reference, is imprinted on the high caliber test gages and provides for a precise laboratory method of correcting inaccuracies caused by extreme temperature variations or errors resulting from inadvertent rough handling. Readjusting the damaged gage to another gage at the zero reference level restores the original accurate geometric relationship of movement to the bourdon tube without automatic devices that are subject

to over or under compensation. These instruments are also manufactured for vacuum ranges of 15 psig (800 to 0 mm Hg).

The average pressure of a pneumatic system for industrial use is usually about 90 psi. An instrument commonly used for measuring these lower pressures is shown in Fig. 7–20. We did, however, see in Chapter 3 that pumps operated by a low gaseous pressure were capable of producing hydraulic pressures as high as 75,000 psi. In the study of hydraulics we learn that the average pressure in industrial plants is from 200 or 300 psi to 600 psi. Pressures as high as 3,000 or even higher

Fig. 7–22. Working mechanism of bourdon gage for pressures from 2,000 to 10,000 psi. (Courtesy of Marsh Instrument Company)

are not uncommon. Since the bourdon gages are used for a liquid as well as a gaseous medium, the pressure ranges may be very high.

Fig. 7–21 shows the working mechanism behind the dial of the gage shown in Fig. 7–20. The fluid, gaseous or liquid, enters at inlet port A, and as the pressure changes the circular tube C of an oval cross-section it has a tendency to straighten with increase in pressure, thus transmitting mechanical motion from its closed end D to a mechanism of levers and gears B. This produces a magnification of the motion of tube C and thus registers the applied pressure to a very high degree

of accuracy by pointer A in Fig. 7–20. This particular instrument is designed for pressure ranges up to 1,500 psi or 105 kg/cm².

Fig. 7–22 illustrates the working mechanism of a bourdon gage with a helical shaped bourdon tube C which is used for pressure ranges from 2,000 psi, or 140 kg/cm², up to 10,000 psi, or 703 kg/cm². A is the inlet port and B is the operating mechanism consisting of levers and gears for transmitting a magnified motion to pointer A in Fig. 7–20 from the motion due to applied pressure created at end D of the helical tube C.

Calibration. As stated previously,

Fig. 7–23. Dead-weight pressure gage tester. (Courtesy of Marsh Instrument Company)

Fluid Power: Pneumatics

the bourdon gages illustrated in Figures 7–20, 7–21 and 7–22 are accurate test gages used for calibrating and checking laboratory as well as industrial gages. As we see in Fig. 7–20, the reference level of the instrument is marked at the upper part of the face of the dial indicated as *L–L.* This level is referred to as *ambient zero datum.* If checking is performed at other levels calculations must be performed to compensate for the head of pressure created by the difference in levels. When checking an industrial gage the reference level is not required.

Test gages must be checked for accuracy against known standards when they are first manufactured and also occasionally as they are used, because after repeated use the elasticity of the bourdon tubes has a tendency to change. A basic instrument for performing this task is shown in Fig. 7–23. This is called a *Dead-Weight- Tester* and is also known under other names such as:

1. Dead- Weight Gage
2. Gage Tester
3. Pressure Balance
4. Piston Manometer

The *piston manometer* description is used in Germany and since this is a very appropriate name, aptly describing the instrument, it might well be used universally. In principle it is a piston inserted into a close fitting cylinder. Weights *A* loaded on one end of the piston are supported by fluid which transmits the pressure accumulated by the weights to bourdon tube *A* in Fig. 7–21 or 7–22. The gage to be tested is shown at *B.*

Construction of piston gages vary as to the method of loading and methods of rotating or oscillating the piston to reduce friction as load is applied. They also vary greatly in the design of piston and cylinder. The pressure registered on instru-

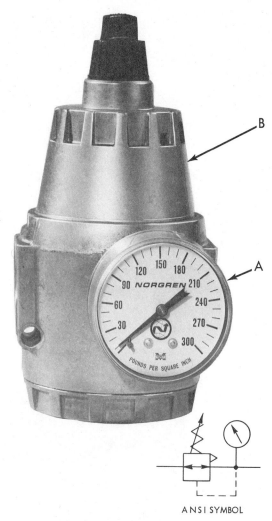

ANSI SYMBOL

Fig. 7–24. Industrial pressure gage mounted on a pressure regulator. (Courtesy of C. A. Norgren Company)

ment *B* is equal to the total weight *A* divided by the active area of the piston.

Fig. 7–24 shows a commonly used industrial pressure gage *A* mounted on a pressure regulator *B.*

Diaphragm Pressure Transducers

Diaphragm type pressure transducers, which put out an electrical signal proportional to the pressure, are more accurate than other types of mechanical gages and are more convenient than liquid gages for test purposes. They are, however, much more expensive and more delicately constructed than liquid manometers. Also they are usually poorer in low pressure response and have higher overall errors. They are principally useful in reducing the time for taking the readings and are sometimes used with a pressure selector switch to read and record electrically a number of pressures in sequence.

These gages usually have strain gages attached to the diaphragm, which are fed into an electrical network to give a voltage output proportional to pressure. They are more sensitive than most mechanical gages to low pressures. They are, however, more easily damaged by overpressures. They have negligible friction errors, but appreciable hysteresis and scale errors as well as temperature errors.

Fluid Probes

Small-diameter angular tubes called *probes* or *pitot tubes* are used in pressure lines to conduct a small portion of the gaseous medium to either mechanical gages such as bourdon gages, bellows type gages, diaphragm pressure transducers, or to liquid manometers, in order to obtain readings with minimum obstruction or pressure drop in the lines. Some of these are described in paragraphs that follow.

Pitot Tubes (pronounced *pētō'*). The pitot tube, named after its eighteenth century French inventor, Henri Pitot, is commonly used for measuring the velocity of gaseous media in motion based on the mathematical relationship of *velocity pressure* (which is the full impact pressure of the moving gaseous medium less the static pressure) and velocity. It is essentially an angular tube inserted in the pressure line at right angles to the moving stream. Its short leg may be surrounded by a short tube, preferably of small diameter and beveled to a fine edge at the entrance end only, or at both ends. The small inside diameter receives the full impact of the gaseous medium in motion.

Fig. 7–25 shows two designs of pressure probes. These instruments are used with suitable gages for measuring total pressure in a fluid stream when direction of flow is unknown or varies with operating condition. The miniature probe shown at (A) has a sharp-edged venturi especially useful for total pressure traverses. A pitot tube is very similar to a traverse rod for curtains or drapes in that the flow moves over, around, and along it in a similar manner. Therefore the word *traverse* is often used in this connection. This can be inserted through a 1/8-inch diameter hole. The probe at (B) has a rounded venturi entrance. This probe has a shorter time constant than the probe shown at (A) due to a higher orifice coefficient and is better for high temperature use, up to 2,000°F (or 1,093°C).

A small diameter probe is in most cases desirable because it offers less restriction

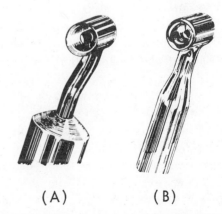

(A) (B)

Fig. 7–25. Standard pitot tubes surrounded by short tubes. (Courtesy of United Sensor & Control Corp.)

to flow. In extreme cases, with too many instruments restricting the flow, compressor efficiency has been observed to drop as much as 5 percent. Free stream total pressure is affected very little by the probe, so this measurement is easy to make. Static pressure, however, is affected quite noticeably by interference. The effect can be estimated by comparing the cross-sectional area of a passage with and without the probe in it. If the probes block as much as 5 percent of the area, the fluid is accelerated 5 percent in going through the measuring section, and the static pressure will drop 10 percent below the unobstructed value.

Usually there is some sustaining pressure drop due to this effect, but it is not as great as the drop at the probe. When static pressures are being measured with probes, it is desirable to limit their cross section to 1 percent of the passage area. Very often wall static pressure can be used instead of probe pressures without introducing any error in the free flow condition.

The taps must be carefully made in a smooth section of the wall and carefully deburred, and positioned at least ten probe diameters from any probe stem for accuracy.

The minimum size of pressure probe is usually determined by the allowable time constant (time required to obtain an accurate reading) and danger of plugging with dirt. In practice, a single orifice probe (Fig. 7–25) can be used down to 0.030″ (or 0.76 mm) diameter with good results, while a two-orifice probe, such as a pitot-static tube, down to .060″ (or 1.5 mm) overall diameter, and three to five-orifice probes down to 0.120″ (or 3 mm) overall diameter. The limiting practical size for pressure tubes is 0.015″ (or 0.38 mm) inside diameter in short lengths up to one

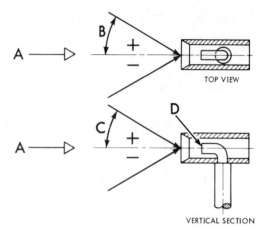

Fig. 7–26. Definition of yaw & pitch angles for pressure probes. (Courtesy of United Sensor & Control Corp.)

inch, and 0.030″ (or 0.76 mm) for longer lengths.

Yaw angle, as illustrated by angle B in the top view of Fig. 7–26 is quite insensitive to probe interference.

Pitch angle as indicated by angle C in the vertical section of Fig. 7–26 can, however, change the measurement noticeably when taken too close to a solid boundary, since this obstructs the flow around the tip D of the probe and changes its calibration. A indicates direction of the fluid flow.

Fig. 7–27 shows five designs of directional total pressure probes of various configurations. (A) has a cylindrical sensing head for measuring yaw angle and total pressure. (B) has a cobra-shaped sensing head for measuring yaw angle and total pressure. This probe is more accurate for boundary layer traverses than probe (A). Probe (C) is a cobra-shaped sensing head for measuring yaw angle, total pressure, and also contains a thermocouple for measuring total temperature. Probe (D) has a prism-shaped sen-

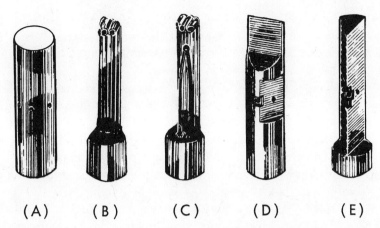

Fig. 7–27. Various designs of pressure probes. (Courtesy of United Sensor & Control Corp.)

sing head for measuring yaw angle, total pressure and static pressure up to pitch angles of 20°. This probe is wind-tunnel calibrated. (E) has a wedge-shaped sensing head for measuring yaw angle, total pressure and static pressure up to pitch angles of 30°. It is also wind-tunnel calibrated.

Fig. 7–28 shows three multiple-hole probes for measuring several different quantities, as listed. Probe (A) has a five-hole, prism-shaped measuring section.

This measures total and static pressure, yaw angle and pitch angle up to 40°. It is applicable up to 0.7 Mach. Probe (B) has five holes and thermocouple. It measures total and static pressure, yaw angle and pitch angle up to 40°, and total temperature. Probe (C) has five holes also. It measures total and static pressure, yaw angle and pitch angle up to 40°. It is applicable up to 0.7 Mach. *Mach number* is defined as the ratio of fluid velocity to the speed of sound in the fluid. When the fluid

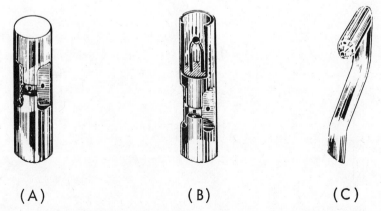

Fig. 7–28. Directional, total and static pressure probes and temperature probes. (Courtesy of United Sensor & Control Corp.)

flow is 1.00 Mach, the velocity of the flow is the same as the speed of sound in that fluid, and the flow is *sonic*. Mach numbers greater than 1.00 are *supersonic* flows, and Mach numbers less than 1.00 are *subsonic* flows.

The long leg of the angular tube probe is connected by pressure lines to measuring instruments or indicators of various types, and sometimes to two instruments. This will be explained in detail in later paragraphs. Some of the most common instruments are: liquid-filled manometers, bourdon gages, bellow-type mechanical gages, and diaphragm pressure transducers which give an electrical output proportional to the diaphragm deflection.

Manometers. The manometer is one of the most common pressure reading devices used in connection with pressure probes for experimental applications. A variety of liquids may be used, depending on a number of requirements. Generally speaking, water is the standard reference for low pressures and mercury is the standard reference for high pressures, because the specific gravity of mercury is 13.6, or 13.6 times as heavy as water. Because of mercury's inability to wet glass, however,

it forms a decided *meniscus* or convexity at the top of the mercury column in the tube, causing it to have a high *meniscus error*.

A simple manometer is shown in Fig. 7–29 at left. A simple slantgage manometer is shown in Fig. 7–29, at right. If we consider p_1 as the atmospheric pressure, the pressure applied at p_2 should be gage pressure registered as h in inches of water (H_2O), mercury (Hg) or other measuring media in the U.S. system, or as millimeters (mm) in the metric system. Water is the standard for measurements, and all other media are based on the relationship of their density to the density of water. Thus:

1 inch of H_2O at 4°C = 0.07355″ H_g
= 0.03613 psi = 0.00254 kg/cm²

It is easily seen that if angle in the slant-gage manometer is small enough so that $c/h = 6$, a 6 to 1 ratio is obtained, and h may be measured in much finer increments, with the measurements being registered along line c.

For low pressures water is one of the best manometer liquids in several re-

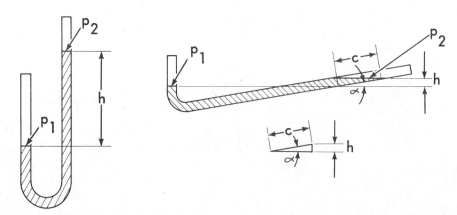

Fig. 7−29. Two types of simple manometers: The U-tube type is shown at left, and the slant-gage type is shown at right.

spects. Its density is accurately known, and it has a low density coefficient change with change in temperature. Water also has a meniscus error although in this case the meniscus is concave. Normally it wets clean glass tubing, but a slight oily deposit will make it non-wetting, causing uncertainty in meniscus elevation. Sometimes a wetting agent is used to counteract this, but after a period of time the agent appears to form deposits on the tube which are as bad as other contaminants.

Because of mercury's non-wetting characteristic its meniscus level tends to stay below the equilibrium pressure point in the tube, but oxidation of the surface or contaminants can make it partially wetting, so an uneven meniscus level is formed or the meniscus depression changes erratically. This gives an uncertainty of about 0.05″ (or 1.25 mm) in a 1/4″ (or 6 mm) inside diameter tube.

All meniscus level errors are more serious with smaller diameter tubes. However, because large tubes create more time lag and are unusable in slant gages, the best compromise is usually a tube with 1/4″ (or 6 mm) to 3/8″ (or 9.5 mm) inside diameter.

Alcohol and alcohol-water mixtures are among the best for low pressure work and in slant gages, since alcohol has a lower surface tension than water, therefore less meniscus elevation, and is a solvent for many contaminants that tend to collect in the tube. Pure alcohol is *hygroscopic* (absorbs water), so its density can change over a period of time in a humid atmosphere. Therefore, alcohol-water mixtures have been found to be more stable, retaining the advantages of pure alcohol. Alcohol-water mixtures of known density are desirable for measuring very low pressures. They have one undesirable feature,

however. They have much larger change of density with temperature change than does pure water. Therefore, in some cases the change in density must be taken into consideration when ambient temperature fluctuates wildly.

In a slant gage with alcohol-water mixtures the uncertainty in meniscus level is usually less than 0.01″ (or 0.25 mm) in terms of vertical height. For a 6:1 slope this would mean a variation of 0.06″ (or 1.5 mm) in slant height. Since this error is a constant vertical error, decreasing the slope angle of the gage does not reduce the error. Slanting the gage has the principal advantage that it makes it easier to read the meniscus deflection. Slopes less than 5° from the horizontal, giving a magnification of 10:1 are not as a rule practical, however, because the shape of the meniscus level is so distorted that it cannot be read accurately.

In addition to water and alcohol-water mixtures, some of the most common liquids for manometers are kerosene and various oils with specific gravities of less than 1.0 down to about 0.8. Also some synthetic compounds, often proprietary mixtures, with specific gravity of over 1.0 are used. Carbon tetrachloride, with a specific gravity of 1.6, and acetylene tetrabromide, with specific gravity of about 3.0, are the most common heavy liquids between water and mercury.

Since these liquids are poisonous, they should be used cautiously. They also attack many of the synthetic hose materials, which is also the case with alcohol mixtures and kerosene. Mercury attacks copper. The heavier liquids mentioned, and also mercury, are normally used in vertical tubes only because in general they have a poor meniscus shape in slant-tube gages, making their use in such gages impractical.

Pressure. The maximum pressure for a liquid manometer is about 35 psi (or 2.5 kg/cm²) and the minimum pressure about 0.0005 psi (or 3.5 gm/mm²). The maximum is for a 6-ft (or 1.82 meter) mercury column, and the minimum is 0.01″ (or 0.25 mm) on an alcohol manometer, which is the minimum random error approximately on an alcohol slant gage. This may, however, be reduced to 0.001″ with some extra effort.

In Chapter 2 we found that the average pressure of the atmosphere was about 14.7 psi. We also saw that this was the equivalent to a mercury column of 29.921 inches. Therefore the practical maximum mercury height of 6 feet which is 72 inches would be:

$$72 \times \frac{14.7}{29.921} = 72 \times 0.4912$$

$$= 35 \text{ psi (approx.)}$$

The low pressure would be measured by a slant gage as explained in the preceding paragraph. Since, however, due to the meniscus of the fluid level in the tube it is difficult to read with absolute accuracy and several individuals may vary slightly in their interpretation of the same reading. The term *random error* applies to an error of this type. In practice, a reading based on the average of several individual readings would be used.

For still lower pressure, special types of gages have been devised which are not practical for routine testing. One type uses two different immiscible liquids of specific gravities very close to each other and in contact with each other. In this case the meniscus deflection will be:

$$h = \frac{p_2 - p_1}{\rho_2 - \rho_1}, \text{ where:}$$

h = manometer deflection (inches or centimeters)

p_1 = pressure on one liquid column (psi or kg/cm²)

p_2 = pressure on other liquid column (psi or kg/cm²)

ρ_1 = density of one liquid (lb/ft³ or kg/cm³)

ρ_2 = density of other liquid (lb/ft³ or kg/cm³)

All manometers measure pressure as follows:

$$p_2 - p_1 = h \times \rho$$

It is always important to remember that in our calculations we *must* use the same units of measurements throughout the problem. After the calculations are finished we may then convert to the desired units of measurements.

Often only one pressure fitting is provided on the manometer. In such a case the other pressure is usually the atmospheric pressure. In a few rare cases the other end may be permanently sealed so the measured pressure is absolute, as in the barometer. Usually, where absolute pressure is required, the pressure is measured with respect to the atmospheric pressure and the barometric pressure is added to this.

As shown by the preceding equation, there are no calibration coefficients involved in the indicated pressure. As long as the density of the liquid is accurately known (corrected to ambient temperature if necessary), and the height of the column accurately measured, the reading is exact.

Calibration coefficient is known as the coefficient which the reading should be multiplied by to correct for changes in density in the liquid caused by temperature changes or changes in elevation above or below sea level. For example, the calibration coefficient is as follows:

1.0000 = Pure water (H_2O) at sea level and 4°C (39°F)

1.0010 = Pure water (H_2O) at sea level and 15.5°C (60°F)

1.0018 = Pure water (H_2O) at sea level and 20°C (68°F)

1.0007 = Mercury (H_g) at sea level and 4°C (39°F)

1.0028 = Mercury (H_g) at sea level and 15.5°C (60°F)

1.0036 = Mercury (H_g) at sea level and 20°C (68°F)

There is, however, a slight, irreducible random error due to erratic wetting of the surface of the liquid, and therefore the difficulty in determining the exact level of the irregular surface. This error becomes more serious at lower pressures.

Since the irreducible error tends to be fixed and independent of either the type of liquid used or the pressure being measured, to get the minimum percentage of error a manometer should always be used with the maximum deflection possible and thus read as near to full scale as possible.

Manometers are usually of the plain U-tube type, as shown in Fig. 7–29 (left), the single leg vertical with reservoir, or the slant-gage type with reservoir.

The U-tube type is theoretically the most accurate, since the level of each leg is read and subtracted, so variation in the bore of the tubing has no effect on the results. It is also the cheapest type, but it has the disadvantage that it takes twice as long to read as the single-leg type.

The single-leg type has a special shrunk scale to compensate for the drop in reservoir level with applied pressure. Also, it must have a uniform-bore tube. If the cross-section of the reservoir is large

enough, these factors will have less effect on reading, but the time constant of the manometer is increased.

Within the limits presented, and subject to meniscus errors, liquid-filled manometers are among the most practical gages for visual reading. Their accuracy depends basically on just one length dimension. They are immune to mechanical fatigue induced by pressure fluctuations, and they are cheap and easy to service.

The slant gage has a reservoir also, and is used where a larger deflection is needed for low pressures. The deflection of the meniscus level with pressure is:

$$c = \frac{h \times \rho}{\sin \alpha}, \text{ where}$$

c = manometer deflection along the slant-gage tube

α = angle of tilt from the horizontal (degrees)

For very accurate readings a micromanometer is often used. This usually is built like a slant gage, but has a short slant tube, which is moveable and is connected to the reservoir by a flexible hose. In use, the manometer is always balanced, so the meniscus is at a fixed reference mark on the slant tube. A lead screw is then provided to raise and lower the reservoir or the slant tube and an indicator to show the distance moved.

The gage is first balanced with zero pressure and the height indicator set at zero. For any other setting the height indicator then reads the vertical elevation h in the preceding equation. In effect, this type of manometer combines the sensitivity of the slant gage and the long range of a vertical tube manometer. Then, because the readings are always taken at the same point on the slant tube, errors due to the tilt of the gage, non-uniformity of bore, or irregularity of the meniscus level, do not occur. The principal objections to these gages are their high cost and the long time required to balance them. Balancing may also be more difficult if the gage is connected to a probe with a long time constant.

Connecting Pressure Probes to Measuring Instruments. The connections from pitot tubes (or other pressure probes) to the measuring instruments should be arranged with tees in the lines, where necessary, to allow measuring all differential pressures directly on a single manometer rather than measuring pressures separately and then subtracting them. This avoids the error incurred by taking the difference of two large quantities and

also the error due to pressure changing slightly during a set of readings. The manometer for each pressure can be picked to have a full-scale reading slightly higher than the maximum expected. If the pressure range of any of the readings is more than ten to one, it is advisable to provide two or more manometers with different ranges for the reading.

The pressure ranges can be calculated from the expected difference between the static pressure of the setup, and the atmospheric pressure and velocity pressure, which depends on velocity and density of the gaseous medium.

Fig. 7–30 is a typical pitot-static tube arrangement, in which the gaseous medium to be measured enters at *A*. The

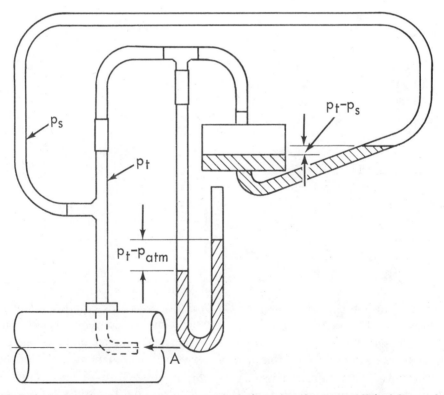

Fig. 7–30. Typical measuring arrangement for a standard pitot tube. (Courtesy of United Sensor & Control Corp.)

required pressures for calculating veloc-ity are p_t, the total absolute pressure, and p_s, the static pressure. Since the total pressure of the setup might be quite a bit higher than the atmospheric pressure while the velocity pressure might be low, high errors could result if the total and static pressures were measured separate-ly with respect to the atmospheric pres-sure on mercury manometers.

By using a sensitive slant gage as shown in Fig. 7–30 to measure the differ-ential pressure directly and a tee from the total pressure line to a mercury tube to

measure total pressure with respect to the atmospheric pressure, the percentage of error in the readings is much less.

To refresh what we have previously learned in Chapter 2 and be in a better way to understand Fig. 7–30, we may refer to Fig. 7–31, which illustrates pres-sure measurements in simpler form.

You will recall that we learned in Chapter 2 that a gaseous medium may be used for accurate measurements of static pressure in a liquid. Bearing this in mind, let us examine Fig. 7–31. If tank A is filled with a liquid to level $O–O$ and an

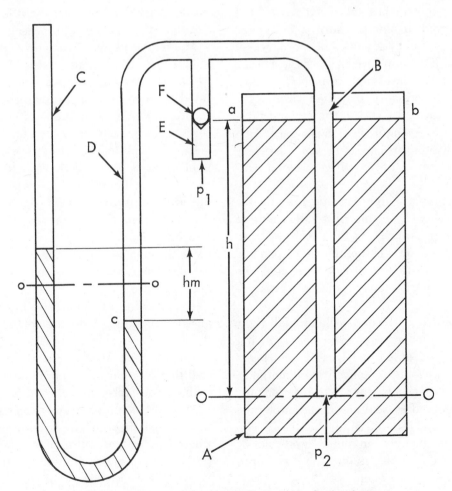

Fig. 7–31. Pressure measurements illustrated in simplest form.

open tube B is fastened in the tank so the open end just contacts the surface of the liquid, and this tube B is connected to a U-tube filled with mercury to level $o-o$, we have equilibrium.

Tube B, connected to U-tube C,D, has a branch E supplied with a check valve F. Now, if air pressure is applied to this check valve, the equilibrium of the mercury would remain undisturbed because the air supplied through the check valve would escape to the atmosphere at the open end of tube B, contacting the surface of the liquid in tank A. If, however, liquid is added to tank A to level $a-b$, the pressure of the liquid has increased to head h, a function of depth and specific gravity of the liquid. If now pressure p_1 is applied through the check valve, the mercury will fall to level c in branch D of the U-tube and rise to level d in branch C. This is when the pressure p_1 applied through the check valve is equal to the upward pressure p_2 of the liquid, which is head h. This is Newton's third law of motion: "To every action there is an opposite and equal reaction."

If a pressure higher than p_1 is applied to check valve E, the mercury will remain at level d in branch C of the U-tube because the excess air is escaping at the open end of tube B to the atmosphere, and the check valve E keeps the enclosed pressure from escaping.

Mounting Errors. Clean and tight connections are essential for reducing errors to a minimum. Locations of leaks are easily found by conventional methods. Determination of leaks in the system may be observed by sealing off the pitot tube orifice and pressurizing the lines. The pressure should then remain steady for at least one minute. A slow drop is evidence of a leak in the system.

Contaminated lines are also a source of error. A drop of water in a small internal diameter will act as a pressure relief valve in sealing off small pressure differences, but passing large pressures. For this reason it is particularly difficult to detect, and can give large, unexplained errors in the probe indications. After checking for leaks, the probe orifice should be opened and the manometer observed. It should drop smoothly to zero. If it stops about 1 or 2 inches (2.5 or 5 cm) of water differential from zero, it is a sign of a drop of water inside the probe. If it stops at a higher differential, it might indicate liquid in connecting tubes in a U-bend, forming a water trap. If the pressure does not drop at all, or very slowly, it is an indication of dirt in the probe passage.

Mach Number. Previously in this chapter we have come across the term *Mach number* and learned how it is related to the speed of sound in a given medium. There is another aspect to this term that is even more important.

In our study of the gaseous media as applied to perform work for industrial use, we have found that the gaseous media are highly compressible in comparison to most engineering materials. Therefore, even when merely pushing a volume of air through a conduit with no mechanical load opposing it, the gaseous medium is compressed.

The measure of compressibility of the gaseous medium is a function of the velocity of the gaseous medium. The Austrian physicist Ernst Mach (1838–1916) realized this relationship, so in honor of him we have the expression *Mach number*.

At low Mach numbers, up to about 0.25, the gaseous medium can usually be considered as an incompressible fluid, and the same equations apply as for liquids. Above this velocity the equations have to be modified to take account of the change in gas density due to its compressibility.

At about 0.7 Mach number, parts of measuring probes fall into zones of sonic velocity due to local acceleration as a result of obstruction of the probe. Therefore large changes in calibration can occur.

At 1.0 Mach number (sonic flow), the whole flow pattern changes around the probe, and its calibration changes so much that, as a rule, the same type of pressure probes cannot be used for subsonic and supersonic flow. Temperature probes, however, are affected much less by Mach numbers, since the shock waves that change total pressure do not change total temperature.

Mach number is defined as the ratio of the velocity of a gaseous medium to the velocity of sound waves in the same gaseous medium under free stream conditions. The Mach number has led to a number of important equations in pneumatics. These are given in following paragraphs.

Symbols enumerated below are used in the equations to follow:

A = Cross section of the measuring area, ft²

c_d = Ratio between average velocity in the section and maximum indicated velocity as determined by the pressure difference

c_p = Specific heat capacity at constant pressure, BTU/lb

c_v = Specific heat capacity at constant volume, BTU/lb

E = Mechanical energy, ft-lbs/lb

g = Acceleration due to gravity, 32.2 ft/sec²

J = The mechanical equivalent of heat, 778 ft lbs, BTU

k = c_p/c_v (See Chapter 3)

M = Mach number

$\overline{p_{t1}}$ = Average total initial pressure

$\overline{p_{t2}}$ = Average total final pressure

p_c = Constant pressure

p_s = Static pressure

p_t = Total pressure

p_{thg} = Total pressure, inches of mercury

p_{sw} = Static pressure, inches of water

p_{tw} = Total pressure, inches of water

Q = Heat energy, ft lbs/lb

q = Volume flow in cubic feet per second

R = Gas constant (see Chapter 3)

$\overline{T_{t1}}$ = Average initial absolute temperature at total pressure (Rankine)

$\overline{T_{t2}}$ = Average final absolute temperature at total pressure (Rankine)

T_s = Absolute temperature at static pressure

T_t = Absolute temperature at total pressure (Rankine)

T_{t1} = Initial absolute temperature at total pressure (Rankine)

T_{t2} = Final absolute temperature at total pressure (Rankine)

V = Linear flow, ft/sec

W = Weight flow in pounds per second

ρ_t = Density at total pressure, lbs/ft³

ϵ_v = Expansion factor for dry air

η_a = Adiabatic shaft efficiency

V_{max} = Maximum linear velocity in the measuring section, ft/sec

Velocity. For liquids at all velocities and gaseous media when $p_t - p_s/p_t$ is less than 0.025 we have:

$$V = 8.03 \times \sqrt{\frac{p_t - p_s}{p_t}}$$

As a practical example assume:

$p_t = 16$ psi

$p_s = 15.648$ psi

$$\frac{p_t - p_s}{p_t} = \frac{16 - 15.648}{16} = 0.022$$

$$V = 8.03 \times \sqrt{\frac{p_t - p_s}{p_t}} = 8.03 \times \sqrt{0.022}$$

$$= 8.03 \times 0.1483 = 1.191 \text{ ft/sec}$$

The velocity in this sub-sonic stream of air is therefore 1.191 ft/sec.

$$V = 18.28 \times \sqrt{\frac{p_{tw} - p_{sw}}{\rho_t}}$$

For dry air when $p_t - p_s/p_t$ is less than 0.025 we have:

$$V = 15.90 \times \sqrt{\frac{(p_{tw} - p_{sw}) \times T_t}{p_{thg}}}$$

For dry air when $p_t - p_s/p_t$ is above 0.025 we have:

$$V = 15.90 \times \epsilon_v \times \sqrt{\frac{(p_{tw} - p_{sw}) \times T_t}{p_{thg}}}$$

$$\epsilon_v = 1 + .212 \times \sqrt{\frac{p_t - p_s}{p_c}}$$

For gaseous media at all velocities we have:

$$V = \sqrt{2g \times J \times C_p \times T_t \times \left[1 - \left(\frac{p_s}{p_t}\right)^{\frac{k-1}{k}}\right]}.$$

The velocity equation for gaseous media at low mach numbers are the same as for liquids. At a ratio of $p_t - p_s/p_t = 0.025$, (mach number of 0.20), the error in the first three equations is 1/2%. The last equation eliminates this error, and may be accurately calculated with the now available pocket computers.

For mach numbers less than 0.2 or $p_t - p_s/p_t$ less than 0.025, we have:

$$M = .179 \times \sqrt{R} \times \sqrt{\frac{p_t - p_s}{p_t}}$$

For dry air we have:

$$M = 1.31 \times \sqrt{\frac{p_t - p_s}{p_t}}$$

For all velocities we have:

$$M = \sqrt{\frac{2}{k-1} \times \left[\left(\frac{p_c}{p_s}\right)^{\left(\frac{k-1}{k}\right)} - 1\right]}$$

Since mach number can be expressed in terms of pressure ratio $p_t - p_s/p_t$, it is more convenient to use this as a calibration parameter than the mach number itself, or an approximate equivalent $p_1 - p_2/p_1$.

The expression is then used for calibration of pressure probes and is: M_r = mach number ratio.

If calculated with a slide rule, the error would be too great and would probably exceed the 1/2% for the first three equations.

Where single pressures or pressure ratios occur in the equations, absolute pressure must be used. When a differential appears, gage pressures can be used, or better still, the differential may be measured directly.

Adiabatic Equations. When work is performed on a gaseous medium or derived from it without any transfer of heat, pressures, densities and temperatures are related as follows:

$$\left(\frac{p_1}{\rho_1}\right)^k = \left(\frac{p_2}{\rho_2}\right)^k$$

$$\frac{\rho_1}{\rho_2} = \left(\frac{p_1}{p_2}\right)^{\frac{1}{k}}$$

$$\frac{T_1}{T_2} = \left(\frac{p_1}{p_2}\right)^{\frac{k-1}{k}}$$

Any rapid expansion or compression in a cylinder or turbine is assumed to follow this relation as a first approximation.

Total and Static Pressure and Temperature. Static pressure p_s and total pressure p_t are the pressures of the gaseous or liquid media moving at free stream velocity and the same fluid stagnated by being brought to rest suddenly in striking an obstruction, or passing through a diffuser. This results, in the case of a gaseous medium, in adiabatic compression, which raises the temperature as well as the pressure. Static temperature T_s and total temperature T_t are corresponding temperatures in a gaseous medium, under free stream conditions and when stagnated. These pressures and temperatures are related as the adiabatic equation:

$$\frac{T_t}{T_s} = \left(\frac{p_t}{p_s}\right)^{\frac{k-1}{k}}$$

Total and static temperatures can also be expressed in terms of the velocity equation:

$$T_t - T_s = \frac{V_2}{2g \times J \times C_p}$$

and for dry air:

$$T_1 - T_s = \frac{V^2}{12,000}$$

Total temperature is important in itself as a measure of the total energy per pound of gas, but is also important in being the only temperature that can be measured accurately. It is impossible to measure static temperature directly, because boundary layer friction always creates a temperature rise adjacent to a fixed probe, even when the gas is not deliberately stagnated. By designing proper

stagnation shields, total temperature can be accurately measured and static temperature can be calculated from it by using the above three equations.

Unshielded probes at low temperatures and high velocities, where conduction and radiation errors are negligible, indicate a temperature between total and static temperature. A bare wire probe indicates static temperature plus about 75% of the differential, $T_t - T_s$. At a velocity of 1,000 feet per second (or 400 meters per second) this means an error of about 21°F (or 6.1°C) below total temperature and 62°F (or 16.6°C) above static temperature.

Thermodynamic Static Points and Physical Properties. The three measurements p_t, p_s and T_t are sufficient for calculation of velocity and T_s, T_s and p_s together define the thermodynamic static point from which internal energy and density can be calculated. They also determine such physical properties as viscosity and conductivity.

Energy. The total energy input into a gaseous stream is measured by the total temperature rise:

$$\frac{Q_{12}}{J \times c_p} + \frac{E_{12}}{J \times c_p} = T_{t2} - T_{t1}$$

Weight Flow and Volume Flow. The general equations for all liquids and gaseous media are:

$$W = c_d \times A \times V_{max} \times \rho_s$$
$$Q = c_d \times A \times V_{max}$$

With a smooth approach nozzle, c_d can be as high as 0.995 and is rarely below 0.95, the difference from 1.000 being caused by the boundary layer in the throat. With a plate orifice, the flow contracts beyond the plate, so the flow area

Fluid Power: Pneumatics

is less than the nozzle area and the coefficient c_d has to allow for this, so it averages about 0.60. With both types of orifices additional corrections are included in c_d to correct for difference between measured pressure drop and the drop corresponding to V_{max}, the main correction being for velocity of approach.

In terms of measured variables, the equation for liquid and gaseous media when $p_1 - p_2/p_1$ is below 0.025, is:

$$W = [\sqrt{2g \times \rho_s \times (p_1 - p_2)}] \times c_d{}^A$$

For higher velocities of gaseous media a correction must be applied, not only for the effect of compressibility and measured velocity, but also on the orifice coefficient.

Compressor and Turbine Efficiencies. These efficiencies can be determined for overall performance, as well

as performance of each stage, by the use of probes alone without any mechanical measurements of thrust or horsepower. The efficiencies are adiabatic shaft efficiencies, or roughly equal to indicated efficiencies as measured on steam engines, not brake efficiencies, since they do not include the effect of bearing and gear friction. For compressors we have:

$$\eta_a = \frac{\overline{T}_{t1}\left[\left(\dfrac{\overline{p}_{t2}}{\overline{p}_{t1}}\right)^{\frac{k-1}{k}} - 1\right]}{\overline{T}_{t2} - \overline{T}_{t1}}$$

and for turbines we have:

$$\eta_a = \frac{(\overline{T}_{t1} - \overline{T}_{t2})\left(\dfrac{\overline{p}_{t1}}{\overline{p}_{t2}}\right)^{\frac{k-1}{k}}}{\overline{T}_{t1}\left[\left(\dfrac{\overline{p}_{t1}}{\overline{p}_{t2}}\right)^{\frac{k-1}{k}} - 1\right]}$$

Review Questions

1. Describe the beneficial effects of installing filters in pneumatic lines.

2. What adverse effect should be considered when a filter is added to a supply line?

3. Describe the main function of a filter element.

4. What is usually the range in size of contaminating particles filtered out in

filter elements for industrial use?

5. Where is a drip-leg automatic drain used? What is its main function?

6. What is considered standard air, and what is the identifying letter in the metric system?

7. Why is a pressure regulator used in a pneumatic system?

8. Describe the functional advantage of

a pressure relieving type instrument.

9. What adverse effect should be considered when a pressure regulator is added to a supply line?

10. Why is a lubricator used in a pneumatic supply line and what is the main principle of operation?

11. Describe the principal operating parts of a simple spray gun and how pressurized air performs this operation.

12. What is an aneroid barometer?

13. Describe the operation of a bourdon pressure gage.

14. What is a pitot tube?

15. Name some of the common instruments used for measuring fluid pressure with a pitot tube?

SEE END OF BOOK FOR ANSWERS TO QUESTIONS

Industrial Applications

There are innumerable cases where a gaseous medium, generally air, is used to perform useful work in industry. Variations are almost limitless, and space in this chapter allows only a few examples to stimulate the imagination as to what really can be done with pneumatic power.

In most industrial plants the pneumatic pressure generated by compression and stored in a receiver tank is about 100 psi, or 7 kg/cm². As you have learned in previous chapters, a certain amount of pressure drop is unavoidable, and pneumatic tools are designed for maximum efficiency at an operating pressure of 80 to 90 psi, or 5.6 to 6.3 kg/cm². In order to stay within this range, every effort should be made to design the circuits with adequate capacities, using large diameter pipes with few bends and permitting sufficient flow with minimum restrictions. In some cases it may even be economical and advisable to install a booster pump to keep the pressure within this range. This may be of importance particularly where the majority of applications are just for cleaning or similar uses where the pressure has dropped to 60 to 65 psi, or 4.2 to 4.6 kg/cm², while an isolated use of a high quality tool is required.

Examples of Actual Pneumatic Applications

In previous chapters throughout the text we have discussed various types of ordinary pneumatic applications. Now we are ready to examine some more interesting examples of actual applications in use today. From these we can infer, correctly, that some of these will lead to further developments in years to come.

Improved Machine Slides

A fine application of pneumatics that has not yet been utilized to its full potential is that of applying compressed air under a heavy machine tool slide, thus making it possible to move the massive slide with a small force. The resistance between the air and a solid body above it is very small at slow rates of speed.

In making accurate adjustments of a heavy machine tool slide in small increments, a common phenomenon known as "stick slip" is encountered when the heavy slide is sliding on plain bearings. After making a noticeable adjustment it may sometimes be observed that no motion of the slide has taken place. Then, after adjusting it a little more, the slide may suddenly move a considerable amount, going beyond the intended adjustment. The energy applied to move the slide in the first instance has been stored up in the elasticity of the adjusting media until enough additional energy has been applied to overcome the friction of the slide. This condition can be entirely eliminated when the slide is suspended a very minute amount on an air cushion.

Only 100 psi applied to an area of one square foot (or 7 kg/cm² applied to an area of one square meter) would exert a force of 14,400 lb (or 70,000 kg). Since one cubic foot of pure iron weighs approximately 491 lb (or one cubic meter of this iron weighs 7,819 kg), it is easily seen that this pressure would support a column of iron measuring 1 ft × 1 ft × 29 ft high (or one square meter of iron almost 9 meters high). Then if this pressure has dropped to 60 psi (or 4.2 kg/cm²), this reduced pressure would still support a column over 17 feet high (or 5 meters high).

Fig. 8–1 illustrates an actual case. Here a machine slide C, with superstructure D, slides on a bed B. The slide C and superstructure D weigh a total of 1,300 lb (or 590 kg). The area of slide C is 9 square ft (approximately 0.835 square meter) or

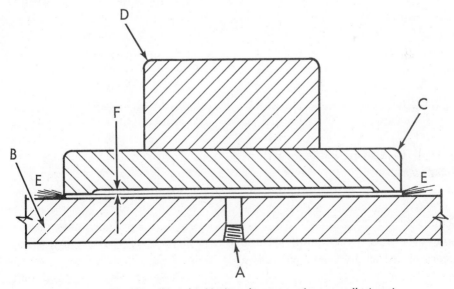

Fig. 8–1. Machine slide raised by low air pressure for easy adjustment.

9 × 144 = 1,296 square inches (above 8,350 square centimeters). Pressure required to lift the slide and superstructure would therefore be 1,300/1,296 = 1 psi, approximately, or 590/8,350 = 0.0707 kg/cm² in the metric system.

Therefore if a pressure regulator of the type described in Chapter 7 is adjusted to only 5 psi, or 0.35 kg/cm², this would be more than enough pressure to keep the slide C a minute distance above bed B. With such a low unit pressure, the escaping air around the edges at E would hardly be noticeable. It is important, however, to make sure that the slide is controlled in all directions, because a small inclination from the horizontal plane would let the slide move under the force of gravity if not controlled.

In operation, the air enters at A, fills up the shallow recessed area F and escapes to the atmosphere at edges E. Recess F may be only a few thousandths of an inch, say 0.005″ or 0.127 mm. A slide of this type, cushioned by air, was successfully applied by the author many years ago.

Air Cushion Vehicles (ACV's)

Much research has been carried out in this area of engineering over a period of years and gave rise to the development of the Hovercraft, a British industry. This type of transportation vehicle was invented by Sir Christopher S. Cockerell, CBE, FRS, who was awarded the Howard N. Potts medal of the U. S. Franklin Institute in 1965, the Royal Medal of the Royal Society in London (followed by election to its Fellowship), the RAC Diamond Jubilee Trophy, the Thulin Medal of the Swedish Society of Aeronautics, the Philadelphia John Scott Award, and, in 1966, the Albert Medal of the Royal Society of Arts.

This type of vehicle is generally known as an *air cushion vehicle* (ACV) and is supported with a cushion of air generated and retained below the vehicle with sufficient pressure to support the machine so it rides clear of the surface, thus reducing the friction to an extent never before achieved and making it possible to drive the vehicle horizontally with considerably less power than for other types of vehicles.

The ACV was made possible by the development of a flexible segmental skirt which would conform closely to any irregular surface. Further development of the skirt has resulted from actual experience in cross-Channel commercial services of the craft.

Fig. 8–2 shows the same hovercraft shown as Fig. 1–3 in Chapter 1. In Fig. 8–2 the vehicle is actually located on land, ready to proceed across the English Channel.

B is the rear section of the skirt, which is flexible to adjust to unevenness of the terrain. Four propellers are seen at A. These propellers drive the hovercraft horizontally, and since the ship is actually lifted a considerable distance above the rough surface by the air confined inside the skirt B, the horizontal friction when traveling horizontally is very low. The height the Hovercraft is lifted above the surface depends on the design of the skirt B underneath the ship.

Possibilities in this line for industrial applications are many, such as material handling over rough, uneven floors in restricted places or moving heavy machine tools on air cushions in industrial plants.

Perhaps the most spectacular application of ACV's so far has been the relocating of two oil storage tanks for Esso Petroleum Company. The method developed by HDL at Hythe, England employs a special version of the segmental skirt

Fig. 8−2. Hovercraft ready to take off. (Courtesy of British Rail Hovercraft Ltd.)

which enables it to be attached to the tank by two steel straps around the bottom end of the tank.

Hovertrailers, using the same principles as hovercrafts, have been used for carrying exceptionally heavy equipment, especially electrical generating equipment, over bridges or soft ground. A 30-ton hovertrailer is used for transporting oil and mineral drilling equipment over the tundra areas of the Canadian Artic Region.

A high-speed hoverkiln, in which an air cushion is used to support the load during firing in the pottery industry by Shelley Furnaces Ltd. of Stoke-on-Trent, England is claimed to cut fuel cost by half and to reduce the firing time.

A hoverbed, in which severely burned hospital patients float on a cushion of warm air, has been developed and successfully tested.

A small hovercraft, 14 ft long, weighing 1/2 ton, has been designed in Britain for crop spraying and inspection. Instead of a flexible skirt as on the hovercraft, it has an inflatable plastic bag around its base to prevent damage to crops.

Pneumatically Preloaded Bearings

Air pressure may be used for accurate, resilient preload of a pair of anti-friction bearings in industrial use. The air pressure may be accurately controlled thermostatically if the bearings should heat up due to too much preload.

Fig. 8−3 illustrates an effective application of pneumatic power by the author in preloading bearings. The pressure applied to the outer race B of the single ball bearing by piston C pulls the inner races D in firm contact with the outer races E.

When the main bearing load then is applied during service, initial looseness or elasticity has already been removed, thus minimizing inaccuracy in bearing performance due to load. The pneumatic power is applied to piston C through a valve operated by an electrical signal from a relay in the control panel as soon

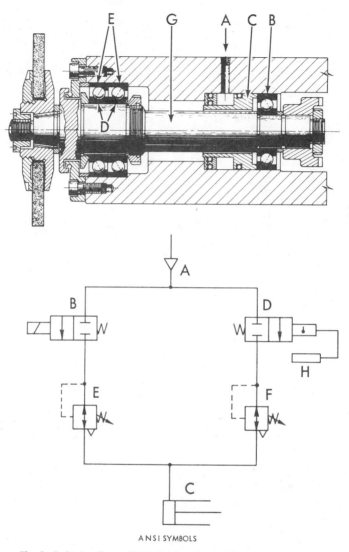

ANSI SYMBOLS

Fig. 8–3. Preloading anti-friction bearings with compressed air.

as the motor driving the spindle is start-ed. If the bearing should heat up during service above the maximum recommend-ed temperature, a temperature-sensing device can be arranged to change the power supply to a lower pressure.

The pneumatic diagram is shown with ANSI symbols. Here, *A* indicates the supply line, *B* is a solenoid-operated, spring-loaded, two-position normally

closed valve. As soon as the main drive motor is started, an electrical signal from a relay in the control panel will cause the solenoid to open the valve, directing the flow of the gaseous medium through a pressure-adjustable and relieving valve *E*. The pressure of this valve would be ad-justed to a value recommended by the bearing manufacturer for actual running conditions.

The gaseous medium then normally continues to cylinder C. If the bearings during service should heat up above a value normally recommended, a temperature-sensing device H will deactivate the solenoid in valve B, closing this valve. At the same time, it will open the spring-loaded normally closed valve D, causing the gaseous medium to flow through an adjustable pressure relieving valve F, which is set to a lower pressure than valve E. When the temperature has been lowered to a normally recommended value, valve D will close and valve B will open, being actuated by electrical relays. The electrical circuit in this case is not shown.

It may be of interest to know that no energy is wasted by the pneumatic system in preloading the bearings in this manner.

Air Gages for Precision Measurement

Fig. 8–4 illustrates the operation of an air gage by which the bore of the inside

race of a tapered roller bearing may be measured to very close tolerances using an air stream. This type of inspection has several advantages over conventional gaging:

1. It can be performed while the bearing race is in process or after the hole is finished.
2. The hole being measured is automatically cleaned by the blast of compressed air, removing oil and other contaminants for accurate inspection.
3. Wear and maintenance of this type of instrument is very low.
4. After initial adjustment for a particular job, this instrument provides high accuracy and is easily checked against standard gages.
5. It is not unusual to find magnifications as high as 10,000 to 1. Thus a variation of 0.00001″ (or 0.00025 mm) would show 0.1″ (or 2.5 mm) on the calibrated instrument.

ANSI symbols shown in the diagram are: A is a high precision pressure regulator such as the one described and illustrated in Chapter 7. B is a calibrated flow meter, and C is a hole plug with restricted air passages, with arrows indicating that variation in space between bore and plugs is expected. The actual plug is shown in the bore at D.

Pneumatic Control for Calendar Rolls

Fig. 8–5 shows schematically how air pressure is used to control calendar roll loading. This is one of a great many variations that are possible using the same principles.

This illustration shows an arrangement of calendar rolls used for the manufacturing of paper. Air is supplied at constant preselected pressure through a pressure regulator A to a diaphragm type

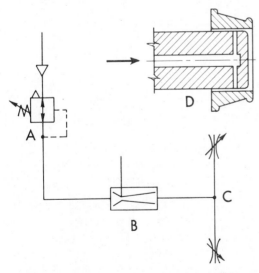

Fig. 8–4. Air gage. (Courtesy of Bellofram Corporation)

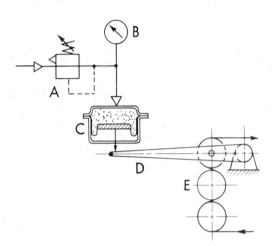

Fig. 8–5. Pneumatic system to control calendar roll loading. (Courtesy of Bellofram Corporation)

actuator C. This actuator then applies pressure to lever D, which applies a high tonnage pressure on calendar rolls E, squeezing the paper to a close tolerance thickness as it is being processed.

The pressure indicator B may be calibrated directly in tonnage. After the correct tonnage has been determined for the right thickness of paper, the precision pressure regulator A will hold this tonnage and thus the thickness of paper to a constant value, with no waste in pneumatic energy.

Pneumatic Measurement of Web Tension

Fig. 8–6 shows schematically how air pressure is used to measure web tension in the printing industry. In the printing of paper it is often desirable to have a constant monitoring of the actual tension on the paper web as it is being processed. This can easily be arranged as is shown.

Air is supplied to the pressure regulator A. As the tension F in the paper web varies, causing the roll C to swing through a limited path, lever D transmits this variation to pressure regulator A through rod E in the pressure regulator. The indicator at B, showing the variation, may be calibrated to values easily recognized by the operator, or a pressure switch may energize an audible signal when the tension exceeds the maximum.

Surge Control System

Fig. 8–7 shows schematically a surge control system to control pressure fluctuations in a liquid, using a gaseous medium. Pump A (a hydraulic pump) is pumping water from a reservoir E to tank C on a higher level. If the pump is suddenly shut off, the air-charged accumulator or surge arrestor D will supply air pressure, eliminating voids in the hydraulic

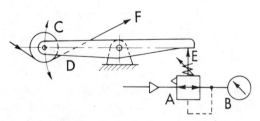

Fig. 8–6. Web tension measurement. (Courtesy of Bellofram Corporation)

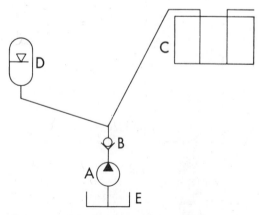

Fig. 8–7. Surge control system. (Courtesy of American Air Filter Co., Inc., Pulsco Division)

system, thus preventing resurge, and will also eliminate high pressures. Check valve *B* prevents the water from returning to the pump.

Pneumatic Power Chuck

Fig. 8–8 shows a typical installation of a pneumatically operated power chuck for a modern machine tool. The pneumatic

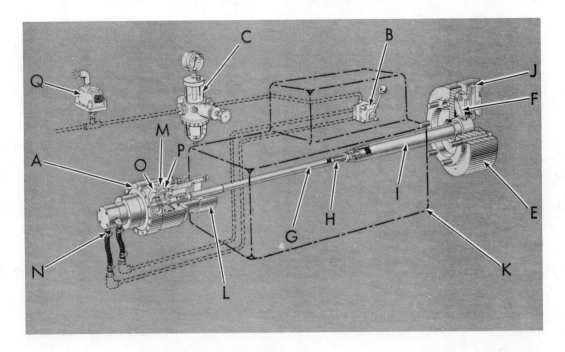

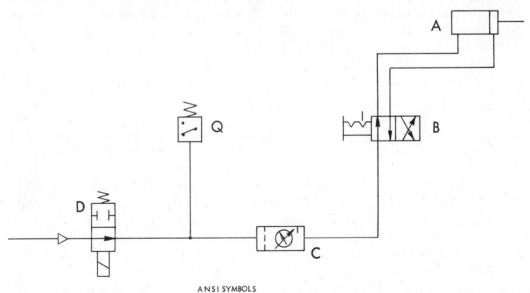

ANSI SYMBOLS

Fig. 8–8. Pneumatic power chuck for machine tool. (Courtesy of Cushman Industries, Inc.)

working components are also shown with ANSI symbols.

A is a double-acting cylinder. *B* is a manually operated four-way, two-position valve. *C* is a simplified symbol showing a combination of air line filter, pressure regulator, and lubricator, with pressure-indicating gage. *D* is a two-way spring-loaded, solenoid-operated normally closed valve.

Valve B is shown in the unloaded position, which is indicated by the short line over the inside notch in the ANSI symbol. Lever *F* on chuck *E* is then in the forward (out) position, pushing the jaws *J* radially outward to the released position, ready to receive the workpiece.

The gaseous medium then pressurizes the left side of piston *M* at *O* in cylinder *A*, pushing draw rod *G* to the right. Draw rod *G* is connected by screw *H* to a hollow tube *I* so the chuck can receive a workpiece having a shank.

The cylinder assembly is fastened to the headstock *K* of the machine tool with the adapter *L*. At *N* is shown a swivel connection for the pneumatic lines. *C* in the illustration shows the air line filter at the bottom, the adjusting screw on the near side for adjusting the pressure to the desired value as indicated by the gage at the top of the lubricator on the combined component. *Q* shows a pressure switch which will stop the main drive motor of the machine tool if the pneumatic pressure should fall below the minimum acceptable value.

D, shown only with the ANSI symbol, is a normally closed two-way, two-position, solenoid-operated valve. As soon as the electric power is turned on for the machine tool, the solenoid operates the valve *D* to the open position as shown in the diagram, permitting the air to flow to valve *B*.

When the workpiece has been loaded in the chuck *E*, valve *B* is manually operated to pressurize side *P* of piston *M*. Air pressure then puts draw rod *G*, bolt *H*, and tube *I* in tension, pulling lever *F* inward to the left. This moves jaws *J* radially inward to clamp the workpiece.

Rotary Motion by Linear Actuator

In industrial manufacturing plants rotary motion is often used to perform operations in processing equipment. Without a thorough investigation it might appear that the best solution would be a rotary actuator. This, however, is not the case. With a little ingenuity in design, rotary motion can always be performed much easier, at low cost, with a linear actuator. With careful analysis it has been found that not only the initial cost can be reduced but also the operating and maintenance costs can be considerably lower. Rotary actuators are very difficult to seal because in many cases they must be sealed on the end surfaces as well as on the peripheral surfaces.

Many clamping devices require rotary motion. Fig. 8–9 illustrates a device for performing rotary motion with a linear actuator.

C is a double-end piston which is effectively sealed with O-rings *G*. This piston is provided with teeth *E* in the middle section, engaging spur gear *F*. The spur gear is fastened to a righthand screw *H*, which is provided with a head *I* to keep it from moving axially. Cap *L* encloses head *I* of screw *H*. O-rings *J* in end caps *K* provide a perfect seal.

If pressure is applied to port *B*, the piston *C* will move in the direction of the arrow to the left. This motion turns the spur gear *F* in a counterclockwise direction, moving clamp block *M* in the direc-

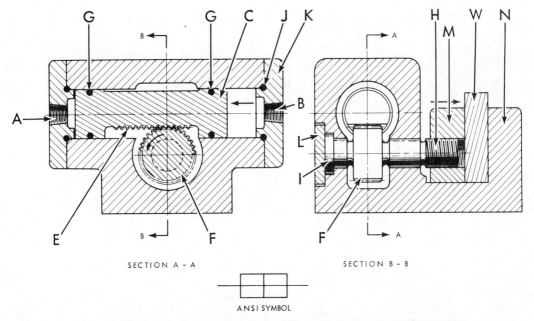

SECTION A – A   SECTION B – B

ANSI SYMBOL

Fig. 8–9. Rotary-actuated clamping device operated by linear pneumatic actuator.

tion of the arrow, clamping workpiece *W* between *M* and *N*.

When pressure is applied to port *A*, the piston *C* moves in the opposite direction, releasing the clamping pressure from the workpiece.

Rotary Unloading System

Fig. 8–10 illustrates schematically a system for gradual unloading that has many uses. This is a good, practical example of air being used in conjunction with oil for performing work.

Because air is used as the driving power, the unit can be stopped at any position of the cycle and the container *J* can be held at any position with no consumption of power or waste of energy. And, because oil is used as the final drive medium, very accurate speed adjustments are possible. The device shown in Fig. 8–10 is another example of how rotary

motion can be performed with a spur gear, which is mounted on shaft *O* driven by a spur gear rack on the central portion of a double-end piston similar in design to the one previously shown in Fig. 8–9.

Because the control is performed with oil, very close step-by-step unloading of container *J* is possible. The compressed air enters through air line filter, pressure regulator and airline lubricator at *A*, where there is also a pressure indicator shown in the ANSI symbol.

The control valve *A* is a spring-centered, manually operated 4-way, 3-position valve. The air line pressure is blocked when the valve is in the neutral position, or centered, and the cylinder ports are on exhaust.

By actuating one end of valve *A* the air pressure is directed to the top portion of tank *C*. The oil in this tank is then under pressure to the normally closed valve *E*.

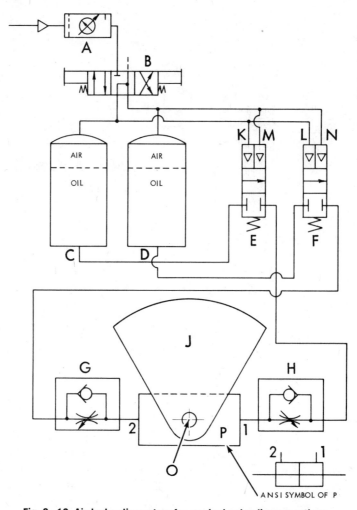

Fig. 8−10. Air-hydraulic system for gradual unloading operations.

The air flowing to the tank C is also directed to air pilot valves K and L. Oil then flows from tank C through the actuated valve E and through the free-flow bypass portion of adjustable valve H to port 1 of rotary actuator P. The oil flowing out of port 2 is controlled by the adjustable portion of valve G, controlling the speed of container J to the preselected rate as it is descending. As soon as valve B is released to center itself, container J will stop.

To raise the container, valve B is actuated in the opposite direction. Air then flows to tank D and operates pilot valves M and N to send the oil pressure in tank D through valve F and the bypass portion of valve G to port 2 of rotary actuator P. The oil flowing out of port 1 is then controlled by the adjustable portion of valve H to raise container J at a preselected speed. Many variables of this arrangement are possible.

Automobile Elevator

Fig. 8–11 shows schematically the operation of an automobile elevator of the

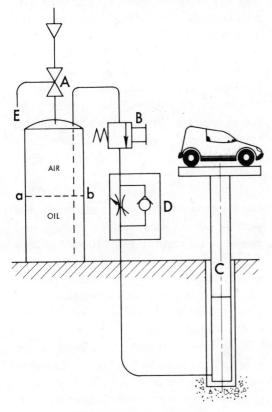

Fig. 8–11. Automobile elevator.

type used by gasoline service stations and repair shops. This is a familiar use of a simple linear actuator — in this case a vertically mounted underground cylinder for lifting an automobile. Here, air is the energy medium and oil, which also serves as a good lubricant for the piston, transmits the force of the air to the object to be lifted. No energy is wasted as the automobile is held at any desired height while work on it is being performed.

Air supply is turned on at shutoff valve *A*. This builds up the pressure so the elevator is ready for an instantaneous start. As soon as normally closed hydraulic valve *B* is opened, the pressure from the air on liquid surface *a*–*b* is transmitted to the bottom of piston *C*, raising the automobile.

The liquid bypasses the adjustable side of valve *D* for maximum speed-up.

To lower the automobile, the shutoff valve *A* is closed, putting the air in the reservoir on exhaust at *E*. The oil under the piston *C* can then flow only through the adjustable side of valve *D* for a slow downward motion. This may, of course, be done with the motion of one handle, but for simplicity it is illustrated as shown.

Possible Solution of an Ancient Mystery

We have discussed all the practical examples of pneumatic power for industrial use and can afford to consider a conjecture that has no historical proof but is a plausible explanation of a mystery that has puzzled many people for ages.

Some years ago the author stood in the King's Chamber, which is approximately 160 feet above the base of the inside of the Great Pyramid of Khufu at Giza, near present-day Cairo, Egypt. The original dimensions of the this pyramid were approximately as shown in Fig. 8–12. This massive structure, classed as one of the Seven Wonders of the World, covers an area of over 13 acres, standing on solid

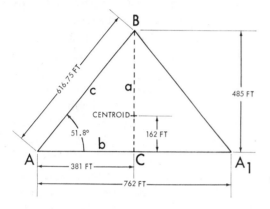

Fig. 8–12. Approximate dimensions of the Great Pyramid at the time it was built, about 4,660 years ago. Most of the smooth, white facing masonry on the sides and apex of the pyramid has been removed for use as building stones. Also, sand has accumulated around the base. These facts, together with some natural erosion, have reduced the original dimensions.

rock covered with sand that extends many miles in all directions. Its construction, begun around 2680 or 2690 B.C., required from 12 to 20 years to complete, with a labor force estimated between 40,000 and 100,000 men.

Originally the Great Pyramid contained about 2,300,000 building blocks cut from limestone or granite. According

to the Greek historian Herodotus, writing about it in the 5th century B.C., the work took 100,000 men 20 years to build. Modern archeologists doubt these figures and have reduced his estimate considerably, but the fact of the stones remains. The majority of these building blocks were rectangular pieces of limestone approximately 2 × 4 × 2 feet. Some of the blocks in the inside chambers were larger and made of polished red granite. The blocks were set in place by some method that has never been explained, and there have been many unsatisfactory conjectures.

Unsolved questions are how these blocks, each weighing an average of 2,400 pounds, could have been moved and raised to a height of over 40 stories at a time thousands of years before there were any derricks or power machinery of any kind. As a matter of fact, even power derricks would not have worked well on shifting sand.

The most common conjecture about raising the blocks is that they were somehow transported on a long, inclined plane of dirt and sand that was gradually built up in increments of about two feet in height for each tier of stones.

As far as it goes, this conjecture has a lot of merit. With a tremendous amount of manual labor this could have been done. Suppose the sand ramp shown in Fig. 8–13 were 30 ft wide in the center and long enough for a maximum incline

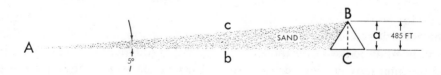

Fig. 8–13. An inclined plane of dirt and sand may have lead to the apex of the Great Pyramid when it was built, around 2,680 B.C.

of 5°. Here the triangle ABC is a right triangle. Angle $A = 5°$ and altitude $a = 485$ ft. By the Law of Sines, c/sin C = a/sin A, but angle C is a right angle, so its sine = 1, so that c = a/sin A. The sine of a 5° angle = 0.0872. Then c = 485/0.0872 = 5,562 ft (approx.), a little over 1 mile, which is 5,280 ft. The distance along the base line b is then b/c = cos A, or b = c cos A. The cosine of 5° = 0.9962. Substituting numbers, b = 5,562 × 0.9962 = 5,541 ft (approx.), which is only 261 ft beyond a mile. However, sand at the base line would extend only to the side of the pyramid, which is 1/2 of the pyramid base length from the center at C. So this amount, 381 ft, would be subtracted from b; that is, 5,541 − 381 = 5,160 ft, the distance from point A to the pyramid's base. And this is less than 1 mile.

Another favorable fact is that fewer blocks would be required for each tier above the base. The center of mass, and average condition, would be at the centroid, 1/3 the height from the base to the apex, or 1/3 × 485 ft = 161.666 . . . , say 162 ft. If *point A* were left at 5,160 ft from the pyramid's base, *angle A* to the centroid would be figured as: tan A = 162/5160 = 0.0314, and this is the tangent of 1.8°, a very slight incline.

The hard part of the problem is how the heavy blocks could be moved up the incline. The usual conjectures suppose that these blocks were pushed or dragged over large poles or bars which acted as wheels, or that some sort of carts with wide wheels supported the blocks. Such methods would not work well on sand or sandy soil, however, and the effort would be tremendous. A much better method would be essentially the same as used for moving heavy machine tables and hovercrafts, moving the limestone blocks on cushions of compressed air. This would not be im-

possible even thousands of years ago.

The surface area on the bottom of each block is about 24″ × 48″, and the weight is about 2,400 lb. The unit pressure is therefore 2,400/24 × 48 = 2.08 psi. About 2.1 psi above atmospheric pressure would lift the block off the ground. This is a very low pressure for compressed air, but with just this much pressure the block could be suspended above the surface. There would be no complications, because the blocks are symmetrical and pressure could be applied equally to the entire bottom surface of the block; also, no force would tend to move the block laterally.

Nowadays, with compressors available, the source of pressure would be no problem, but how about 4,660 years ago?

The answer to the last question is easy. Fabric was abundant in those days, so a runner of fabric could be laid on the sand along the ramp. A present-day compressor was not available, of course, but low pressures could be obtained with a manually operated bellows-type compressor much as air is compressed in an old-fashioned blacksmith's forge bellows.

A wooden structure such as that shown in D of Fig. 8–14 could be constructed with a flexible skirt, as for the hovercraft. For simplicity, the skirt is omitted from the drawing. Section $A–A$ in Fig. 8–14 shows such a compressor. Animal skin or airtight fabric was available for the compressor lining E. This lining could be fastened to the uprights F, which could be secured to the base D. The lining could also be fastened to the lever arm G.

As the lever arm is moved through angle α, the air inside lining E is compressed to a higher pressure and escapes through an opening in lining E at the bottom, moving to the bottom of base D. The opening of the lining E at the bottom could be constructed similar to flap J,

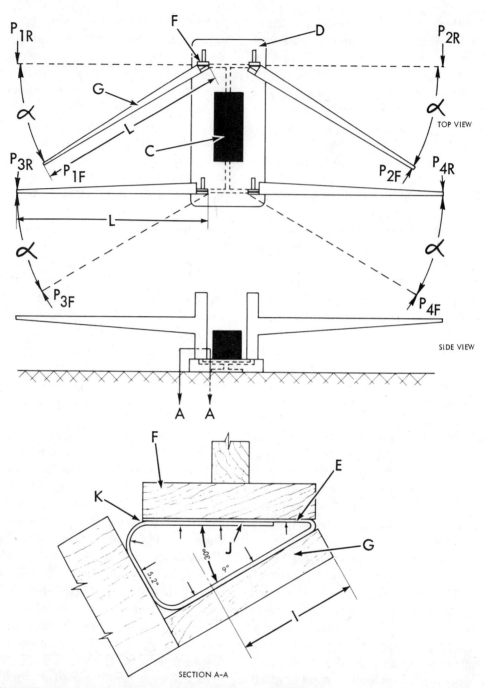

Fig. 8–14. Rig for transporting stone blocks to build the Great Pyramid, using manually operated bellows-type compressor to obtain the low-pressure air to support the 2,400-lb block by an air cushion. This rig could be operated by a 4-man team of stone bearers.

which prevents pressure from leaking out to the atmosphere.

Pressure, as you know, is exerted equally, perpendicularly to all surfaces. This flap would prevent pressure under base *D* from returning to the bellows chamber when lever *G* is returned.

When lever *G* is returned, a partial vacuum would be created inside lining *E*, and flap *J* would permit the atmospheric pressure to enter at *K*.

To raise the pressure (to about 2.1 psi above atmospheric pressure), the lever *G* would have to move only a very small angle. As soon as the pressure is raised a very little above what is required to keep the base *D* off the ground, the base *D*, with block *C*, could be moved forward with little effort.

Assume that angle α is 30° at the beginning of compression, and the long adjacent leg of the lining *E* is 9 inches. The sides opposite to the lining would then be approximately 5.2 inches in length. If *h* is 72 inches, the initial volume V_1 would be 5.2 × 9 × 72/2 = 1,685 cubic inches. To raise the pressure 2.1 psi, we would have:

$$V_2 = \frac{V_1 \times p_1}{p_2} = \frac{1,685 \times 14.7}{16.8} = 1,474 \text{ in.}^3$$

$$V_1 - V_2 = V_3;\ 1,685 - 1474 = 211 \text{ in.}^3$$

$$V_3 = \frac{9 \times 72 \times y}{2},\ y = \frac{9 \times 72}{2 \times 211} = 1.536 \text{ in.}$$

In other words, leg 5.2″ of lining would have to be shortened to about 1.54″, so that lever *G* would have to move less than 9°. However, in action there are two levers which could be moved simultaneously, so these levers would only have to move about 4-1/2 degrees to raise the block and start moving it forward.

The operation would be as follows:

Four men would operate the rig, with one man at the end of each lever. To start, the levers would be positioned as shown by the solid lines in the plan view of Fig. 8–14. The two men in front would then take 3 short steps (2-1/2 ft per step) to move the levers to the dotted line position. This moves the base *D*, with stone block *C*, forward, while the two men at the rear are resting, holding their levers so they are retracted to the dotted line.

As soon as the two men in front stop, the two rear men take 3 short steps forward while the two men in front are resting, holding their levers until they again assume the starting position.

The force required to move each lever forward would be figured in this way:

$$L = 15 \text{ ft} = 180 \text{ in.}$$

$$l = 6 \text{ in.}$$

$$\text{Then, } \frac{2,400 \times 6}{180 \times 2} = 40 \text{ lb.}$$

A few blocks inside the pyramid are heavier than the block in our illustration. These heavier blocks could, of course, be moved just as easily by doubling or tripling the number of levers and men. Also, it would be easy to design and construct fairly shallow containers for sand and dirt in the same manner as the stones, to facilitate building the ramp.

Many seemingly impossible problems have been solved by application of a gaseous medium. There is, of course, no proof that the method demonstrated was used. It is, however, a plausible conjecture. If it seems a bit far-fetched to you now, think about it again sometime when you are traveling in a 150-ton jet airplane 37,000 ft above the ground or ocean, supported by the lift of air on the wings.

Comparison of Pneumatic and Hydraulic Systems

As was pointed out in the introductory Chapter 1, there are two basic media used for fluid power for industrial use:

1. Gaseous Media
2. Liquid Media

Each of these two media for transmitting a force has several subdivisions. We have found in studying the gaseous media that air is the principal medium in importance and the one most commonly used. In the study of hydraulics for industrial use you will discover that oil is the principal and most commonly used liquid medium.

Basic laws of behavior for the two media, gaseous and liquid, are so different that they are best studied separately. Although hydraulic systems now outnumber pneumatics systems in industry, pneumatics was used earlier than hydraulics as a principal source for transmitting a force. Hydraulics was used to a limited extent, and at first the medium used was water. Besides its availability, water had the great advantage of having uniform density. However, it had the disadvantage of causing corrosion of the parts or materials it contacted.

It was not until oil could be economically refined that this medium was adopted as the principal liquid medium for fluid power. Another difficulty that delayed the widespread use of hydraulics by industry was that when oil was used as a medium for transmitting force for industrial processing and manufacturing machinery it was found that a gaseous medium could cause serious trouble if it was trapped or inadvertently introduced in the liquid medium. As we have seen in previous chapters, there are many applications where a gaseous medium is used as the primary driving force in conjunction with a secondary liquid medium to transmit this force. For these various reasons it is to our advantage to have a thorough understanding of the behavior of the gaseous media before making a detail study of the liquid media.

To say that one medium is superior to the other for fluid power applications is not correct. There are a great many factors to consider, so a thorough study should be made of both types of media before adopting one in preference to the other. In his long contact with many industrial processing plants, the author has found that the tendency has been to go more and more to the liquid media, especially for complicated industrial machinery where accuracy is of prime importance. With liquid as a medium there is no bounce on delivery. Because the gaseous medium is highly compressible, there is always a bounce, and this is more pronounced if the speed is high. In some instances, as we have seen, it is also true that the compressibility of a gaseous medium is its chief advantage.

Even in simple forms we have seen in our study of the gaseous media that they are often used in conjunction with liquid media to obtain the best results.

Some of the tools powered by a gaseous medium are identical or similar to the tools operated by a liquid medium. In many cases the only difference is the material used in their construction, because in all cases the material must be compatible with the fluid medium used. This is equally true of valves, accessory equipment of all kinds, and instruments. Pneumatic and hydraulic components are essentially the same in operation, differing only in details.

One important thing to consider is that the sealing of a gaseous powered component is more difficult than a similar component powered by hydraulic oil. For this reason the pneumatic tools require O-rings or other resilient sealing and very accurate machining. The liquid media, on the other hand, can be effectively sealed where two metal surfaces are sliding in close proximity provided the metal surfaces have been honed to a reasonably smooth finish. The hydraulic oil will then act as a lubricating medium. Some types of valves, such as ball valves, are highly effective for either pneumatic or hydraulic supply lines.

In proceeding through this book we saw that a valve was used for the purpose of starting, directing, and stopping flow of the gaseous medium. Also we found that a change in the valve could be initiated by various means:

1. Manual Operation
2. Mechanical Operation, by means of Cams
3. Pneumatic Operation
4. Electric Operation, by means of Solenoids
5. Springs

These various methods of operation are illustrated by simple ANSI symbols listed in Appendix A.

Timers are also available for holding a valve closed or open, following a preselected flow pattern, for a predetermined time. The electrical timers are more dependable and accurate than pneumatic or hydraulic timers, and they will energize or deenergize a solenoid operating the valve. These electrical timers are called *time delay relays*.

Many components described in this book are now identical or very similar to components used for hydraulic systems. The supply lines and fittings are also now identical or at least similar. In most cases the only question is compatibility of material to the medium used for transmission of power. In the past few years much progress has been made in the design and standardization of supply lines and fittings for fluid power.

Before taking up hydraulics, let us remember that in many cases a gaseous medium is the best source of power. This is particularly true for equipment of an auxiliary nature, such as:

1. Clamping Devices
2. Hoists
3. Nut Setters or Screwdrivers
4. Small Presses

For more complicated automatic machinery demanding high accuracy, the modern tendency is definitely to favor hydraulic systems, and where these machines are required the auxiliary equipment has also been changed to hydraulic. Pneumatic pressure in the average shop or factory seldom exceeds 100 psi (or 7 kg/cm²), whereas the average hydraulic pressure is from 200 to 600 psi (or 14 to 42 kg/cm²). Therefore, using the available hydraulic system, all working parts can be made much smaller while delivering the same force as a larger pneumatic part. Also, in a hydraulic system, lubrication is no problem.

Review Questions

1. Why may a booster pump be advisable for a pneumatic system in some cases?

2. What is the most economical pressure for most pneumatic systems in industrial plants?

3. (a) What unit pressure in psi would be required to suspend a machine slide weighing 1,000 lb and measuring 10×20 inches?

(b) What unit pressure in kg/cm² would be required to suspend a machine slide weighing 500 kg and measuring 25×50 cm?

4. Give some examples of how air cushions may be used commercially.

5. Give some examples of air cushions for industrial application.

6. Give two examples of how air pressure may be used in industry with no waste of pneumatic energy after pressure has been applied.

7. Give one example of how rotary motion can be performed with a linear actuator.

8. Give two examples of how pneumatic power may be used in conjunction with hydraulic power for performing useful work.

9. Name two of the main fluid media for transmitting power for industrial use.

10. Which fluid medium is superior for transmitting power?

11. Name some of the conditions to consider in determining whether a pneumatic component is useful for a hydraulic system.

12. What are some of the most common means for initiating a change in a control valve?

13. When is a timer used in a fluid power system and which type is most dependable and accurate?

SEE END OF BOOK FOR ANSWERS TO QUESTIONS

Appendices

Appendix

A

Appendix A:
ANSI Standard
Graphic Symbols for
Fluid Power Diagrams

1. Introduction

1.1 General
Fluid power systems are those that transmit and control power through use of a pressurized fluid (liquid or gas) within an enclosed circuit.

Types of symbols commonly used in drawing circuit diagrams for fluid power systems are Pictorial, Cutaway, and Graphic. These symbols are fully explained in the USA Standard Drafting Manual (Ref. 2).

1.1.1 *Pictorial symbols* are very useful for showing the interconnection of components. They are difficult to standardize from a functional basis.

1.1.2 *Cutaway symbols* emphasize construction. These symbols are complex to draw and the functions are not readily apparent.

1.1.3 *Graphic symbols* emphasize the function and methods of operation of components. These symbols are simple to draw. Component functions and methods of operation are obvious. Graphic symbols are capable of crossing language barriers, and can promote a universal understanding of fluid power systems.

Graphic symbols for fluid power systems should be used in conjunction with the graphic symbols for other systems published by the USA Standards Institute (Ref. 3–7 inclusive).

1.1.3.1 Complete graphic symbols are those which give symbolic representation of the component and all of its features pertinent to the circuit diagram.

1.1.3.2 Simplified graphic symbols are stylized versions of the complete symbols.

1.1.3.3 Composite graphic symbols are an organization of simplified or complete symbols. Composite symbols usually represent a complex component.

1.2 Scope and Purpose

1.2.1 *Scope*
This standard presents a system of graphic symbols for fluid power diagrams.

1.2.1.1 Elementary forms of symbols are:

Circles	Triangles	Lines
Squares	Arcs	Dots
Rectangles	Arrows	Crosses

1.2.1.2 Symbols using words or their abbreviations are avoided. Symbols capable of crossing language barriers are presented herein.

1.2.1.3 Component function rather than construction is emphasized by the symbol.

1.2.1.4 The means of operating fluid power components are shown as part of the symbol (where applicable).

1.2.1.5 This standard shows the basic symbols, describes the principles on which the symbols are based, and illustrates some representative composite symbols. Composite symbols can be devised for any fluid power component by combining basic symbols.
Simplified symbols are shown for commonly used components.

1.2.1.6 This standard provides basic symbols which differentiate between hydraulic and pneumatic fluid power media.

1.2.2 *Purpose*

1.2.2.1 The purpose of this standard is to provide a system of fluid power graphic symbols for industrial and educational purposes.

1.2.2.2 The purpose of this standard is to simplify design, fabrication, analysis, and service of fluid power circuits.

1.2.2.3 The purpose of this standard is to provide fluid power graphic symbols which are internationally recognized.

1.2.2.4 The purpose of this standard is to promote universal understanding of fluid power systems.

1.3 Terms and Definitions
Terms and corresponding definitions found in this standard are listed in Ref. 8.

2. Symbol Rules (See Section 10)

2.1 Symbols show connections, flow paths, and functions of components represented. They can indicate conditions occurring during transition from one flow path arrangement to another. Symbols do not indicate construction, nor do they indicate values, such as pressure, flow rate, and other component settings.

2.2 Symbols do not indicate locations of ports, direction of shifting of spools, or positions of actuators on actual component.

2.3 Symbols may be rotated or reversed without altering their meaning except in the cases of: a.) Lines to Reservoir, 4.1.1; b.) Vented Manifold, 4.1.2.3; c.) Accumulator, 4.2.

Extracted from USA Standard Graphic Symbols for Fluid Power Diagrams (USAS Y 32.10–1967) with the permission of the publisher. The American Society of Mechanical Engineers, United Engineering Center, 345 E. 47th Street, New York, N. Y. 10017.

NOTE: Name of the former United States of America Standards Institute (USAS) was changed in October, 1969, to American National Standards Institute, Inc. (ANSI)

2.4 Line Technique (See Ref. 1)

Keep line widths approximately equal. Line width does not alter meaning of symbols.

2.4.1 Solid Line

(Main line conductor, outline, and shaft)

2.4.2 Dash Line

(Pilot line for control)

2.4.3 Dotted Line

(Exhaust or Drain Line)

2.4.4 Center Line

(Enclosure outline)

2.4.5 Lines Crossing

(The intersection is not necessarily at a 90 deg angle.)

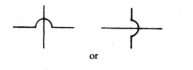

or

IEC

IEC

2.4.6 Lines Joining

IEC

or

IEC

2.5 Basic symbols may be shown any suitable size. Size may be varied for emphasis or clarity. Relative sizes should be maintained. (As in the following example.)

2.5.1 Circle and Semi-Circle

2.5.1.1 Large and small circles may be used to signify that one component is the "main" and the other the auxiliary.

2.5.2 Triangle

2.5.3 Arrow

2.5.4 Square

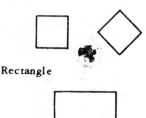

Rectangle

2.6 Letter combinations used as parts of graphic symbols are not necessarily abbreviations.

2.7 In multiple envelope symbols, the flow condition shown nearest an actuator symbol takes place when that control is caused or permitted to actuate.

2.8 Each symbol is drawn to show normal, at-rest, or neutral condition of component unless multiple diagrams are furnished showing various phases of circuit operation. Show an actuator symbol for each flow path condition possessed by the component.

2.9 An arrow through a symbol at approximately 45 degrees indicates that the component can be adjusted or varied.

2.10 An arrow parallel to the short side of a symbol, within the symbol, indicates that the component is pressure compensated.

2.11 A line terminating in a dot to represent a thermometer is the symbol for temperature cause or effect.

See Temperature Controls 7.9, Temperature Indicators and Recorders 9.1.2, and Temperature Compensation 10.16.3 and 4.

2.12 External ports are located where flow lines connect to basic symbol, except where component enclosure symbol is used.

External ports are located at intersections of flow lines and component enclosure symbol when enclosure is used, see Section 11.

2.13 Rotating shafts are symbolized by an arrow which indicates direction of rotation (assume arrow on near side of shaft).

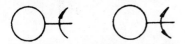

3. Conductor, Fluid

3.1 Line, Working (main)

3.2 Line, Pilot (for control)

3.3 Line, Exhaust and Liquid Drain

3.4 Line, sensing, etc. such as gage lines shall be drawn the same as the line to which it connects.

3.5 Flow, Direction of

   3.5.1 Pneumatic

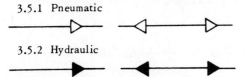

   3.5.2 Hydraulic

3.6 Line, Pneumatic
Outlet to Atmosphere

   3.6.1 Plain orifice, unconnectable

   3.6.2 Connectable orifice (e. g. Thread)

3.7 Line with Fixed Restriction

3.8 Line, Flexible

3.9 Station, Testing, measurement, or power take-off

   3.9.1 Plugged port

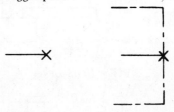

3.10 Quick Disconnect

   3.10.1 Without Checks

     Connected

     Disconnected

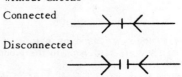

   3.10.2 With Two Checks

     Connected

     Disconnected

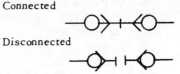

   3.10.3 With One Check

     Connected

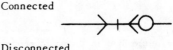

     Disconnected

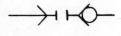

3.11 Rotating Coupling

Fluid Power: Pneumatics

4. Energy Storage and Fluid Storage

4.1 Reservoir

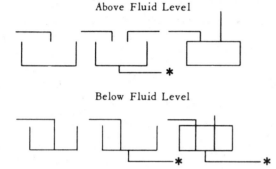

Vented

Pressurized

Note: Reservoirs are conventionally drawn in the horizontal plane. All lines enter and leave from above. Examples:

4.1.1 Reservoir with Connecting Lines

Above Fluid Level

Below Fluid Level

4.1.2 Simplified symbol

The symbols are used as part of a complete circuit. They are analogous to the ground symbol of electrical diagrams. ⎯⎯‖ᵢ IEC. Several such symbols may be used in one diagram to represent the same reservoir.

4.1.2.1 Below Fluid Level

4.1.2.2 Above Fluid Level

(The return line is drawn to terminate at the upright legs of the tank symbol.)

4.1.2.3 Vented Manifold

---

* Show line entering or leaving below reservoir only when such bottom connection is essential to circuit function.

4.2 Accumulator

4.2.1 Accumulator, Spring Loaded

4.2.2 Accumulator, Gas Charged

4.2.3 Accumulator, Weighted

4.3 Receiver, for Air or Other Gases

4.4 Energy Source
(Pump, Compressor, Accumulator, etc.)

This symbol may be used to represent a fluid power source which may be a pump, compressor, or another associated system.

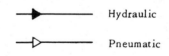

Hydraulic

Pneumatic

Simplified Symbol

Example:

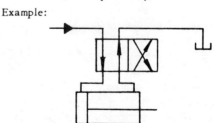

5. Fluid Conditioners

Devices which control the physical characteristics of the fluid.

5.1 Heat Exchanger

5.1.1 Heater

Inside triangles indicate the introduction of heat.

Outside triangles show the heating medium is liquid.

Outside triangles show the heating medium is gaseous.

5.1.2 Cooler

  or

Inside triangles indicate heat dissipation

(Corners may be filled in to represent triangles.)

5.1.3 Temperature Controller
(The temperature is to be maintained between two predetermined limits.)

  or

5.2 Filter — Strainer

5.3 Separator

5.3.1 With Manual Drain

5.3.2 With Automatic Drain

5.4 Filter — Separator

5.4.1 With Manual Drain

5.4.2 With Automatic Drain

5.5 Dessicator (Chemical Dryer)

5.6 Lubricator

5.6.1 Less Drain

5.6.2 With Manual Drain

6. Linear Devices

6.1 Cylinders, Hydraulic & Pneumatic

6.1.1 Single Acting

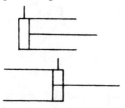

6.1.2 Double Acting

6.1.2.1 Single End Rod

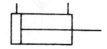

6.1.2.2 Double End Rod

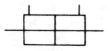

6.1.2.3 Fixed Cushion, Advance & Retract

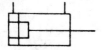

6.1.2.4 Adjustable Cushion, Advance Only

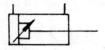

6.1.2.5 Use these symbols when diameter of rod compared to diameter of bore is significant to circuit function.

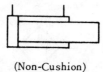

(Non-Cushion)

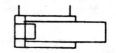

(Cushion, Advance & Retract)

6.2 Pressure Intensifier

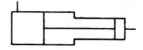

6.3 Servo Positioner (Simplified)

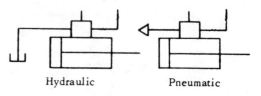

Hydraulic   Pneumatic

6.4 Discrete Positioner

Combine two or more basic cylinder symbols.

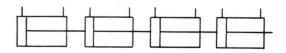

7. Actuators and Controls

7.1 Spring

7.2 Manual

(Use as general symbol without indication of specific type; i.e., foot, hand, leg, arm)

7.2.1 Push Button

7.2.2 Lever

7.2.3 Pedal or Treadle

7.3 Mechanical

7.4 Detent

(Show a notch for each detent in the actual component being symbolized. A short line indicates which detent is in use.) Detent may, for convenience, be positioned on either end of symbol.

7.5 Pressure Compensated

7.6 Electrical

7.6.1 Solenoid (Single Winding)

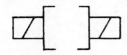

7.6.2 Reversing Motor

7.7 Pilot Pressure

7.7.1

Remote Supply

7.7.2

Internal Supply

7.7.3 Actuation by Released Pressure

by Remote Exhaust

by Internal Return

7.7.4 Pilot Controlled, Spring Centered

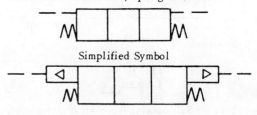

Simplified Symbol

Complete Symbol

7.7.5 Pilot Differential

Simplified Symbol

Complete Symbol

7.8 Solenoid Pilot

7.8.1 Solenoid or Pilot

External Pilot
Supply

Internal Pilot
Supply and
Exhaust

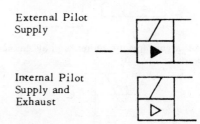

7.8.2 Solenoid and Pilot

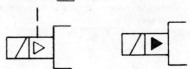

7.9 Thermal

A mechanical device responding to thermal change.

7.9.1 Local Sensing

7.9.2 With Bulb for Remote Sensing

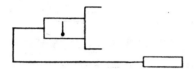

7.10 Servo

(This symbol contains representation for energy input, command input, and resultant output.)

7.11 Composite Actuators (and, or, and/or)

Basic One signal only causes the device to operate.

And One signal and a second signal both cause the device to operate.

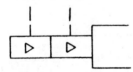

Or One signal or the other signal causes the device to operate

And/Or The solenoid and the pilot or the manual override alone causes the device to operate.

The solenoid and the pilot or the manual override and the pilot

The solenoid and the pilot or a manual override and the pilot or a manual override alone.

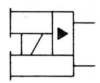

8. Rotary Devices

8.1 Basic Symbol

8.1.1 With Ports

8.1.2 With Rotating Shaft, with control, and with Drain

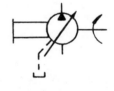

8.2 Hydraulic Pump

8.2.1 Fixed Displacement.

8.2.1.1 Unidirectional

8.2.1.2 Bidirectional

8.2.2 Variable Displacement, Non-Compensated

8.2.2.1 Unidirectional

Simplified

Complete

8.2.2.2 Bidirectional

Simplified

Complete

8.2.3 Variable Displacement, Pressure Compensated

8.2.3.1 Unidirectional

Simplified

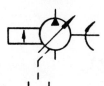

Complete

8.2.3.2 Bidirectional

 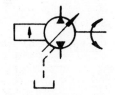

Simplified   Complete

8.3 Hydraulic Motor

8.3.1 Fixed Displacement

8.3.1.2 Bidirectional

8.3.2 Variable Displacement

8.3.2.1 Unidirectional

8.3.2.2 Bidirectional

8.4 Pump-Motor, Hydraulic

8.4.1 Operating in one direction as a pump. Operating in the other direction as a motor.

8.4.1.1 Complete Symbol

8.4.1.2 Simplified Symbol

8.4.2 Operating one direction of flow as either a pump or as a motor.

8.4.2.1 Complete Symbol

8.4.2.2 Simplified Symbol

8.4.3 Operating in both directions of flow either as a pump or as a motor.
(Variable displacement, pressure compensated shown)

8.4.3.1 Complete Symbol

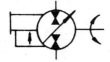

8.4.3.2 Simplified Symbol

8.5 Pump, Pneumatic

8.5.1 Compressor, Fixed Displacement

8.5.2 Vacuum Pump, Fixed Displacement

8.6 Motor, Pneumatic

8.6.1 Unidirectional

8.6.2 Bidirectional

8.7 Oscillator

8.7.1 Hydraulic

8.7.2 Pneumatic

8.8 Motors, Engines

8.8.1 Electric Motor

IEC

8.8.2 Heat Engine (E.G. internal combustion engine)

9. Instruments and Accessories

9.1 Indicating and Recording

9.1.1 Pressure

9.1.2 Temperature

9.1.3 Flow Meter

9.1.3.1   Flow Rate

9.1.3.2   Totalizing

9.2 Sensing

9.2.1 Venturi

9.2.2 Orifice Plate

9.2.3 Pitot Tube

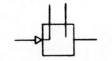

9.2.4 Nozzle

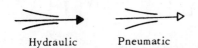

Hydraulic   Pneumatic

9.3 Accessories

9.3.1 Pressure Switch

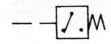

9.3.2 Muffler

10. Valves

A basic valve symbol is composed of one or more envelopes with lines inside the envelope to represent flow paths and flow conditions between ports. Three symbol systems are used to represent valve types: single envelope, both finite and infinite position; multiple envelope, finite position; and multipe envelope, infinite position.

10.1 In infinite position single envelope valves, the envelope is imagined to move to illustrate how pressure or flow conditions are controlled as the valve is actuated.

10.2 Multiple envelopes symbolize valves providing more than one finite flow path option for the fluid. The multiple envelope moves to represent how flow paths change when the valving element within the component is shifted to its finite positions.

10.3 Multiple envelope valves capable of infinite positioning between certain limits are symbolized as in 10.2 above with the addition of horizontal bars which are drawn parallel to the envelope. The horizontal bars are the clues to the infinite positioning function possessed by the valve re-represented.

10.4 Envelopes

10.5 Ports

10.6 Ports, Internally Blocked

Symbol System 10.1

Symbol System 10.2

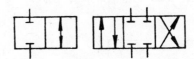

10.7 Flow Paths, Internally Open (Symbol System 10.1 and 10.2)

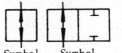
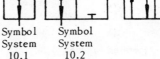

Symbol System 10.1   Symbol System 10.2

10.8 Flow Paths, Internally Open (Symbol System 10.3)

Fluid Power: Pneumatics

10.9 Two-Way Valves (2 Ported Valves)

10.9.1 On-Off (Manual Shut-Off)

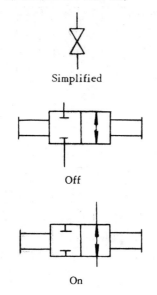

Simplified

Off

On

10.9.2 Check

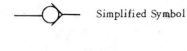

Simplified Symbol

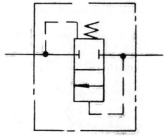

Flow to the right is blocked. Flow to the left is permitted)

(Composite Symbol)

10.9.3 Check, Pilot-Operated to Open

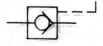

10.9.4 Check, Pilot-Operated to Close

10.9.5 Two-Way Valves

10.9.5.1 Two-Position

Normally Closed   Normally Open

10.9.5.2 Infinite Position

Normally Closed   Normally Open

10.10 Three-Way Valves

10.10.1 Two-Position

10.10.1.1 Normally Open

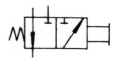

10.10.1.2 Normally Closed

10.10.1.3 Distributor (Pressure is distributed first to one port, then the other)

10.10.1.4 Two-Pressure

10.10.2 Double Check Valve
Double check valves can be built with and without "cross bleed". Such valves with two

210

poppets do not usually allow pressure to momentarily "cross bleed" to return during transition. Valves with one poppet may allow "cross bleed" as these symbols illustrate.

10.10.2.1 Without Cross Bleed (One Way Flow)

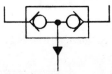

10.10.2.2 With Cross Bleed (Reverse Flow Permitted)

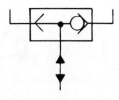

10.11 Four-Way Valves

10.11.1 Two Position

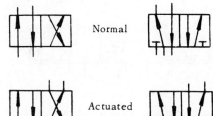

Normal

Actuated

10.11.2 Three Position

(a) Normal

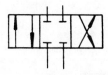

(b) Actuated Left

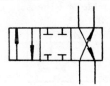

(c) Actuated Right

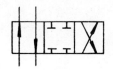

10.11.3 Typical Flow Paths for Center Condition of Three Position Valves

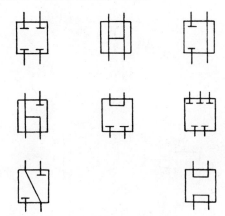

10.11.4 Two-Position, Snap Action with Transition.

As the valve element shifts from one position to the other, it passes through an intermediate position. If it is essential to circuit function to symbolize this "in transit" condition, it can be shown in the center position, enclosed by dashed lines.

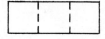

Typical Transition Symbol

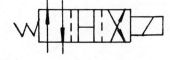

10.12 Infinite Positioning (Between Open & Closed)

10.12.1 Normally Closed

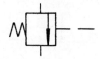

211

10.12.2 Normally Open

10.13 Pressure Control Valves

10.13.1 Pressure Relief

Simplified Symbol
Denotes

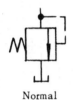

Normal   Actuated
               (Relieving)

10.13.2 Sequence

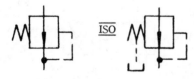

10.13.3 Pressure Reducing

$\overline{ISO}$

10.13.4 Pressure Reducing and Relieving

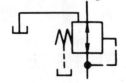

10.13.5 Airline Pressure Regulator (Adjustable, Relieving)

10.14 Infinite Positioning Three-Way Valves

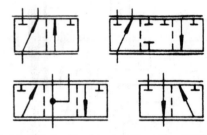

10.15 Infinite Positioning Four-Way Valves

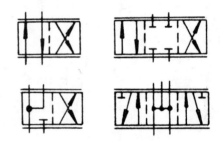

10.16 Flow Control Valves (See 3.7)

10.16.1 Adjustable, Non-Compensated (Flow control in each direction)

10.16.2 Adjustable with Bypass

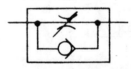

Flow is controlled
to the right
Flow to the left by-
passes control

10.16.3 Adjustable and Pressure Compensated
With Bypass

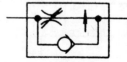

10.16.4 Adjustable, Temperature & Pressure Compensated

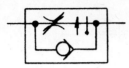

11. Representative Composite Symbols

11.1 Component Enclosure

Component enclosure may surround a complete symbol or a group of symbols to represent an assembly. It is used to convey more information about component connections and functions. Enclosure indicates extremity of component or assembly. External ports are assumed to be on enclosure line and indicate connections to component.

Flow lines shall cross enclosure line without loops or dots.

11.2 Airline Accessories
  (Filter, Regulator, and Lubricator)

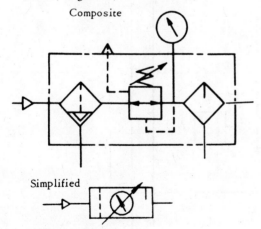

11.3 Pumps and Motors

  11.3.1 Pumps

    11.3.1.1 Double, Fixed Displacement, One

Inlet and Two Outlets

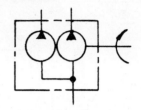

11.3.1.2 Double, with Integral Check Unloading and Two Outlets

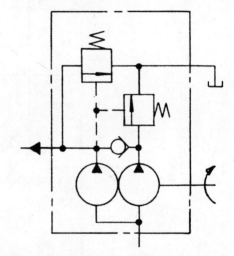

11.3.1.3 Integral Variable Flow Rate Control with Overload Relief

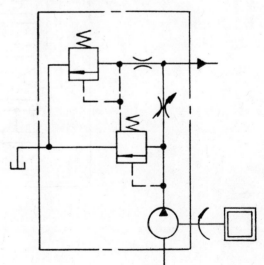

11.3.1.4 Variable Displacement with Integral Replenishing Pump and Control Valves

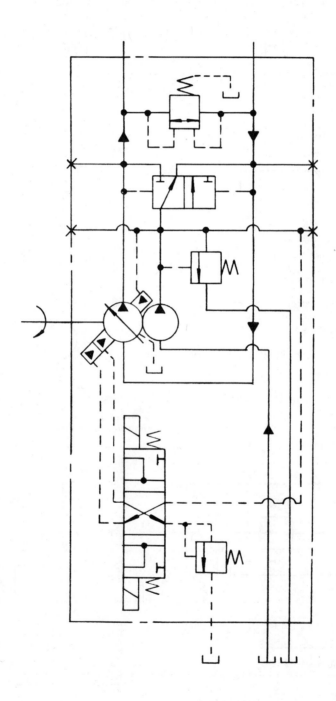

11.3.2 Pump Motor

Variable displacement with manual, electric, pilot, and servo control.

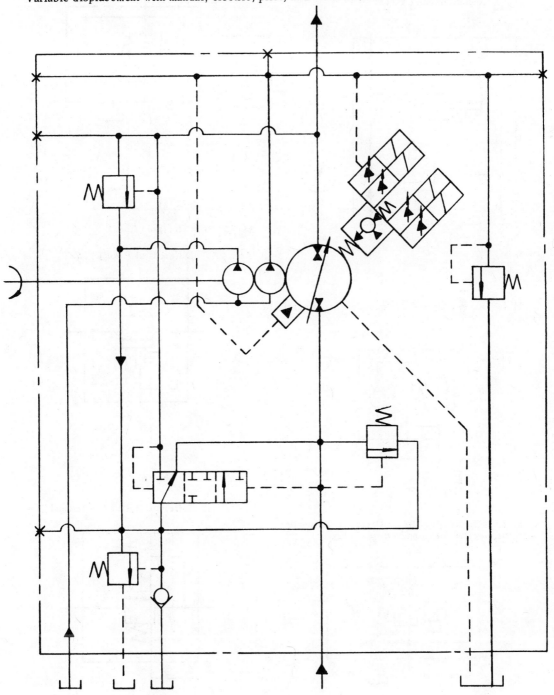

Fluid Power: Pneumatics

11.4 Valves

11.4.1 Relief, Balanced Type

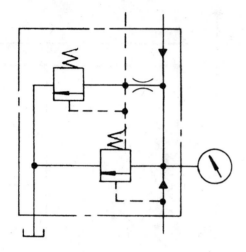

11.4.2 Remote Operated Sequence with Integral Check

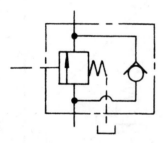

11.4.3 Remote & Direct Operated Sequence with Differential Areas and Integral Check

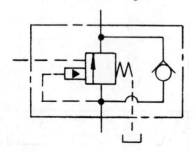

11.4.4 Pressure Reducing with Integral Check

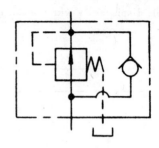

11.4.5 Pilot Operated Check

11.4.5.1 Differential Pilot Opened

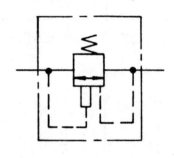

11.4.5.2 Differential Pilot Opened and Closed

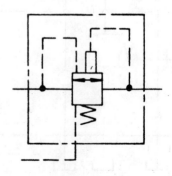

11.4.6 Two Positions, Four Connection Solenoid and Pilot Actuated, with Manual Pilot Override.

Simplified Symbol

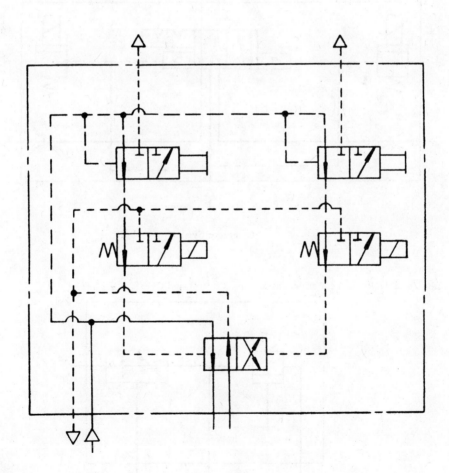

Complete Symbol

11.4.7 Two Position, Five Connection, Solenoid Control Pilot Actuated with Detents and Throttle Exhaust

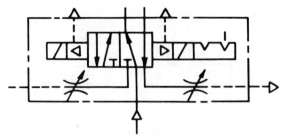

Symplified Symbol

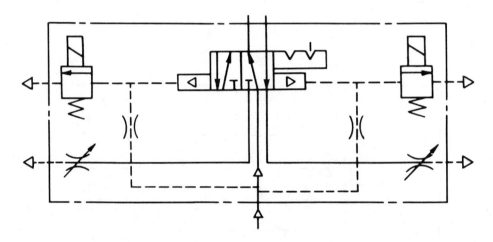

Complete Symbol

11.4.8 Variable Pressure Compensated Flow Control and Overload Relief

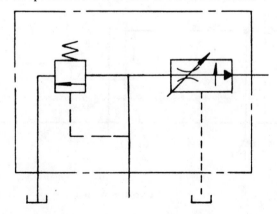

11.4.9 Multiple, Three Position, Manual Directional Control with Integral Check and Relief Valves

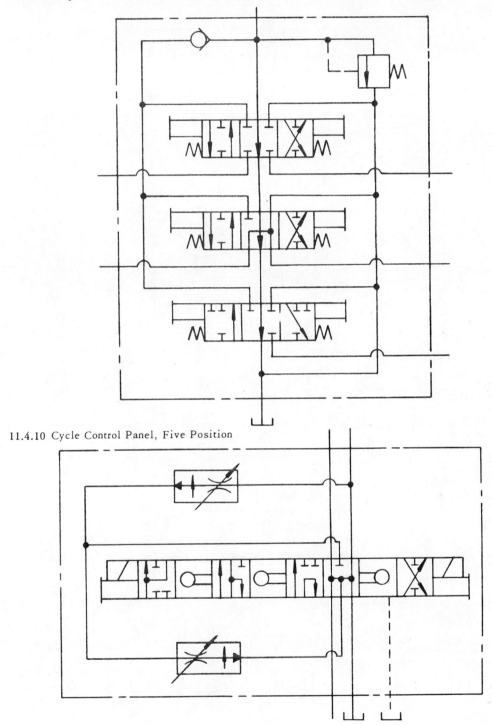

11.4.10 Cycle Control Panel, Five Position

11.4.11 Panel Mounted Separate Units Furnished as a Package (Relief, Two Four-Way, Two Check, and Flow Rate Valves)

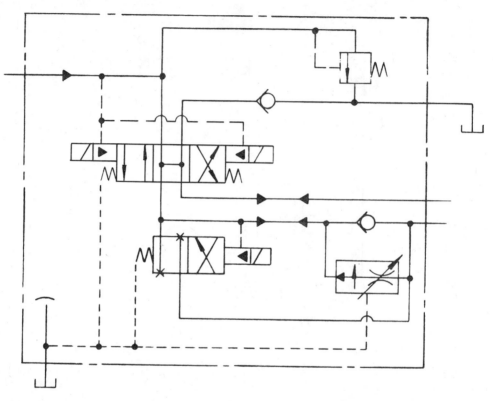

11.4.12 Single Stage Compressor with Electric Motor Drive, Pressure Switch Control of Receiver Tank Pressure

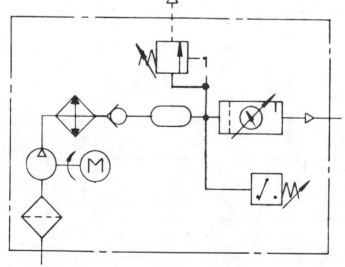

Appendix B:
Metric Measurements

Space does not permit a full account of the history of the metric system, which was officially legalized in France in 1793 but made little progress until 1841. Since that time it has been adopted in one form or another by 92 percent of the world. Although metric units were officially accepted and legalized in the United States in 1866, they were never really adopted for ordinary and practical uses in this country, where their use has been largely limited to scientific and medical purposes. Only one branch of engineering (electricity and electronics) routinely uses metric units, for the simple reason that electrical science had its origin in Europe. Even so, the electrical engineer must also deal with customary U.S. units as electricity interfaces with mechanical engineering, manufacturing, etc.

Despite considerable pressure for metrication, which nearly succeeded in becoming law in 1921 and again in 1974, the United States in 1975 is still officially uncommitted to a planned program of conversion to the metric system. The writers and publishers of textbooks on industrial and engineering subjects are thus forced into an untenable position. Current pressures to convert to the SI (*Système International*) or International System of metric units, however laudable, do not make such a conversion an accomplished fact. The SI version of metric units was adopted by ISO (*International Standards Organization*) in 1960 to replace earlier metric measurements and, hopefully, become universally used.

While various metric countries which have officially agreed to convert from earlier units of measurement to those of the SI in due course, the fact remains that this aim has not been fully attained. Conversion is not the easiest of tasks, and there is a vast amount of still valid and useful technical data to be converted. Also, there are valid objections to an instant changeover by certain industries. Following the example of the United Kingdom, we refer to these metric but pre-SI units of measurement as MT or "Metric Technical". On the whole, they are easier to relate to the customary U.S. measurements than are some of those in the SI system.

TABLE B-1. DECIMAL EQUIVALENTS OF A FOOT

0″	0.0000	1″	0.0833	2″	0.166667	3″	0.2500
1/16	.0052	1 1/16	.0885	2 1/16	.171875	3 1/16	.2552
1/8	.0104	1 1/8	.09375	2 1/8	.1771	3 1/8	.2604
3/16	.015625	1 3/16	.0990	2 3/16	.1823	3 3/16	.265625
1/4	0.0208	1 1/4	0.1042	2 1/4	0.1875	3 1/4	0.2708
5/16	.0260	1 5/16	.109375	2 5/16	.1927	3 5/16	.2760
3/8	.03125	1 3/8	.1146	2 3/8	.1979	3 3/8	.28125
7/16	.0365	1 7/16	.1198	2 7/16	.203125	3 7/16	.2865
1/2	0.0417	1 1/2	0.1250	2 1/2	0.2083	3 1/2	0.2917
9/16	.046875	1 9/16	.1302	2 9/16	.2135	3 9/16	.296875
5/8	.0521	1 5/8	.1354	2 5/8	.21875	3 5/8	.3021
11/16	.0573	1 11/16	.140625	2 11/16	.2240	3 11/16	.3073
3/4	0.0625	1 3/4	0.1458	2 3/4	0.2292	3 3/4	0.3125
13/16	.0677	1 13/16	.1510	2 13/16	.234375	3 13/16	.3177
7/8	.0729	1 7/8	.15625	2 7/8	.2396	3 7/8	.3229
15/16	.078125	1 15/16	.1615	2 15/16	.2448	3 15/16	.328125
4″	0.3333	5″	0.416667	6″	0.5000	7″	0.5833
4 1/16	.3385	5 1/16	.421875	6 1/16	.5052	7 1/16	.5885
4 1/8	.34375	5 1/8	.4271	6 1/8	.5104	7 1/8	.59375
4 3/16	.3490	5 3/16	.4323	6 3/16	.515625	7 3/16	.5990
4 1/4	0.3542	5 1/4	0.4375	6 1/4	0.5208	7 1/4	0.6042
4 5/16	.359375	5 5/16	.4427	6 5/16	.5260	7 5/16	.6093
4 3/8	.3646	5 3/8	.4479	6 3/8	.53125	7 3/8	.6146
4 7/16	.3698	5 7/16	.453125	6 7/16	.5365	7 7/16	.6198
4 1/2	0.3750	5 1/2	0.4583	6 1/2	0.5417	7 1/2	0.6250
4 9/16	.3802	5 9/16	.4635	6 9/16	.546875	7 9/16	.6302
4 5/8	.3854	5 5/8	.46875	6 5/8	.5521	7 5/8	.6354
4 11/16	.390625	5 11/16	.4740	6 11/16	.5573	7 11/16	.640625
4 3/4	0.3958	5 3/4	0.4792	6 3/4	0.5625	7 3/4	0.6458
4 13/16	.4010	5 13/16	.484375	6 13/16	.5677	7 13/16	.6510
4 7/8	.40625	5 7/8	.4896	6 7/8	.5729	7 7/8	.65625
4 15/16	.4115	5 15/16	.4948	6 15/16	.578125	7 15/16	.6615
8″	0.666667	9″	0.7500	10″	0.8333	11″	0.916667
8 1/16	.671875	9 1/16	.7552	10 1/16	.8385	11 1/16	.921875
8 1/8	.6771	9 1/8	.7604	10 1/8	.84375	11 1/8	.9271
8 3/16	.6823	9 3/16	.765625	10 3/16	.8490	11 3/16	.9323
8 1/4	0.6875	9 1/4	0.7708	10 1/4	0.8542	11 1/4	0.9375
8 5/16	.6927	9 5/16	.7760	10 5/16	.859375	11 5/16	.9427
8 3/8	.6979	9 3/8	.78125	10 3/8	.8646	11 3/8	.9479
8 7/16	.703125	9 7/16	.7865	10 7/16	.8698	11 7/16	.953125
8 1/2	0.7083	9 1/2	0.7917	10 1/2	0.8750	11 1/2	0.9583
8 9/16	.7135	9 9/16	.796875	10 9/16	.8802	11 9/16	.9635
8 5/8	.71875	9 5/8	.8021	10 5/8	.8854	11 5/8	.96875
8 11/16	.7240	9 11/16	.8073	10 11/16	.890625	11 11/16	.9740
8 3/4	0.7292	9 3/4	0.8125	10 3/4	0.8958	11 3/4	0.9792
8 13/16	.734375	9 13/16	.8177	10 13/16	.9010	11 13/16	.984375
8 7/8	.7396	9 7/8	.8229	10 7/8	.90625	11 7/8	.9896
8 15/16	.7448	9 15/16	.828125	10 15/16	.9115	11 15/16	.9948

The main concern in presenting a textbook intended for the U.S. market is to set forth the information in units presently used, which are the customary U.S. units. To extend the use of the book, some of this information is also presented in MT metric units still in current use. As a third objective, subordinate to these, the corresponding SI units are presented to acquaint readers and students with them. All tables included in this appendix show clearly the customary U.S. units, the corresponding MT units, and the SI units which in time probably will replace all earlier measurements in metric countries and one day, perhaps, become widely used in the United States also.

For purposes of this book, only common units of everyday use and those applying to fluid power and related mechanical calculations are included. Others of equal importance but applying to electricity, illumination, astronomy, etc. have been omitted as irrelevant.

The chief advantage of the metric system is its decimal nature, the second advantage is the logical relationship between the various units, and the third advantage is international trade and exchange of information. Engineers in the United States long ago modified the customary U.S. measurements by dividing the foot and inch into decimals to facilitate calculations. They also developed conversion tables such as the chart shown in Table B–1, to avoid the troublesome use of common fractions. Also, manufacturers had to resort to thousandths of an inch measurements in order to obtain interchangeable parts. This same practice was followed by the United Kingdom and other English-speaking countries long before they converted or had initiated plans to convert to metric measurements.

Because the SI system has the support of the National Bureau of Standards, the ANSI (American National Standards Institute) and the ASTM (American Society for Testing and Materials) it seems likely that the metric units finally adopted by the United States will be the SI units. Even then, some industries such as the relatively new U.S. vacuum industry (which is already using some pre-SI metric units) may be reluctant to accept these newer units.

First, Learn the Construction of Metric Language

Table B–2 lists the prefixes, symbols, and their mathematical meanings, used in the metric system. These, coupled with words meaning the base units, make up the metric vocabulary. Learning these first and thoroughly is highly important. Positive powers of ten are *multiplies* of the base units; thus, $1 \text{ m} \times 10^3 = 1000 \text{ m} = 1$ kilometer. Notice the meaning of the prefix "kilo" and associate it with 10^3, the multiplier. Negative powers of ten are *sub-multiples* of the base units; thus, $1 \text{ m} \times 10^{-3} = 10^{-3} \text{ m} = 1$ millimeter. Notice the meaning of the prefix "milli" and associate it with 10^{-3}. The one exception, where the base unit has a prefix, is the kilogram, originally derived from the gram. The gram has been abandoned as a base unit for practical and engineering purposes because it is too small.

TABLE B-2. STANDARD PREFIXES, THEIR SYMBOLS AND MAGNITUDES

FACTOR BY WHICH UNIT IS MULTIPLIED	PREFIX	SYMBOL	OLD PREFIX & SYMBOL (IF DIFFERENT)	
10^{12}	tera-	T		
10^{9}	giga-	G	kilomega-	km
10^{6}	mega-	M		m
10^{3}	kilo-	k		
10^{2}	hecto-	h		
10^{1}	deka-	da		
10^{-1}	deci-	d		
10^{-2}	centi-	c		
10^{-3}	milli-	m		
10^{-6}	micro-	μ		
10^{-9}	nano-	n	millimicro-	$m\mu$
10^{-12}	pico-	p	micromicro-	$\mu\mu$
10^{-15}	femto-	f		
10^{-18}	atto	a	KI	

EXAMPLES:

kilometer = km	milligram = mg
millimeter = mm	hectoliter = hl
decimeter = dm	microvolt = μV

Notice particularly the distinction between capital letter symbols and lower case letter symbols; thus, *M* stands for "mega" or $\times 10^6$ (multiplied by a million), while *m* stands for "milli" or 10^{-3} (divided by a thousand).

Next, make sure you know how to make calculations using powers of ten. Space does not allow instructions on this easy but powerful method. The "powers of ten" method is simply an extension of the ordinary decimal system using 10 coupled with an exponent as a multiplier. A knowledge of decimals plus the laws of exponents is all that is required. Actually this method could be taught at a fairly elementary level but usually isn't in this country.

Major Changes in SI Units

The main units causing some difficulty in the SI version of metrics are the *newton* (unit of force) and *pascal* (unit of pressure), the *joule* (unit of work), etc. derived from the newton.

In the customary U.S. system

(including most engineering and industrial calculations) force and weight have been treated as synonymous although sometimes the word "pound" is qualified as "pound-force" to clarify the application but not the numerical value. The same is true in the customary (pre-SI) metric uses, including MT. Thus a "kilogram" might be a kilogram (mass) or a "kilogram-force" (kgf). For this reason a great many ordinary engineering calculations are fairly easy to understand in earlier metric form despite the fact that the kilogram is roughly equal to 2.2 pounds.

The SI tells us that this concept is erroneous and does not recognize either the U.S. pound-force or the pre-SI metric kilogram-force as valid. Reluctantly, however, SI tables list the pound-force as numerically equivalent to 4.448 222 newtons. Also, note that the kilogram-force is equivalent to roughly 9.81 newtons (actually 9.806 650 newtons).

Now, reviewing some typical engineering calculations, we see that many involve units of force, such as:

$$\text{work} = \text{force} \times \text{distance}$$

$$\text{power} = \frac{\text{work}}{\text{time}} = \frac{\text{force} \times \text{distance}}{\text{time}}$$

$$\text{pressure} = \frac{\text{force}}{\text{area}}$$

In the MT metric usage these units are rather transparent, thus:

ft-1bf (work) becomes kgf.m

ft-1bf/sec (power) becomes kgf.m/s

lb/in.² or psi (pressure) becomes kg/cm² or, more properly, kgf/cm²

The newton (N), however, is defined as the force required to give a mass of one kilogram an acceleration of 1 meter per second per second, or 1 meter per second squared; thus, $1\ N = 1\ kgf \cdot m/s^2$. The standard acceleration of free fall, which is also standard gravity, is established as 9.806 650 m/s². Therefore 1 kgf (in pre-SI metrics) = 9.806 650 N. 1 newton is therefore 0.101 971 6 kgf, very nearly one-tenth of a kilogram (force). 1 newton is also 0.224 808 9 1bf or pound-force in customary U.S. measurements. Acceleration of free fall, or gravity, actually varies slightly (up to about 0.5 percent) even on the earth and a great deal more in space. This fact, important to scientific investigations, is of no real concern in practical engineering work other than space technology.

Derived units have special names in honor of certain scientists. While these names are conveniently brief, they have the disadvantage of not showing the derivations. The ones of most concern in fluid power are the *joule* (J) for work or energy, the *watt* (W) for mechanical power and generation of heat as well as electric power, and the *pascal* (Pa) for pressure.

Work, expressed as ft-lb (force) in the customary U.S. measurements or as kilogram (force) meters in MT metrics, is expressed in SI as joules. $1\ J = 1\ N \cdot m$. The *joule* is thus a special name for the newton-meter.

Power, expressed as foot-pound force per second in customary U.S. measurements or as kilogram-force meters per second (kgf m/s) in MT metrics, is expressed in SI as *watts*, applied to mechanical power as well as electrical power and rate of thermal generation. $1\ W = 1\ J/s$ in mechanical calculations.

Pressure, expressed as pounds (force) per square inch (psi) in customary U.S. measurements or as kilogram-force per square centimeter (kgf/cm²) in MT metrics, is expressed in SI as pascals. 1 Pa = 1 N/m². This is a very small unit of pressure because of the fact that the newton itself is a small unit of force, and this is divided by the square meter, a relatively large area. For example, 1 psi = 6 894.757 Pa. For most practical purposes the prefix

"kilo" or "mega" would have to be used. Quite ordinary gage pressure for compressed air is 100 psi, equivalent to 689 475.7 Pa. More practically this would be 689.475 7 kilopascals (kPa) or 0.689 475 7 megapascals (MPa).

Using the Metric Tables

In the following tables only one conversion factor is given for both U.S. to metric (MT or SI) or metric (MT or SI) to U.S. To convert from U.S. to metric units multiply by the conversion factor. To convert from metric to U.S. units, divide by the same factor. In some cases the MT unit is not shown and in other cases the SI unit is not shown. In these cases SI does not recognise the MT unit, or vice versa.

As stated previously, these tables are far from complete, but cover most of the units encountered in connection with fluid power and mechanics. The full SI listings and definitions are given in ANSI Z210.1-1973 and published in ASTM Metric Practice Guide, Published by the American Society for Testing and Materials, 1916 Race Street, Philadelphia, Pennsylvania 19103.

For convenience, the conversion tables are arranged alphabetically. Following the practice of metric countries, digits are

placed in groups of threes separated by spaces rather than commas. More digits are given than are used in most engineering applications. The user of these tables is expected to round these numbers to the degree justified by the requirement for precision and the accuracy of the data used.

Conversions are, in a sense, translations, and translations are cumbersome. The full benefits and advantages of the metric system can be realized only when the changeover is completed, standards have been developed, and people can think in metric terms. Then there is no further need to think of conversions. If and when the United States as a nation decides to make the changeover there will undoubtedly be an awkward period such as an untutored person feels trying to speak a foreign language by using a dictionary.

Review Questions

1. From the studies made in the metric appendix how may:
   (a) psi (pounds per square inch) be converted to kg/cm² (kilogram per square centimeter)?
   (b) How may kg/cm² be converted to the

latest SI pressure units kPa (kilopascal)?

2. How is the U.S. horsepower related to the metric horsepower and what is the equivalent value in the latest SI units?

SEE END OF BOOK FOR ANSWERS TO QUESTIONS

TABLE B-3. ACCELERATION MEASUREMENTS

U.S. CUSTOMARY Units & Symbols	MULTIPLY ⟶ OR DIVIDE ⟵	MT Units & Symbols	SI Units & Symbols
MILE PER HOUR SQUARED mi/hr²	1.609 344	KILOMETER PER HOUR SQUARED km/h²	KILOMETER PER HOUR SQUARED km/h²
FOOT PER SECOND SQUARED ft/sec²	0.304 800	METER PER SECOND SQUARED m/s²	METER PER SECOND SQUARED m/s²
INCH PER SECOND SQUARED in/sec²	0.025 400	METER PER SECOND SQUARED m/s²	METER PER SECOND SQUARED m/s²
INCH PER SECOND SQUARED in/sec²	2.540	CENTIMETER PER SECOND SQUARED cm/s²	(SI discourages use of centimeter, preferring m/s² or mm/s² in technical work)
STANDARD ACCELERATION OF GRAVITY (32.17 ft/sec²)	9.806 650	METER PER SECOND SQUARED m/s²	METER PER SECOND SQUARED m/s²

TABLE B-4. AREA MEASUREMENTS

U.S. CUSTOMARY Units & Symbols	MULTIPLY ⟶ OR DIVIDE ⟵	MT Units & Symbols	SI Units & Symbols
SQUARE MILE mi²	2.589 988	SQUARE KILOMETER km²	SQUARE KILOMETER km²
ACRE	0.404 686	HECTARE (ha) or SQUARE HECTOMETER hm²	(SI uses the m² unit for large areas up to 1 km², as shown below)
ACRE	4 046.686	SQUARE METER m²	SQUARE METER m²
SQUARE YARD yd²	0.836 127	SQUARE METER m²	SQUARE METER m²
SQUARE FOOT ft²	0.092 903	SQUARE METER m²	SQUARE METER m²
SQUARE INCH in.²	6.451 600	SQUARE CENTIMETER cm²	SQUARE CENTIMETER cm²
SQUARE INCH in.²	645.160	SQUARE MILLIMETER mm²	SQUARE MILLIMETER mm²

TABLE B-5. DENSITY MEASUREMENTS

U.S. CUSTOMARY Units & Symbols	MULTIPLY → OR DIVIDE ←	MT Units & Symbols	SI Units & Symbols
POUND PER CUBIC FOOT lb/ft³	16.018 46	KILOGRAM PER CUBIC METER kg/m³	KILOGRAM PER CUBIC METER kg/m³
POUND PER CUBIC INCH lb/in³	27.679 90	GRAM PER CUBIC CENTIMETER g/cm³	GRAM PER CUBIC CENTIMETER g/cm³
U.S. LIQUID OUNCE (Avoirdupois) PER CUBIC INCH oz/in³	1.729 994	GRAM PER CUBIC CENTIMETER g/cm³	GRAM PER CUBIC CENTIMETER g/cm³
POUND PER U.S. GALLON lb/gal (U.S. Liquid)	119.826 4	MT PREFERS THE LITER (dm³) UNIT (See below)	KILOGRAM PER CUBIC METER kg/m³
POUND PER U.S. GALLON lb/gal (U.S. Liquid)	0.119 826	KILOGRAM PER LITER kg/1	

TABLE B-6. ENERGY AND WORK MEASUREMENTS

U.S. CUSTOMARY Units & Symbols	MULTIPLY → OR DIVIDE ←	MT Units & Symbols	SI Units & Symbols
FOOT-POUND FORCE ft/lb	1.355 818	(MT does not use the joule as unit for mechanical work.)	JOULE J (1 J = 1 N · m)
FOOT-POUND FORCE ft/lb	0.138 250	KILOGRAM (Force) - METER kgf · m	(SI recognizes only the joule as base unit for energy and work.)
BRITISH THERMAL UNIT (Thermochemical) BTU	1 054.350	(MT does not use the joule as unit for mechanical work.)	JOULE J
BRITISH THERMAL UNIT (International Table) BTU	1 055.056	(MT does not use the joule as unit for mechanical work.)	JOULE J

TABLE B-7. FLUID CAPACITY MEASUREMENTS

U.S. CUSTOMARY Units & Symbols	MULTIPLY → OR DIVIDE ←	MT Units & Symbols	SI Units & Symbols
GALLON gal (U.S. Liquid)	3.785 412	LITER l or CUBIC DECIMETER dm^3	LITER l or CUBIC DECIMETER dm^3
GALLON gal (U.S. Liquid)	0.003 785	CUBIC METER m^3	CUBIC METER m^3
QUART qt (U.S. Liquid)	0.946 353	LITER l or CUBIC DECIMETER dm^3	LITER l or CUBIC DECIMETER dm^3
PINT pt (U.S. Liquid)	0.473 176	LITER l or CUBIC DECIMETER dm^3	LITER l or CUBIC DECIMETER dm^3
OUNCE oz (U.S. Liquid)	0.029 574	LITER l or CUBIC DECIMETER dm^3	LITER l or CUBIC DECIMETER dm^3
OUNCE oz (U.S. Liquid)	29.573 53	MILLILITER ml	MILLILITER ml

TABLE B-8. FORCE MEASUREMENTS

U.S. CUSTOMARY Units & Symbols	MULTIPLY → OR DIVIDE ←	MT Units & Symbols	SI Units & Symbols
TON-FORCE tonf (Based on U.S. short ton of 2000 lb-force)	8.896 444	(MT does not use the newton or its multiples or submultiples.)	KILONEWTON kN (SI recognizes only the newton (N) as base unit of force.)
TON-FORCE tonf (Based on U.S. short ton of 2000 lb-force)	0.907 185	TONNE (Metric Ton) tf	(SI recognizes only the newton (N) as base unit of force.)
TON-FORCE tonf (Based on U.S. short ton of 2000 lb-force)	907.185	KILOGRAM-FORCE kgf	(SI recognizes only the newton (N) as base unit of force.)
KIP kip (1000 lb-force)	0.453 593	TONNE (Metric Ton) tf	(SI recognizes only the newton (N) as base unit of force.)
KIP kip (1000 lb-force)	4.448 222	(MT does not use the newton or its multiples or submultiples.)	KILONEWTON kN
POUND-FORCE lbf (lbf avoirdupois)	4.448 222	(MT does not use the newton or its multiples or submultiples.)	NEWTON N
POUND-FORCE lbf (lbf avoirdupois)	0.453 592	KILOGRAM-FORCE kgf	(SI recognizes only the newton (N) as base unit of force.)
OUNCE-FORCE ozf (ozf avoirdupois)	0.278 014	(MT does not use the newton or its multiples or submultiples.)	NEWTON N
OUNCE-FORCE ozf (ozf avoirdupois)	28.349 523	GRAM-FORCE gf	(SI recognizes only the newton (N) as base unit of force.)

TABLE B-9. LENGTH MEASUREMENTS

U.S. CUSTOMARY Units & Symbols	MULTIPLY ⟶ OR DIVIDE ⟵	MT Units & Symbols	SI Units & Symbols
MILE mi	1.609 344	KILOMETER km	KILOMETER km
YARD yd	0.914 400	METER m	METER m
FOOT ft	0.304 800	METER m	METER m
INCH in.	2.540 000	CENTIMETER cm	(SI recommends use of mm unit for small lengths.)
INCH in.	25.400 000	MILLIMETER mm	MILLIMETER mm

TABLE B-10. MASS MEASUREMENTS

U.S. CUSTOMARY Units & Symbols	MULTIPLY ⟶ OR DIVIDE ⟵	MT Units & Symbols	SI Units & Symbols
TON, SHORT ton (2000 lb)	0.907 185	TONNE (Metric Ton) t or MEGAGRAM Mg	(SI discourages use of metric ton, preferring the kilogram.)
TON, SHORT ton (2000 lb)	907.185	KILOGRAM kg	KILOGRAM kg (Mass)
POUND lb (Avoirdupois)	0.453 592	KILOGRAM kg	KILOGRAM kg (Mass)
POUND lb (Avoirdupois)	453.592 37	GRAM g	GRAM g (Mass)
OUNCE oz (Avoirdupois)	28.349 523	GRAM g	GRAM g (Mass)
OUNCE oz troy (Troy)	31.103 477	GRAM g	GRAM g (Mass)
GRAIN gr	0.064 799	GRAM g	GRAM g (Mass)
GRAIN gr	64.798 91	MILLIGRAM mg	MILLIGRAM mg (Mass)

TABLE B-11. POWER MEASUREMENTS

U.S. CUSTOMARY Units & Symbols	MULTIPLY ⟶ OR DIVIDE ⟵	MT Units & Symbols	SI Units & Symbols
U.S. HORSEPOWER (550 Foot-Pounds per second) HP (Mechanical)	76.061 15	KILOGRAM METER PER SECOND kgf · m/s	(SI recognizes only the watt as base unit for power measurements.)
U.S. HORSEPOWER (550 Foot-Pounds per Second) HP (Mechanical)	745.700	(MT usually uses the watt as unit of electrical power.)	WATT W (1 W = 1 J/s = 1 N m/s)
U.S. HORSEPOWER (Electrical)	746.000	WATT W	WATT W (W = A X V, the DC power equation.)
U.S. HORSEPOWER (Electrical)	0.746	KILOWATT kW	KILOWATT kW
U.S. HORSEPOWER (550 Foot-Pounds per Second) HP (Mechanical)	1.014	METRIC HORSE-POWER (Equivalent to 735.499 W)	(SI recognizes only the watt as base unit for power mea-surements.)
FOOT-POUND PER SECOND ft-lb/sec (Mechanical)	1.355 818	(MT usually uses the watt as unit of electrical power.)	WATT W
FOOT-POUND PER SECOND ft-lb/sec (Mechanical)	0.138 293	KILOGRAM METER PER SECOND kgf · m/s	(SI recognizes only the watt as base unit for power measure-ments.)
FOOT-POUND PER MINUTE ft-lb/min (Mechanical)	0.022 597	(MT usually uses the watt as unit of electrical power.)	WATT W
BTU (International Table) PER HOUR (Heating) BTU/hr	0.293 071	WATT W	WATT W (Thermal equivalent of mechanical power.)
BTU (International Table) PER MINUTE (Heating) BTU/min	17.584 26	WATT W	WATT W (Thermal equivalent of mechanical power.)

U.S. CUSTOMARY Units & Symbols	MULTIPLY → OR DIVIDE ←	MT Units & Symbols	SI Units & Symbols
U.S. (Short) TON FORCE PER SQUARE INCH tonf/in.²	13.789 514	(MT does not use the pascal or its multiples or sub-multiples.)	MEGAPASCAL MPa 1 MPa = 1 Pa × 10⁶ (1 Pa = 1 N/m²)
U.S. (Short) TON FORCE PER SQUARE INCH tonf/in.²	0.140 6	METRIC TON FORCE PER SQUARE CENTI-METER tf/cm²	(SI recognizes only the pascal as base unit for pressure measurement.)
POUND FORCE PER SQUARE INCH psi	6.894 757	(MT does not use the pascal or its multiples or sub-multiples.)	KILOPASCAL kPa 1 kPa = 1 Pa × 10³
POUND FORCE PER SQUARE INCH psi	0.070 310	KILOGRAM FORCE PER SQUARE CENTI-METER kgf/cm²	(SI recognizes only the pascal as base unit for pressure measurement.)
POUND FORCE PER SQUARE INCH psi (Gage Pressure or psig)	0.068 655	BAR bar (1 bar = 14.5 psi)	(SI recognizes only the pascal as base unit for pressure measurement.)
POUND FORCE PER SQUARE INCH psi (Pressures Below Atmospheric)	51.700 681	TORR torr (1 torr = 1 mm of mercury)	(SI recognizes only the pascal as base unit for pressure measurement.)
INCH OF MERCURY in. Hg (Low Pressure Measurement)	25.400 221	TORR torr or MILLIMETER OF MERCURY mm Hg	(SI recognizes only the pascal as base unit for pressure measurement.)
FOOT OF WATER ft H₂O (at 4°C or 39.2°F)	2.988 98	(MT does not use the pascal or its multiples or sub-multiples.)	KILOPASCAL kPa
INCH OF WATER in. H₂O (at 4°C or 39.2°F)	249.082	(MT does not use the pascal or its multiples or sub-multiples.)	PASCAL Pa
INCH OF WATER in H₂O (at 4°C or 39.2°F)	0.002 540	KILOGRAM FORCE PER SQUARE CENTI-METER kgf/cm²	(SI recognizes only the pascal as base unit for pressure measurement.)
STANDARD ATMO-SPHERE (14.7 psi)	101.325	(MT does not use the pascal or its multiples or sub-multiples.)	KILOPASCAL kPa
STANDARD ATMO-SPHERE (14.7 psi)	1.013 250	BAR bar	(SI recognizes only the pascal as base unit for pressure measurement.)
STANDARD ATMO-SPHERE (14.7 psi)	51.700·	TORR torr or MILLIMETER OF MERCURY mm Hg	(SI recognizes only the pascal as base unit for pressure measurement.)

TABLE B-13. TEMPERATURE MEASUREMENTS
(U.S. TO METRIC CONVERSIONS)

U.S. SYSTEM	CONVERSION EQUATIONS	METRIC SYSTEM (MT and SI)
DEGREES FAHRENHEIT (°F) (CUSTOMARY SCALE)	$\frac{5}{9}(°F - 32) = °C$	DEGREES CELSIUS (°C) (CUSTOMARY SCALE)
DEGREES RANKINE (°R) (ABSOLUTE SCALE BASED ON FAHRENHEIT DEGREES) ABSOLUTE ZERO: RANKINE = −459.67°F	$\frac{°R}{1.68} = K$	KELVIN K (ABSOLUTE SCALE BASED ON CELSIUS DEGREES) ABSOLUTE ZERO: KELVIN = −273.15° C

TABLE B-14. TEMPERATURE MEASUREMENTS
(METRIC TO U.S. CONVERSIONS)

METRIC SYSTEM (MT and SI)	CONVERSION EQUATIONS	U.S. SYSTEM
DEGREES CELSIUS (°C) (CUSTOMARY SCALE)	$(°C \times 1.8) + 32 = °F$	DEGREES FAHRENHEIT (°F) (CUSTOMARY U.S. SCALE)
KELVIN K (ABSOLUTE SCALE BASED ON CELSIUS DEGREES) ABSOLUTE ZERO: KELVIN = −273.15° C	$K \times 1.68 = °R$	DEGREES RANKINE (°R) (ABSOLUTE SCALE BASED ON FAHRENHEIT DEGREES) ABSOLUTE ZERO: RANKINE = −459.67° F

TABLE B-15. TORQUE OR BENDING MOMENT MEASUREMENTS

U.S. CUSTOMARY Units & Symbols	MULTIPLY ⟶ OR DIVIDE ⟵	MT Units & Symbols	SI Units & Symbols
POUND FORCE-FOOT lb-ft	1.355 818	(MT does not use the newton-meter unit.)	NEWTON-METER N·m
POUND FORCE-FOOT lb-ft	0.138 250	KILOGRAM-FORCE METER kgf·m	(SI recognizes only the newton-meter as base unit for bending moments.)
POUND FORCE-INCH lb-in.	0.112 985	(MT does not use the newton-meter unit.)	NEWTON-METER N·m
POUND FORCE-INCH lb-in.	0.011 521	KILOGRAM-FORCE METER kgf·m	(SI recognizes only the newton-meter as base unit for bending moments.)
POUND FORCE-INCH lb-in.	1.152 080	KILOGRAM-FORCE CENTIMETER kgf·cm	(SI recognizes only the newton-meter as base unit for bending moments.)

TABLE B-16. VELOCITY MEASUREMENTS

U.S. CUSTOMARY Units & Symbols	MULTIPLY ⟶ OR DIVIDE ⟵	MT Units & Symbols	SI Units & Symbols
MILE PER HOUR mph	1.609 344	KILOMETER PER HR km/h	KILOMETER PER HR km/h
FOOT PER MINUTE ft/min	0.005 08	METER PER SECOND m/s	METER PER SECOND m/s
FOOT PER SECOND ft/sec	0.304 800	METER PER SECOND m/s	METER PER SECOND m/s
FOOT PER SECOND ft/sec	30.480	CENTIMETERS PER SECOND cm/s	(SI discourages use of centimeters per second, preferring m/s.)

TABLE B-17. VISCOSITY MEASUREMENTS

U.S. CUSTOMARY Units & Symbols	MULTIPLY ⟶ OR DIVIDE ⟵	MT Units & Symbols	SI Units & Symbols
DYNAMIC OR ABSOLUTE			
POUND/FOOT-SECOND lb/ft-sec	14.878 738	(MT does not use the pascal unit.)	PASCAL-SECOND Pa·s
POUND/FOOT-SECOND lb/ft-sec	14.878 738	CENTIPOISE cP or GRAM PER CENTI-METER-SECOND g/cm·s	
KINEMATIC			
SQUARE FOOT PER SECOND ft²/sec	0.092 903	CENTISTOKES cSt or SQUARE METER PER SECOND m²/s	CENTISTOKES cSt or SQUARE METER PER SECOND m²/s
SAYBOLT UNIVERSAL SECONDS SUS (at 38°C or 100°F)	0.215 750	CENTISTOKES cSt or SQUARE METER PER SECOND m²/s	CENTISTOKES cSt or SQUARE METER PER SECOND m²/s

Appendix B: Metric Measurements*

TABLE B-18. VOLUME MEASUREMENTS

U.S. CUSTOMARY Units & Symbols	MULTIPLY → OR DIVIDE ←	MT Units & Symbols	SI Units & Symbols
CUBIC YARD yd³	0.764 555	CUBIC METER m³	CUBIC METER m³
CUBIC FOOT ft³	0.028 317	CUBIC METER m³	CUBIC METER m³
CUBIC FOOT ft³	28.316 85	LITER l or CUBIC DECIMETER dm³	CUBIC DECIMETER dm³
CUBIC INCH in.³	16.387 064	CUBIC CENTIMETER cm³	(Prefers use of cubic meter or cubic millimeter for tech. uses.)
CUBIC INCH in.³	16 387.064	CUBIC MILLIMETER mm³	CUBIC MILLIMETER mm³

TABLE B-19. VOLUME FLOW RATE MEASUREMENTS

U.S. CUSTOMARY Units & Symbols	MULTIPLY → OR DIVIDE ←	MT Units & Symbols	SI Units & Symbols
CUBIC FOOT PER MINUTE ft³/min	0.471 947	LITER PER SECOND l/s or CUBIC DECIMETER PER SECOND dm³/s	CUBIC DECIMETER PER SECOND dm³/s
CUBIC FOOT PER SECOND ft³/sec	28.316 85	LITER PER SECOND l/s or CUBIC DECIMETER PER SECOND dm³/s	CUBIC DECIMETER PER SECOND dm³/s
CUBIC INCH PER SECOND	16.387 1	CUBIC CENTIMETER PER SECOND cm³/s	CUBIC CENTIMETER PER SECOND cm³/s
U.S. GALLON PER MINUTE gal/min (Liquid)	0.063 090	LITER PER SECOND l/s or CUBIC DECIMETER PER SECOND dm³/s	CUBIC DECIMETER PER SECOND dm³/s
U.S. GALLON PER SECOND gal/sec (Liquid)	3.785 412	LITER PER SECOND l/s or CUBIC DECIMETER PER SECOND dm³/s	CUBI DECIMETER PER SCECOND dm³/s

Answers to Review Questions

1. The origin of a tornado.

2. Air and oil.

3. Yes. Heat has a great influence on the performance of pneumatics. Mechanical devices are, however, the main source of power for performing useful work.

4. The Archimedes water screws.

5. There are many similar screws in modern industry. Practical, efficient application was, however, only possible after a drive source was available.

6. A fluid in a closed system exerts pressure equally in all directions.

7. The Italian scientist Torricelli (1608–1647).

8. The German physicist Otto von Guericke (1602–1686).

9. The French physicist Edme Mariotte (1620–1684) formulated the *Boyle's law* which states: For a gaseous substance at constant temperature the volume is inversely proportional to the pressure.

10. The French physicist Jacques Charles (1746–1823) was the first to discover that the volume of a given mass of a gaseous substance increases or decreases 1/273 for each degree centigrade of temperature change.

11. Gay Lussac, a French physicist (1778–1850), discovered the law of expansion of gases when heated.

12. The French mathematician Jean Baptiste Joseph Fourier (1768–1830) made important contributions to the calculation of heat conduction.

13. The British chemist John Dalton (1766–1844) discovered that for a mixture of gases which do not react chemically, each gas exerts its own pressure independently, as if no other gas were present.

14. The Italian physicist Amadeo Avogadro (1776–1856) advanced the theory that at the same temperature and pressure, equal volumes of different gases contain equal numbers of molecules.

15. The German physicist Julius Robert von Mayer (1814–1878) was the first to formulate clearly the principle of the conservation of energy.

16. The British physicist James Prescott Joule (1818–1889) determined the mechanical equivalent of heat as related to electrical energy.

17. Joule also established that a perfect gas has no latent heat.

18. The British chemist Sir James Dewar (1842–1923) was the first to liquefy hydrogen, in 1889, and to solidify it, in 1899.

19. Synthetic production of ammonia was actually first developed by the German chemist Fritz Haber (1868–1934). He produced ammonia by direct combination of nitrogen and hydrogen. In the same time period another German chemist, Karl Bosch (1874–1940), developed an economical method for producing hydrogen by a combination of carbon monoxide obtained catalytically by passing steam at 500°C through a hydrocarbonous substance and water gas. He then adopted Haber's method for fixing nitrogen in the synthetic production of ammonia.

20. The German chemist Karl Bosch.

21. The German chemist Friedrich Bergius (1884–1949) developed a method for producing crude mineral oil by combining coal dust and hydrogen under high pressures.

22. Air is the principal gaseous medium used for transmitting a force in fluid power for industrial use.

23. A receiver for storing a compressed gaseous medium is also called a pressure tank.

24. A compressor is the source of energy when using a gaseous medium for transmitting a force in industry.

Chapter 2, Pages 21—22

1. By a barometer.

2. When all gaseous substances have been removed from the inside of a container we have a vacuum.

3. Gage pressure is the actual pressure above atmospheric pressure.

4. An instrument that measures atmospheric pressure.

5. 76 cm Hg in the metric system and 29.921 inches Hg in the U.S. system.

6. The *mole* is the unit measurement for molecules in a gaseous medium.

7. The unit for pressure measurement in the vacuum industry is the torr. Average atmospheric pressure is considered 760 mm Hg in the metric system, the system of measurement used in the vacuum industry. 1 torr = 1 mm Hg.

Fluid Power: Pneumatics

8. Two contemporary scientists, Boyle and Mariotte, discovered simultaneously the behavior of a gaseous medium if compressed or expanded under constant temperature. Mariotte formulated the following expressions:
   1. The volume is inversely proportional to the absolute pressure.
   2. The weight per cubic unit is inversely proportional to the volume.
   3. The weight per cubic unit is directly proportional to the pressure.

9. 78.03% nitrogen, 20.99% oxygen and 0.98% argon. By molecular weight this is: 28.016 nitrogen, 32.000 oxygen and 39.950 argon.

10. Free air is ambient air at the intake of a compressor.

11. Absolute humidity is the actual quantity of water present in the air. This is expressed as units of weight per cubic units of air.

12. Relative humidity is the amount of water or water vapor present in the air expressed as a pecentage of the maximum amount of water possible for the air to hold at the temperature considered.

13. Dew point is the temperature to which moisture-laden air must be cooled to start to release the moisture.

14. Relative humidity is most accurately measured with a wet bulb thermometer and a dry bulb thermometer simultaneously. The wet bulb thermometer reading should be subtracted from the dry bulb thermometer reading. The relative humidity may then be found by comparing the result to a standard table. See Table 2–6.

Chapter 3, Page 65

1. The gaseous media have no fixed shape or volume. They do, however, completely fill and take the exact shape of the container they occupy. The gaseous media are highly compressible and therefore very useful for storing up energy for future use.

2. The Pascal law states that a fluid (gaseous medium) in a closed system exerts pressure equally in all directions.

3. According to Boyle's Law for a gaseous medium at constant temperature the volume is inversely proportional to the pressure. Mariotte formulated this law.

4. Charles discovered that the volume of a given mass of a gaseous substance increases or decreases 1/273 for each degree centigrade of temperature change.

5. Adiabatic compression and expansion occurs when the gaseous medium is compressed or expanded without transmission of heat from it or to it.

6. Isothermal compression and expansion occurs when the gaseous medium is compressed or expanded with withdrawal or addition of heat to keep the temperature constant.

7. Gage pressure is defined as the pressure above the atmospheric pressure. Gages for measuring of a gaseous medium for industrial use are set at zero for the prevailing atmospheric pressure.

8. Atmospheric pressure is absolute pressure. If atmospheric pressure is reduced or increased by compression or expansion the resulting total pressure is absolute pressure. For calculations involving proportions in pressure, absolute pressure is always used.

9. Theoretically, vacuum may be defined as an enclosure devoid of all matter.

10. One *torr* is 1/760 of atmospheric pressure. One *micron* is 1/1,000 of a torr.

11. The expression *partial pressure* is generally used where more than one gaseous medium is contained in the same enclosure.

12. Dalton's law states: The pressure one gas exerts on an enclosure is not affected by the pressure that another or other gases in the same container exert on the same enclosure.

13. The following industrial processes depend on vacuum technology:
    1. Coating an object with metallic or non-metallic substances.
    2. Drying and impregnating electrical components.
    3. Freeze-drying in processing food.
    4. Distillation of liquids at lower temperatures than under atmospheric pressure.
    5. Cryogenic insulation (the thermos bottle).
    6. Space environment simulation.

14. The zero point of absolute temperature is defined as the point where no further cooling is considered possible. In the U.S. system pure water freezes at 459.7° Rankine or absolute temperature. In the metric system pure water freezes at 273.2° Kelvin or absolute temperature.

15. Charles proved that the volume of a confined gaseous medium would increase or decrease 1/273 of its original volume for every one degree centigrade change in temperature. This would be an increase or decrease of 1/459.7 of its original volume for every degree Fahrenheit change in temperature. The absolute temperature is directly proportional to the product of absolute pressure and volume.

16. The *gas constant* is an experimental value found to be: $R = \dfrac{1544}{M}$ for any perfect gas where *M* is the molecular weight of the gas or mixture of gases.

17. One of the greatest energy wastes in compressing a gaseous medium is the generation of heat in the compression process.

18. Clearance in a compressor is the volume of the gaseous medium in the compressor at the end of the stroke.

19. The smaller the clearance in the compressor is in proportion to the displacement, the better the volumetric efficiency.

20. This is the volume of the gaseous medium left in the compressor at the end of the stroke for useful work.

21. A true hyperbola.

22. Mariotte formulated the Boyle Law which states: At constant temperature the volume is inversely proportional to the pressure.

23. *Energy* is the force required to overcome resistance.
    Work is the product of force necessary to overcome the resistance and the distance traveled to perform the work.
    Power is the product of force and distance traveled divided by the time required to perform the work.
    Horsepower is the unit of power for engineering work. In the U.S. system we have: 1 horsepower = 33,000 foot-pounds per minute or 550 foot-pound per second. In the metric system we have: 1 horsepower = 75 kilogram-meters per second.

24. Indicated horsepower is the actual power developed within the cylinder.

25. Brake horsepower is the actual power required to drive the compressor under load. This power is measured by a dynomometer.

26. Volumetric efficiency is the ratio of the actual number of cubic units of standard free air compressed per unit of time to the number of cubic units of piston displacement during that time.

27. For a reciprocating compressor the compression ratio is the volumetric piston displacement plus the volumetric clearance at the end of the stroke divided by the volumetric clearance. This usually ranges between 3-1/2 to 1 to 8 to 1.

28. *Compressor efficiency*: The ratio of theoretical power required to compress the amount of air actually delivered, to the actual power developed in the air cylinder.
    Mechanical efficiency: The ratio of air indicated horsepower divided by the brake horsepower.
    Slip efficiency: The ratio of air actually measured to the apparent volume accounted for by the indicator diagram.
    Overall efficiency: The product of efficiency of each element.

29. A single-acting, single-stage compressor compresses the air from atmospheric pressure to the final pressure for each forward stroke of the piston.
    A double-acting, single-stage compressor compresses the air from atmospheric pressure to the final pressure on forward as well as return stroke of the piston.

30. High volumetric efficiency is obtained in a multi -stage compressor by reducing the compressor clearance for each stage and continuously maintaining a low temperature in the process of compression.

Chapter 4, Page 101

1. The greatest theoretical height to which water may be pumped by a single-acting suction pump is:

   (approx.) 34 feet $\left(\dfrac{14.7 \times 144}{62.4}\right)$ in the U.S. system

   (approx.) 10 meters $\left(\dfrac{1.033 \times 100}{1 \times 10}\right)$ in the metric system

2. Air-driven pumps are used for developing pressure of tremendous magnitudes in the liquid media. No energy is expended in holding these high pressures for long periods of time.

3. In the most commonly used vacuum pump in industry, a true compressor, the gaseous medium is compressed to a higher pressure to cause the gaseous medium to move to the lower pressure of the atmosphere.

4. A mechanical vacuum pump is really a true compressor.

5. A single-stage rotary piston pump can evacuate an enclosure to approximately 10^{-2} torr. A double-stage rotary piston pump can evacuate an enclosure to approximately 10^{-3} torr.

6. The most important requirements for a storage tank are:
   1. Adequate strength.
   2. Safety protection.
   3. Capacity to meet emergency demands.

7.
   1. Cylindrical tanks used in a vertical or horizontal position for storage or transportation.
   2. Flat-bottom tanks with a dome shaped top, usually for storage.
   3. Spherical tanks, usually used for storage.

8. The desired storage temperature in a liquid nitrogen container may be maintained by the following methods:
   1. Frequent refilling.
   2. Adjustment of the stored item to maintain the distance between the item stored and the liquid level as the liquid nitrogen evaporates.
   3. Conduction devices to conduct the heat from the stored item to the liquid nitrogen.

9. *Cryogenics* was coined from the Greek *kryos* meaning "icy cold" and *genes* meaning to *become* or *produce*.

10. The major uses of liquid oxygen are for the manufacture of steel, the propulsion of rocket engines, the chemical industry, and environmental use.

11. Liquid oxygen reduces the heat time in steel making.

12. The fastest growing market potentials for liquid nitrogen are the missile industry and the food and chemical industries.

13. Argon is mainly used at present in the arc welding industry as a shield to protect stainless steel, aluminum and other metals from oxydation as they are being welded. It is also used in the production of incandescent bulbs to retard filament evaporation.

14. The storage temperature of liquefied natural gas, LNG, varies from $-250°F$ to $-290°F$ ($-157°C$ to $-173°C$).

15. Peak shaving of liquefied natural gas is the storing of the liquefied gas during periods of low consumption, for future distribution.

16. Ethylene, C_2H_4, is the basic building block for the production of most of our plastics.

17. The usual vapor space for a cryogenic tank in percent of liquid capacity is in the range of 5% to 10%.

18. The inner tank of a cryogenic vessel must be designed for internal pressure arising from vapor-phase pressure and liquid weight.

19. The outer tank of a cryogenic vessel must be designed considering wind, snow, and dead loads, and the internal pressure from insulating powder and insulating-space gas pressure.

20. The common practice in designing foundations for cryogenic vessels is to design the foundation for the total weight of the contained product and to hydrostatic test of 1.25 times the product weight. For flat bottom tanks in locations where the temperature is likely to fall below freezing of water, a heat source should be supplied to the surface soil to prevent heaving, which whould occur if the soil should freeze.

21. Storage tanks for natural gas and manufactured gases are usually spherical.

22. The cylindrical supports for natural and manufactured gas tanks are usually designed to

carry the dead weight of the shell plus a 100 mile per hour wind load. This is 160 kilometer per hour in the metric system.

23. Natural and manufactured gas tanks are usually given the following inspection tests: After applying a soap film to all seams that have not been 100% radiographed with low pressure air in the tank, the air pressure is increased until shell joints are stressed to 125% of the design stress. A magnetic particle inspection is also made of all nozzles and manholes after welding.

Chapter 5, Page 128

1. No damage of the tool is caused by stalling, and there is no shock load in operation of the tool.

2.
   1. Rotary vane motors.
   2. Radial piston motors.
   3. Axial piston motors.
   4. Percussion motors.

3. Air operated tools are sometimes the only safe tools where hazardous environmental conditions exist and other sources of power could cause an explosion.

4. The principal function of a pneumatic actuator is to move an object from one place to another, or to hold an object in a clamped position.

5. The pressure should be checked with no load and also under maximum load to make sure that the volume delivered is sufficient. The pressure should be within 5 to 10% of the pressure the motor was designed for.

6. If the pressure is high enough at the receiver, but too low at the point of application, the supply lines may have too many sharp bends or the diameter of the pipes may be too small.

7. Clean, dry air well supplied with lubricant is essential for efficient operation of a pneumatic motor.

8. Clean air is assured by the installation of a filter.

9. Pneumatic components are usually best lubricated with a lubricator in the supply line.

10. Noise may be reduced with a muffler.

11. The torque in an air-operated rotary vane motor may be changed by one of the following three methods or all three methods:
    1. Change in pressure applied.
    2. Change in the exposed vane area.
    3. Change in the length of moment arm.

12. As the number of vanes is increased, starting torque and reliability of operation is increased.

13. The inherent characteristic of piston type motors is high starting torque. These motors are also well balanced, usually having five pistons. This design provides for even torque at all speeds.

14. The free speed is usually kept at 3,000 rpm or under, and maximum horsepower is usually developed at 1,000 rpm. The smooth overlapping power flow and accurate balancing make these motors vibrationless at all operating speeds.

15. The most dependable and oldest type of air-operated actuator is a piston sliding in a cylinder.

16. A diaphragm cylinder is a virtually frictionless actuator depending on a highly flexible diaphragm to seal the air and center the piston in the cylinder.

17. A pneumatic actuator may be slowed down or cushioned at the end of the stroke by restricting the exhaust.

18. The best way is to use a linear actuator, converting the linear motion to rotary motion by mechanical design.

19. Because there is always a pressure drop in supply lines. The magnitude of the pressure drop depends on the length and diameter of lines, the number of bends, and various components in the lines.

20. The speed may be adjusted in an actuator by adjusting the exhaust flow.

Chapter 6, Pages 144–145

1. A hose is made of flexible material and expands when pressure is applied, consuming energy. A rigid tube does not expand measurably.

2. Pneumatic supply lines must be smooth, of material compatible to the medium conducted.

3. Supply lines must be of adequate diameter. Where bends are necessary they should be of large diameters.

4. Compressor temperatures should not rise above 150°F (65°C).

5. A separator/pulse-trap dampens pulsations in a compressor and extracts undesirable mist.

6. The temperature is several degrees higher at the ceiling level than at the ground level. When the temperature of a gaseous medium is lowered condensation takes place. If excessive moisture is not eliminated, damage to the tools may be the result.

7. A pressure switch stops the compressor when maximum pressure is supplied to the receiver.

8. A relief valve guarantees that the pressure does not exceed a safe value.

9. A branch line should always be taken from the top side of a horizontal supply line so most of the moisture and contaminants may be blasted to the end of the main line and removed there.

10. One compressor valve is located at the intake and one at the discharge location. They admit and discharge an adequate volume of the gaseous medium. They prevent the gaseous medium from leaking back to a lower pressure. They prevent admission of a large percentage of solid contaminants.

11. The main purpose of an unloader device for a compressor valve is to lower power consumption.

12. A leaf-spring compressor valve has the advantage that the moving parts are light, reducing the inertial forces.

13. The springs in a compressor valve must be strong enough to prevent chatter.

14. Three main methods of operating flow control valves are:
    1. Manual operation or mechanical operation.
    2. Electrical operation.
    3. Pneumatic operation.

15. A two-way valve is required to start and stop flow.

16. A three-way valve is required to supply and exhaust the gaseous medium to and from one point of application.

17. A four-way valve is required to supply and exhaust the gaseous medium alternately to and from two points of application.

18. Amplitude of noise is the result of the force applied. Frequency level of noise is the result of the speed applied.

19. A phase shift acoustic filter is designed to split the main stream of air at the entrance of the component into two branches, throwing these two streams 180° out of phase.

Chapter 7, Pages 176–177

1. Filters in pneumatic lines assure trouble-free operation of components and tools.

2. Filters always cause some pressure drop.

3. A filter element is designed to filter out small particles of contamination.

4. The usual size of solid contaminants filtered out in filters for industrial use range from 5 to 50 microns. 1 micron = 0.001 mm or 0.000039"

5. A drip-leg automatic drain is used close to ground level at the end of a main supply line. The main function is to remove contaminants and condensation of moisture.

6. Standard air is air under normal conditions, having a density of 0.075 lbs per cubic foot at 68°F and barometric pressure of 29.921 inches of mercury with a relative humidity of 36 percent. This condition is identified in the U.S. system by the letter S. In the metric system the identifying letter is N.

7. There are always pressure fluctuations in a pneumatic system, and several components in the supply line will cause a pressure drop. The pressure must therefore be high enough at the receiver to assure enough pressure at the point of application. The pressure regulator is required to keep the pressure at the desired level at the point of application.

8. A pressure relieving type instrument prevents excessive pressure from damaging a pneumatic component.

9. All in-line instruments contribute to pressure drop. Therefore the pressure delivered from the receiver must be adequate to meet all needs.

10. A lubricator is used in a pneumatic system to supply oil to moving parts. The oil is usually atomized and when suspended in the air stream it will reach all parts.

11. Part of the air is directed through a venturi tube, causing a differential in pressure. This forces a mist of liquid to follow the main stream of air.

12. An aneroid barometer is an instrument for measuring low pressures. Its inside has been evacuated to partial vacuum.

13. The principal part of a bourdon pressure gage is a circular or helical tube closed at one end. The pressure is admitted to the open end, and, as the pressure is increased, the tube has a tendency to straighten. The motion of the tube is magnified by levers and gears to a pointer registering the pressure on the face of a dial.

14. A pitot tube is used for measuring the velocity of gaseous media in motion.

15. Liquid-filled barometers, bourdon gages, bellow-type mechanical gages, and diaphragm pressure transducers.

Chapter 8, Page 196

1. A booster pump may be adviseable in a pneumatic system when the majority of applications are for cleaning or similar tasks. In such cases the pressure may have dropped considerably below the accepted limit if the occational use of a small high precision tool is needed.

2. The most economical pressure for most pneumatic systems in industrial plants is 80 to 90 psi or 5.5 to 6 kg/cm². ·

3. (A) The unit pressure required to suspend a machine slide weighing 1,000 pounds and measuring 10×20 inches would be: $\dfrac{1,000}{10 \times 20} = 5$ psi

   (B) The unit pressure required to suspend a machine slide weighing 500 kg and measuring 25×50 cm would be: $\dfrac{500}{25 \times 50} = 0.4 \, \text{kg/cm}^2$

4. Air cushions may be used commercially for moving objects over rough surfaces with very little friction. Hospital hoverbeds are now successfully in use for severely burned patients. In these beds the patients float on a cushion of warm air to ease their pain.

5. Machine slides may be suspended by an air cushion when making fine adjustments with virtually frictionless motion.

6. Air pressure may be used for preloading an anti-friction bearing. No energy is wasted. Also, a pneumatic chuck will hold a workpiece tightly with no waste of energy.

7. Linear motion may be changed to rotary motion with a rack and gear.

8. Pneumatic power used in conjunction with hydraulic power is seen in two frequent applications:
   1. Pneumatic power may be applied to a liquid medium for raising and holding a heavy object suspended.
   2. Pneumatic power may be applied to a liquid medium, transmitting the power to a

Fluid Power: Pneumatics

linear actuator connected to a rack in mesh with a gear. The rack may then cause rotary motion to a heavy load. The load may be held at any position with no waste in energy.

9. The two main fluid media for transmitting power in industry are *air* and *oil*.

10. No fluid medium can be considered superior. The selection is based on individual requirements.

11. The pressures for hydraulic systems are higher. The materials used must be compatible to the fluid medium.

12. Mechanical, electrical, or pneumatic.

13. A timer is used for holding a valve closed or open for a preselected time. The electrical timer is the most dependable.

Appendix B, Pages 226–227

1. (A)   One U.S. pound = 0.4536 kilogram
One U.S. inch = 2.54 cm
One square inch = 2.54 × 2.54 = 6.451 6 cm²

One psi is therefore $\frac{0.4536}{6.4516} = 0.070\ 3\ \text{kg/cm}^2$

(B)   One kg. (force) = 9.806 65 N(newton) which is equal to the acceleration one kilogram attains per second squared at sea level at the latitude of Paris.
N/m² = Pa (pascal) the SI unit of pressure
One kg/cm² = 9.806 65 N/cm²
m² = cm² × 10⁴; therefore
9.806 65 ×10⁴ = 98 066.5 pascal which also is expressed as 98.066 5 kPa (kilopascal)

2. Power is work expressed in a given time. In the U.S system one horsepower is 33,000 ft.lbs per minute. In the *original* metric system one horsepower is 75 kilogram meter per second. One U.S. horsepower is 1.014 metric horsepower. In the SI units of measurement one U.S. horsepower is 745.7 watts. One metric horsepower is 735.499 watts.

Index